THE WARSHIP IN HISTORY

The

THE MACMILLAN COMPANY

Warship
in
History

PHILIP COWBURN

Senior Lecturer, Department of Humane Studies
Royal Naval College, Greenwich, England

NEW YORK

FOR ANNE AND STEPHEN

AND THEIR MOTHER

WITH LOVE

Second Printing 1967

Table of Contents

Preface

The chapters that make up this book are really a collection of essays intended to illustrate the main stages in the development of the warship. My material is not the result of original research on my part, but it seemed to me that there was room for a book that brought together into convenient proximity the kind of information that is to be found here. When I was invited to undertake this work, my first feeling was that it must have been attempted before, but I found that, in fact, this was not so. There are many admirable and detailed books on ships in general and on particular kinds of warship and on the navies of different countries, but there seems to be no single book that brings together detailed information about the ancient warships of the Mediterranean, that moves on to the oared vessels of Venice and then to the navies of Northwestern Europe and North America. Nor have many writers on naval subjects been allowed the freedom given me by my publishers to accompany the text with so many illustrations. I am most grateful to The Macmillan Company of New York for planning the book on a scale that made this possible.

Inevitably there are omissions. I have decided to ignore large areas of the world, such as the Arab countries and the Far East, even though ships in those parts of the globe have been used throughout history for the transportation of warriors as well as of merchandise.

My purpose, then, in writing this book, is straightforward. It is simply to present in convenient form and without too daunting a wealth of detail a historical account of some of the main developments in the evolution of the warship. Though I have made many references to sea battles—those occasions when warships were actually brought to the test—I have not attempted to give a detailed account of a single one of them; indeed, some of the most famous and important have received little more than a casual mention. This is intentional, because the book is not a full naval history, and I felt that its scale could easily have been thrown out of shape by the inclusion of such matter, even though, in some cases, such information might have thrown considerable light on the general principles I have been enunciating. I realized too that there would still have been gaps, and readers might have been led to expect a different kind of book altogether. Instead, my intention has been to set down some general propositions on the growth of warships, their changing roles, and the logistical problems arising from their maintenance and, in the footnotes and the bibliography, to give readers the information they need to pursue the study more fully. This approach became particularly necessary in the writing of the later chapters, for I found myself confronted with an ever-mounting bulk of material, both printed and photographic, and saw that the task of condensing it effectively was almost impossible.

At the end of the book, I have listed the sources by chapter. This has been for two reasons: that I might acknowledge my own debt to those who have explored this subject before me, but also that I might point the way toward further research for those who have a taste for it. I should, however, like to list here some books that I have found particularly useful, as they seem to me to be an excellent basic library for any sustained study of the warship in history:

Lionel Casson, *The Ancient Mariners,* Gollancz, London, 1959
Romola and R. C. Anderson, *The Sailing Ship,* Harrap & Co., London, 1926
R. C. Anderson, *Oared Fighting Ships,* Percival Marshall, London, 1962
G. S. Laird Clowes, *Sailing Ships: Their History and Development,* Her Majesty's Stationery Office, London, 1932, reprinted 1959
Björn Landström, *The Ship: A Survey of the History of the Ship from the Primitive Raft to the Nuclear-Powered Submarine with Reconstructions in Words and Pictures,* George Allen & Unwin, London, 1961
A. W. Brøgger and H. Shetelig, *The Viking Ships: Their Ancestry and Evolution,* Dreyers Forlag, Oslo, and Edward Stanford, Ltd., London, 1950

Alethea Wiel, *The Navy of Venice,* John Murray, London, 1910

M. A. Lewis, *The Navy of Britain,* George Allen & Unwin, London, 1948

T. D. Manning and C. E. Walker, *British Warship Names,* Putnam, London, 1959

G. J. Marcus, *A Naval History of England, Vol. I: The Formative Centuries,* Longmans, Green, London, 1961

M. Oppenheim, *The Administration of the Royal Navy, 1509–1660,* Shoe String Press, Inc., 1961, and Bodley Head, London, 1896

F. L. Robertson, *The Evolution of Naval Armament,* Constable, London, 1921

Donald Macintyre, *The Thunder of the Guns: A Century of Battleships,* Frederick Muller, London, 1959

S. W. Roskill, *The War at Sea 1939–45,* Vols. I, II, and III, Parts 1 and 2, Her Majesty's Stationery Office, London, 1954–1961

Howard I. Chapelle, *The History of American Sailing Ships,* Putnam, London, 1936

S. E. Morison, *The Two Ocean War,* Little, Brown and Company, Boston, 1963

There are a great many people to whom I owe debts of gratitude for help and encouragement while I was writing this book, far more than I can hope to acknowledge. Some of them are personal friends, and among these I should like to mention Dr. M. A. Lewis and Professor C. C. Lloyd, under whom I am glad to have worked at the Royal Naval College, Greenwich, England. They first awakened in me an interest in naval history, and it is because of their help and encouragement that I have been emboldened to take my first tentative steps into the historical field that they have made their own. That I do not feel a trespasser there is a proof of their kindness to me. Among those who have helped me, but are not known to me personally, I should like to cite Dr. R. C. Anderson, through whose careful scholarship and wide knowledge the study of ships and their history has been enriched during the last forty years.

I should like to thank the Navy Records Society, London, for allowing me to print a number of extracts from their publications, the details of which have been listed in the appropriate places; the Society for Nautical Research, London, for allowing me to use material from

The Mariner's Mirror, their quarterly journal; Messrs. Constable and Company, London, and the Executors of the late Hilaire Belloc for a passage from *The Cruise of the Nona*; Messrs. Hurst and Blackett, London, for passages from *Edward Barlow's Journal*, transcribed and edited by Basil Lubbock; Messrs. George Allen & Unwin, London, and the Executors of the late Professor Gilbert Murray for some lines from Gilbert Murray's translation of Aeschylus' *Persae*; Messrs. Hollis and Carter for a passage from Geoffrey Penn's *Up Funnel, Down Screw!* I should like also to thank those many members of the staff of the National Maritime Museum, Greenwich, England, for their great help in a variety of ways, and among them I should like to mention in particular Miss Sichel of the Print Room, who advised me in the selection of so many of the illustrations.

Lastly, I should like to thank a number of Institutions for giving me permission to reproduce material in their collections. The sources of the illustrations are given at the end of each descriptive caption.

PHILIP COWBURN

London
April 12, 1965

Prologue

Unlike many of his contemporaries, Captain Frederick Marryat, the sailor turned novelist, welcomed the arrival of the steam engine. He thought it marvelous in that it embodied great power in a remarkably small space, and he thought of it, too, as something possessing life— something moving not merely under its own mysterious power, but somehow actually living. Yet perhaps it was not strange for a sailor to think of the inanimate as possessing vitality, since all through history there is evidence that those who have had dealings with ships have thought of them as living things.

Nor is it an accident, surely, that in most languages the amalgam of timber and hemp and sailcloth and, in a later age, iron and steel, seems feminine, endowed with all the grace, waywardness, charm, and, above all, mystery that the sex embodies. This is something that the warship shares with all other ships. For whatever her shape, her armament, her seaworthiness, or, indeed, the extent of her failure to live up to the wishes of her designers, the ship possesses a distinct personality. The ideal form of the warship, using the phrase in Plato's sense, must contain this ingredient at least.

This point seems worth establishing at the outset, for the history of the warship is an instructive chapter in the history of mankind. All over the world, men have struggled to master the sea and, indeed, all waterways that are in any sense navigable. They have built boats as best they could, and through the centuries, sometimes slowly, but sometimes with great leaps ahead in inventive imagination, they have improved the techniques handed down to them by their fathers. Yet it has not really been a solitary struggle. Men have felt themselves to be working *with* their ships, to be undertaking a joint endeavor. It has, in fact, been an impressive example of cooperation, and we should bear this in mind as we read the chapters that make up this book.

Toward the end of his life, John Ruskin wrote that the ship of the line was the most honorable thing that man as a gregarious animal had produced. As an individual, he had done better things, ". . . but as a being living in flocks and hammering out with alternate strokes and mutual agreement what is necessary for him in these flocks to get or produce, the ship of the line is his first work. Into that he has put as much of his human patience, commonsense, forethought, experimental philosophy, self-control, habits of order and obedience, thoroughly wrought handiwork, defiance of brute elements, careless courage, careful patriotism and calm expectation of the judgement of God, as can well be put into a space three-hundred feet long by eighty feet broad— and I am thankful to have lived in an age when I could see this thing so done."[1]

The results of such essays in cooperation were certainly impressive, and though negligence from time to time led to disaster, as in the loss of the *Royal George* in 1782 (Cowper's poem is inaccurate on the details), the wooden warships of the classical age of sail were built to last. It is fascinating to see how long they remained afloat and how few ships' lives, as it were, separate us today from the sixteenth century.[2] The first English ship to be called *Vanguard*, for example, was built in 1586 and survived eighty years till she was scuttled during the Dutch attack on the Medway in 1667. In 1666, however, the second *Warspite* had been built, a second-rate that was to be renamed the *Edinburgh* and was to remain in service till she was broken up in 1771. By that time, the *Victory*, seventh ship of the name, was in existence. She had been launched in 1765, remained afloat till 1922, and can still be seen in dry dock at Portsmouth. Admittedly, she is a special case, and her survival is owing, no doubt, to the particular care taken to keep such a historic ship in a good state of preservation, but the point is that she still does exist.

The *Implacable*, launched in 1798, is another example of a long-lived ship. She was a French third-rate called *Duguay-Trouin*, and though she escaped from the battle of Trafalgar, she was captured soon after.

She was used as an accommodation ship in the Second World War and was ceremonially sunk as late as 1949.

True, in all such cases of longevity, there is a factor that must be taken into account—the uncertainty that surrounds the term "rebuilding." The first-rate three-decker *Prince Royal*, launched in 1670, was "rebuilt" in 1692, we are told, as the *Royal William*, but there is also evidence that she had actually been "broken up" and her sound timbers used in the construction of the new ship. The question is to what extent the first ship can really be said still to exist. On the whole, it seems unlikely that this would have been a complete reconstruction, as good timber was already becoming scarce. It is more probable that the earlier vessel would have been enlarged—perhaps by the insertion of a completely new middle section.

We know very little about what those who sailed in these ships thought about them. We are apt to recall only Smollett's pungent descriptions of life in the Georgian navy or to remember Dr. Johnson's prejudiced opinion that a ship was worse than a jail because the inmates had the added disadvantage of being in danger and that sailors went to sea before they knew of "the unhappiness of that way of life" and then found it "too late to choose another profession." Yet in spite of the view from the quarterdeck that revealed to Johnson "the utmost extremity of human misery; such crowding, such filth, such stench," there were others who thought differently.

About twenty years after Johnson expressed the above opinions, young Thomas Byam Martin, later to become an Admiral of the Fleet, had his first glimpse of a 100-gun ship, and we can still overhear his gasp of excitement and share his enthusiasm as we read his journal. "Ye Gods! What s sight, what a sensation!" he wrote, ". . . if I live to the age of Methuselah it will remain unimpaired. . . . It is impossible to forget the breathless astonishment and delight with which my eyes were fixed upon the ship. Nothing so exquisitely touching has ever occurred to me since to produce the same frantic joy. After the first exclamation of ecstasy I for a time spoke not a word; overwhelmed by a thousand feelings, and almost motionless, until presently, as we approached nearer to the *Royal George*, and went closely under her richly carved stern, I broke into a rapid succession of questions, and, jumping about, and almost springing out of the hands of the strokesman of the boat, who held me as I stood upon the seat, I was told I should tumble into the sea if I was not quiet. What nonsense! Who could be quiet under such circumstances?"[3] This picture is far removed from the nefarious activities of the press-gang, through whose agency so many caught sight of their first man-of-war.

Perhaps a word should be said about some of the survivors from the past, for there are a number of them, reviving poignant memories, perhaps, but testifying also to the stoutness of their build. Of the earliest, the Viking ships found at Oseberg and Gokstad in Norway, and discussed in this book, are also the most complete, but there are earlier fragmentary traces, too, such as those found in England at Sutton Hoo near Woodbridge just before the outbreak of the Second World War. The main interest lies in the wealth of objects found in a burial chamber in a large ship, but the whole outline of the ship herself is of great significance, since she is, in the words of the official guide to the excavations, "the most important, indeed the only monument of our Sixth and Seventh Century pagan ancestors that has yet come down to us."[4] The ship showed certain technical improvements over the Nydam ship of about the year 400, also discussed in this book, and she was an open rowing boat, 80 feet long, with a maximum beam of 14 feet and a depth amidships of 4 feet 6 inches. Clinker-built and without permanent decking, the hull was strengthened with ribs and seems to have accommodated thirty-eight oarsmen. There was no trace of any mast, nor was there any other visible provision for sailing.

In Great Britain, the *Victory* has become a national monument as durable as the square in London that commemorates Trafalgar. Indeed, the ship is so closely associated with Nelson and Trafalgar that it is often forgotten that she had seen nearly thirty years of service before she wore Nelson's flag. Thomas Slade designed her to be an improvement on the *Royal George*, and she was launched at Chatham on May 7, 1765, though work on her was delayed and she was not completed till 1778. Once in service, she proved a good ship, was speedy in the water, was commendably weatherly, and could be handled as though she were a two-decker. Yet in spite of this, and even though she had been the flagship of such notable admirals as Keppel, Hyde Parker, Kempenfelt, Howe, Hood, and St. Vincent, by the end of the century she had become a hospital ship and, later still, a hulk for prisoners of war in the River

Medway. During this period, she may well have been seen by Nelson when his flagship, the *Vanguard*, was refitting at Chatham.

In December, 1799, *Victory* was ordered to be restored to fighting condition, and in May, 1803, when war broke out again after the short-lived Peace of Amiens, she was brought to Spithead to become Nelson's flagship, and with her came her attendant frigate, *Amphion*, commanded by Thomas Masterman Hardy. After Trafalgar, she was reclassified as a second-rate and saw her last service in the Baltic, returning to England finally in 1812. In the 1820's and 1830's, she was made the Port Admiral's flagship at Portsmouth, but it became increasingly clear that she was an embarrassment to the British Admiralty and remained so till, in the early 1920's, she was carefully and scientifically restored and, in 1928, opened to the public for inspection. In view of her long career and the care lavished on her, it is worth recording that on the night of March 10–11, 1941, she narrowly escaped complete destruction by enemy action. A 500-pound high-explosive bomb fell inside the dock and burst under her bow, blowing open a hole 8 feet by 15.[5]

A humbler survivor of the days of sail is the frigate *Foudroyant*, launched in Bombay as the *Trincomalee* in 1817 but later renamed *Foudroyant* after the French ship captured by Nelson and lost in a gale in 1897 after she had been sold by the Admiralty. Apart from the *Victory*, she is the only surviving warship of the sailing navy, since she is preserved as a training ship for parties of young people at Portsmouth and is administered by a special trust.

In a few years time, it will be possible to see fully restored the seventeenth century Swedish 64-gun three-decker *Vasa*, which sank on her maiden voyage on August 10, 1628. Possibly of Dutch design, this magnificent ship was intended to be the royal flagship, but after the tragedy nothing was done beyond the salvaging of some fifty of her guns. Even her position in Stockholm harbor was forgotten. The story of her discovery by Anders Franzén in 1956 must not delay us here, but she was raised to the surface in April, 1961, by being cradled between two pontoons mounting hydraulic jacks and by having hawsers passed beneath her keel. The ship reappeared above the surface of the harbor to become the oldest fully identified ship in the world, bringing with her a great assortment of supplies and equipment and a wealth of baroque carvings, some of which still bear traces of gold leaf and colored paint.

Among them was the 2½-ton figurehead, a representation of the lion of the House of Vasa.[6]

An American survivor is the 44-gun frigate *Constitution*, known as *Old Ironsides*. She is still to be seen in the naval dockyards at Boston, Massachusetts, where she was built to the designs of the well-known shipbuilder Joshua Humphreys and launched in October, 1797. She was restored considerably in 1857, but she still remains as a living memorial of the great days of the sailing warship. She was the largest frigate in the world in her day and perhaps the finest ever built, well-known for her speed and seaworthiness.

Future generations, brought up in the age of nuclear-powered warships, may look back on the early ironclad steam-propelled ships with equally nostalgic feelings, and, indeed, some of these ships may be said to possess a quality of their own, that "keen unpassioned beauty," as Rupert Brooke wrote, that is inherent in a great machine. It remains to be seen whether those who look at the *North Carolina*, preserved at Wilmington, North Carolina, or at Togo's flagship *Mikasa*, at Yokohama, will feel the same emotions that stir those who visit *Constitution* or *Victory*. Perhaps it is because the design of warships changed so much and so quickly after about 1860 that the silhouettes became outdated before they had become easily recognizable. From the sixteenth century till the beginnings of the steam age, all the navies of the Western world had remarkably similar ships, as is demonstrated in several chapters of this book, and the image of the wooden ship of the line became fixed in the minds of even those who were unable to appreciate the finer points of a warship in the age of sail.

Lest, however, it be thought that the ironclad inspired no sense of majesty or awe, let us conclude this introduction by recalling the passage in *The Cruise of the Nona* in which Hilaire Belloc, sitting at the tiller, rounded Start Point at dawn one day at the end of July, 1914. "I chanced to look . . . eastward . . . towards the open sea," he has written, "and then it was that there passed me the vision I shall remember for ever. . . . Like ghosts, like things themselves made out of mist, there passed between me and the newly risen sun a procession of great forms, all in line, hastening eastward. It was the Fleet recalled. The slight haze along that distant water had thickened, perhaps, imperceptibly; or perhaps the great speed of the men of war buried them too quickly in the distance.

But, from whatever cause, this marvel was of short duration. It was seen for a moment, and in a moment it was gone."

It must indeed have been a memorable moment, even though it brought with it the realization that the First World War would soon be declared.[7]

NOTES

[1]John Ruskin, in T. J. Wise (ed.), *The Harbours of England*, 1895, pp. 24–25.

[2]For this line of thought, I am indebted to D. G. Browne in his book *The Floating Bulwark*, Cassell, London, 1962.

[3]Sir Richard Vesey-Hamilton (ed.), *Letters of Sir Thomas Byam Martin, Vol. I*, Navy Records Society, London, 1893, vol. xxiv, p. 4.

[4]R. L. S. Bruce-Mitford, *The Sutton Hoo Burial Ship: A Provisional Guide*, Trustees of the British Museum, London, 1951, p. 38.

[5]See Kenneth Fenwick, *HMS Victory*, Cassell, London, 1959.

[6]See Bengt Ohrelius, *Vasa, Kungers Skepp*, translated by Maurice Michael, Cassell, London, 1962.

[7]See Hilaire Belloc, *The Cruise of the Nona*, Constable, London, 1955, p. 150.

Greek wine jar (probably early fifth century B.C.) showing Odysseus' ship passing the Sirens. Note the all-seeing eye painted on the prow and the boar's snout similar to those on the ships illustrated on pages 22 and 26. Note also the steersman between his two steering oars and the yard hoisted to the top of the mast with the sail brailed up along its whole length. *British Museum, London*

I

 The Ancient World

IF we are not too exact in defining our terms, the early use of the word "warship" can describe only the intentions of people transported and not the actual vessel itself. The inflated bladders, hollowed-out tree trunks, papyrus rafts, and indeed those very early boats depicted on vases, rock carvings, and in tombs in Egypt can in one sense all be called warships, as, no doubt, they were used with hostile intent from time to time.

Usually, however, the warship is a vessel particularly built for the purpose of carrying on war: it may be slim in the beam for speed and maneuverability, or it may even contain such features as an easily movable mast to suit the circumstances for which it was constructed. It is therefore in this sense that we should examine the records.

The Egyptians almost certainly ceased to be solely river folk before 3000 B.C. and were already interesting themselves in overseas ventures to Crete and the coasts of Palestine by that date. Hieroglyphics relate that Pharaoh Snofru sent forty armed ships to Byblos about 2900 B.C. to buy cedarwood especially to build ships, and in 2700 B.C. Pharaoh Sahu-re sent eight ships to the Phoenician coasts to bring back prisoners —presumably the newly established trading stations were being threatened.

We know a good deal about these ships, as there are some very detailed contemporary relief carvings of them on one of the pyramids at Abu Sir. Basically they did not differ much from the river craft of the time, which is hardly surprising, but there were certain distinctive features that suggest that they were more strongly built and were in fact adapted to suit the conditions of war. The bipod mast, for instance, is shown lowered onto a crutch aft and fastened to strong stanchions. This would be done to enable the oarsmen to function more easily when the wind was unfavorable. For fore and aft support, there is a feature already to be seen that remains constant in all large Egyptian seagoing vessels—a rope stretched over several queen posts and made taut by the insertion of a short spar, like the Spanish windlass. The object of this device was to provide longitudinal strength by taking the strain off the bow and stern, which might otherwise drop, or be "hogged," when the vessel was afloat. Other features shown in the reliefs are the upright stem and stern posts, the former bearing the all-seeing eye of Osiris.

We notice that the oarsmen are standing, and this seems characteristic of warships as opposed to merchantmen: it may have given them more impetus, and therefore speed, and it would have done away with the need for thwarts, which must have taken up a great deal of room. Again, we see that support athwartships was given by two ropes lashed around the upper planking and kept taut by a third rope running zigzag between them, though another interpretation is that this feature is not made of ropes at all, but is a stylized band of bark or reeds to make the hull more watertight.

Clearly the link between Egypt and Palestine grew as the centuries passed. In the early fifteenth century B.C., Pharaoh Thutmose III fought eighteen campaigns in Syria and in most of them transported troops thither by sea, which suggests that the ships used, even if they were merely commandeered merchantmen, were large enough and well enough built to make the idea pay off. Several harbors on the Phoenician coast were gained as a result of these wars. They were left in charge of local princes, though annual inspections kept the pharaohs informed about them.

A remarkable hoard of tablets excavated at Tel el Amarna shows how Thutmose's bases were picked off one by one nearly a century later in Ikhnaton's time by determined bands of sea rovers whose aim was to enforce blockades, disrupt convoys, and prey upon maritime commerce in general. Thus it seems that when Thutmose opened up these trade routes, the southeastern corner of the Mediterranean was either comparatively free of pirates or controlled by some other maritime force friendly to Egypt. We shall see presently that the Minoans provided an answer to this quandary, but before we consider the part they were to play before being themselves destroyed by the Mycenaeans from the mainland of Greece, we must remember the general proposition that seaborne merchandise needed an effective convoy system to ensure its safe arrival. This meant a continual challenge to the builders of warships.

Before we leave Egypt, we can see this well illustrated in the ships of the Eighteenth Dynasty in about 1480 B.C. Reliefs in the Temple of Deir el Bahari at Thebes show detailed representations of the ships which Queen Hatshepsut sent to the land of Punt. Wherever this place is to be located—Hadramaut and the Somali coasts seem the most likely alternatives—the fact emerges that it was a long way from Egypt, and the ships would need to be sufficiently strongly built to survive the journeys there and back.

Queen Hatshepsut's ship differs little from her predecessors, even those as far back as the Fifth Dynasty, but in detail she has improved considerably. There are, for example, the same truss and queen posts that we saw in Sahu-re's ships, but the mast and sail are different, showing that the advance had been in this direction and not so much in general design. The carving appears to show a fore and aft sail, but this effect was as conventional as the representation of the full-face human eye in contemporary Egyptian profiles; the square sail was in fact athwartships and, a considerable innovation, was much wider than in earlier vessels. Lastly, the two steering oars in the bows deserve mention, though they were no longer really oars at all. Their central posts rested on forks and passed through ring fixtures below the gunwales to keep them straight. Near the upper ends of the "oars" were tillers perpendicular to the deck for the helmsmen to hold with both hands.

Ramses III was probably the last great pharaoh, and among his other achievements was his victory over "the people from the sea" in about 1190 B.C. These people, also called "the northerners of the isles," came from the southern Aegean islands and the south coast of Asia Minor, and they seem to have sacked the Phoenician coast towns and invaded Egypt by land, with a fleet accompanying them along the coast. On the walls of his temple at Medinet Habu near Thebes, Ramses had the story of his exploit depicted, and it is of special interest in that it is the earliest surviving representation of a naval engagement and also the only one from classical times.

In the ships themselves, it is possible to see a distinct advance that suggests that the Egyptians, not really a maritime nation in spite of their enterprise, copied much from these Levantine seafarers. New features are the high washboards intended to protect the oarsmen, the crow's nests at the tops of the masts, and the furling of the sails by means of vertical brails instead of by lowering the yard. Also, the supporting fore and aft hawser has disappeared. The relief shows that the ships of the invaders are in full sail, but this probably means that they were caught unawares by Ramses and had not had time to adopt the normal method of conducting a sea battle, that is, relying on oars for movement.

After this, Egypt drops back from her leading position, and further developments in warship design come to a standstill. Herodotus visited Egypt in about 450 B.C. and showed the customary Greek interest in shipping he found there. He says that the river ship, the *baris*, was built "like a wall," with planks of "acantha" wood, the *mimosa Nilotica*, about 3 feet long, pinned together, but not ribbed, and caulked with the fiber of papyrus on the inside and then fixed with tar. Though the vessel he thus describes cannot be said to come into the warship category, it may, however, be possible to infer that warships were equally primitive, if only because the Egyptians had ceased to be a serious maritime power.

To the modern historian, the Minoans are no longer the shadowy, semimythical people they were once thought to be. At the time when Thutmose was building up the Egyptian connection with the coasts of Palestine, it was only possible for him to be doing so because there was already in existence a strong police force, based on Crete, to patrol the eastern Mediterranean. Thucydides says that "according to tradition," Minos was the first person to organize a navy, that he controlled the greater part of the Aegean and its islands, and suggests that he did his best to put down piracy in order to secure his own trade in that area.

Whether there ever was such a person as Minos or whether, as seems more likely, the name was just a title, like the word "pharaoh," it is clear that the naval control he and his successors exercised was effective for some centuries, as is perhaps proved by the absence of protective walls around the Cretan towns. It also seems likely that the Minoans' ships were warships in the accepted sense of the word, but very little is known about them. It is indeed a loss that so far nothing on the scale of the Egyptian tomb carvings has come to light. In the rings, sealstones, and their impressions that have been discovered, the vessels are almost invariably shown as single-masted, with one bank of oars and between five and eleven oars a side. They have pointed or beaked bows and high sterns that remind us of the ships of the "people of the sea" whom Ramses III defeated and had depicted on the walls of his temple at Medinet Habu.

The Minoan civilization centered on Crete was mysteriously but completely overthrown some time before 1450 B.C. by the Mycenaeans from the Greek mainland. These people must have had effective ships—and complete confidence in them—to have undertaken such a venture, and they must also have mastered at least some of the problems of logistics involved in attacking a number of city-states almost two hundred miles away from their home base.

With the Mycenaeans, we come to the Greeks themselves and into the classical period proper, but mention must first be made of the Trojan War. This famous episode would seem to be merely one of the longest, though not necessarily of ten years' duration, of many similar "wars," and it undoubtedly owes its immortality to the accident that Homer wrote about episodes connected with it. Even Thucydides suspected that Agamemnon was not really leading a national crusade against Troy to recover his brother's wife, but was anxious to preserve his control over the Aegean and ensure that the routes for ships sailing to and from the Black Sea grainlands remained open to him.[1] On another point, Thucydides is surely right when he argues that if Homer was correct in describing Agamemnon as "King of Argos and *of many islands,*" then he must have had a considerable navy to maintain this power. Fear and the normal obligations of subordinate status may then have led to the size of this particular expedition.

However, Thucydides does not accept Homer's figure of 1,200 ships: he refers to the tendency of poets to exaggerate and concludes that, in any case, the expedition would appear small to his own generation. Another interesting point is that Thucydides accepts the Homeric statements that each Boeotian ship had a crew of 120 and that each of Philoctetes' seven ships had a crew of 50 men, but interprets these as the maximum and minimum figures, as no others are given. He also makes the point that according to Homer all Philoctetes' oarsmen were archers, which suggests that the stage of differentiating between soldier and sailor had not really been reached.

It is interesting to examine the adjectives Homer uses to describe ships. In the famous catalog in the *Iliad*,[2] the detachments of ships are almost invariably "black," that is, smeared with pitch, though the twelve ships brought by Odysseus are "vermilion-prowed"; other stock epithets are "hollow," that is, undecked, "benched," and "well-benched." It would seem, too, that ships at the beginning of the twelfth century B.C. were essentially slender and graceful, inspired by the very shapes of the dolphins that sported around them as they sped over the wine-dark sea.

They were swift too and seem to have been either twenty-oared, which would make them at least 40 feet from stem to stern, or sometimes even fifty-oared and therefore more than twice as long. They were low in the water, with wickerwork spray-deflectors forward, and may have been equipped with a beak, *embolon*, which was later to become such a feature of the trireme. They were flat-bottomed, light, and therefore easily beached—invariably stern first—and, when under oars, the sailing gear would be stowed away and the mast lowered.

Throughout both the *Iliad* and the *Odyssey*, there are references that, taken together, help to supplement the very scanty archaeological evidence in existence. For example, the raft-boat that Odysseus built on Calypso's island, under Athene's instructions for the stage of his journey home that eventually brought him to Phaeacia, was certainly not a warship; but it is more than likely that a contemporary warship would be laid down in this way, with seasoned planks of alder, poplar, and pine, bored through and jointed together and made fast with pegs and tree-nails.[3] Again, certain incidents in the narrative suggest something of the hazards of life in the eastern Mediterranean in those centuries after the Mycenaeans had followed the Minoans into the limbo of prehistory.

Piracy was an everyday activity and, according to Thucydides again, was considered an honorable profession, even in his own lifetime, in some places. We learn that Eurycleia, Odysseus' old nurse, was kidnapped by pirates from her well-to-do home in Sidon and sold into slavery; and when Odysseus at last returns to Ithaca, he conceals his identity by posing as a Cretan raider, a perfectly normal and presumably respectable kind of stranger to arrive on the island.[4] Both these details would be by no means fantastic, nor would be the list of places from which Menelaus told Telemachus he got his treasure:[5] Cyprus, Egypt,

Libya, Phoenicia, and Ethiopia would be exactly the places to attract pirates.

Between 1100 and 800 B.C., the Phoenicians were the dominant naval power in the eastern Mediterranean. Their Greek name was derived from the dark-red color with which they dyed textiles, but they referred to themselves as Sidonians. Carthage, their chief colony, was founded in 800 B.C.; but before that, they had reached the Atlantic coast of Spain and beyond in search of tin and silver. Their ships, designed chiefly for trade but also for aggressive action in pursuing that trade, must have taught the Greeks a great deal about ship development.

Two reliefs from Sennacherib's palace in Nineveh and now in the British Museum show two-banked galleys that are thought to be the earliest known pictures of the Phoenician bireme, and they are very like the galleys of the Greeks that remained in existence for so long. One of the reliefs shows the high upcurved bow and stern, but the other is more obviously a warship, as she has a bow extended into a long projecting ram on the waterline. They both, however, have the two banks of oars, and, to judge from the positions of the arms of the outer row of oarsmen—in front of the supports for the narrow upper deck, itself a novel feature—it seems that these oarsmen sat on thwarts projecting outward from the hull into outriggers, while the inner rows sat on a lower level below the raised deck and used longer oars. This arrangement would mean that the hull of the vessel could still be narrow and therefore maneuverable, while speed and striking power were increased by the greater number of oarsmen.

From about the middle of the eighth century B.C., for two hundred years, the Greeks established colonies all over the Mediterranean area. Hopping from island to island and from coast to coast "like frogs on a pond," as Plato said of them later, they set up daughter communities, which made necessary swift and strong ships to protect their inhabitants in their frequent comings and goings. Herodotus says that the Phocaeans, who lived on the coast of Asia Minor not far to the northwest of Smyrna, were the first of the Greeks to perform long voyages and open up the coasts of the western Mediterranean for the other Greeks.[6] He says too that the vessel they used was "not the round-built merchant ship but the long penteconter." They were, in fact, buccaneers like the Elizabethan navigators and not merely merchants, and the light penteconter with its twenty-five oars a side would have been an admirable vessel for their purposes.

The Phocaeans established a colony at Alalia in Corsica and for a few years successfully harassed the neighboring coasts and islands until the Carthaginians and their Etruscan allies attacked them with sixty ships. For, though the Phocaeans also mustered sixty ships, they lost forty of them, and the remaining twenty "came out of the engagement with their beaks so bent and blunted," according to Herodotus,[7] that they were no longer serviceable. This battle off Alalia in 535 B.C. marks a turning point in Mediterranean history, and not necessarily a minor one, for if the Phocaeans had won, perhaps they might have built up a very considerable thalassocracy and, crowding out Carthage into second place, might have turned the Mediterranean into a Greek lake. This passage from Herodotus also gives us the earliest reference to the introduction of the bronze ram, or "beak," which was to determine the future character of Greek naval warfare, so that, instead of being merely straight fights between archers and spearmen, engagements depended more and more on the skill of the oarsmen and their captain in maneuvering the ship.

Traditionally, the first regular sea fight between two Greek states took place a hundred years earlier than the Alalia battle, between Corinth and her daughter city Corcyra in 664 B.C. The Corinthians, according to Thucydides, were "supposed to have been the first to adopt more or less modern methods in ship-building"[8] and, indeed, to have laid down the first trireme. Björn Landström, in his book *The Ship*, postulates that the modern methods referred to were the replacement of the dug-out warship by a ship built of ribs.[9] The problem the shipwrights of the day had to face up to was the combination of lightness with fore-and-aft strength so that the vessel would stand up to ramming. The keel and the storming bridge (*katastroma* in Greek, *constratum* in Latin) would meet this need. In the biremes, and in the later triremes too, the ends of the keel, the gunwales, and the railings were drawn together into a single bunch, often adorned with a bird's head or a stylized acanthus. Biremes would have been about 80 feet in length, with a beam of just over 10 feet, and invariably they had masts, though sometimes these are shown on vases as lowered, and it is probably that this would always be done when there was a head wind.

The time has come now to consider the most famous Greek ship of all, the trireme, in some detail. As at all stages in the history of early warships, it is impossible to be certain when a new development can be said to have been in universal usage. Just as the penteconters of the eighth century B.C. gave way to the biremes that we have been discussing, by the end of that century the bireme herself was yielding place to the trireme, though this does not mean that both the earlier types of vessels were no longer used. Indeed, as we shall see, the bireme in an improved form came back into favor in the late fourth century B.C.

The main point of interest in the trireme is the additional bank of oars; and this introduces a number of problems connected with the positions of the oarsmen's thwarts, the presence of outriggers, and the length of the oars, which we shall discuss later. What does seem certain is that the light and elegant biremes so delicately portrayed on vases and dishes must have proved too fragile. Possibly, too, the addition of the extra oarsmen on each side made the hulls too long and too hard to maneuver, so the idea of the third bank was put into practice to increase the forward thrust without sacrificing maneuverability. Thucydides records that Ameinocles of Corinth constructed the first triremes,[10] four of them, for the Samians in the late eighth century; but the key moment must have been when some naval architect developed the outrigger some time in the late sixth century B.C. At all events, the trireme came into her own in the Persian Wars and particularly after the Greek victory at Salamis in 480 B.C.

Aeschylus' account of this battle is of great interest, not merely because his play The Persae was performed only eight years later, but because the playwright himself was a marine on board one of the Athenian triremes. Therefore, the messenger who announces the defeat of the Persian fleet to the mother of Xerxes can fairly be assumed to be speaking from Aeschylus' own standpoint, that of an eyewitness. In the following passage, in Gilbert Murray's translation, there are many interesting points:

> The first rammer was a Greek
> Which sheared away a great Sidonian's crest;
> Then close, one on another, charged the rest.
> At first the long-drawn Persian line was strong
> And held; but in those narrows such a throng

Was crowded, ship to ship could bring no aid.
Nay, with their own bronze-fanged beaks they made
Destruction; a whole length of oars one beak
Would shatter; and with purposed art the Greek
Ringed us outside, and pressed, and struck; and we—
Our oarless hulls went over, till the sea
Could scarce be seen, with wrecks and corpses spread.[11]

Here we see the skill of Themistocles' plan, which was simply to entice the far superior Persian fleet into a narrow space, where the greater numbers would cause the greater confusion and where the oncoming ships would be fouled by the wreckage ahead of them that could not be dispersed. It seems that the fight was decided not by the archers and spearmen converting the locked ships into a battleground, but by the jamming of the ships together. Aeschylus uses a vivid phrase when he likens the ships being driven onto the beaches to tunnies driven into shallow water so that they can be struck to death with any piece of available wood. It is significant that after the battle was over, the Greeks did not follow the comparatively few surviving Persian ships across the Aegean. Presumably, Eurybiades realized that his own ships were still in a minority and that this factor would be a distinct disadvantage in the open sea. Also, there would be a natural disinclination to set out on a further campaign so late in the season, for the battle was fought in late September. Thus we find that it is only in the following year, and very soon after the Persian army had been defeated at Plataea, that the Greeks took offensive action across the Aegean that led to the destruction of the surviving Persian ships within their stockade at the point on the coast of Asia Minor south of Ephesus where Mount Mycale juts out toward the island of Samos.

There are very few pictorial records to show us what triremes looked like, but a good deal is known about them all the same. Naturally there were slight variations in design and size: for instance, the Phoenician contingent at Salamis carried more marines and the vessels seem to have stood higher out of the water than the Greek ships did. The Corinthians went in for heavier ships so as to carry more men, but the Athenians in their golden age in the fifty years before the outbreak of the Peloponnesian War in 431 B.C. preferred light vessels that could be used, as Lionel Casson says,[12] as projectiles in themselves.

In general, however, the following details seem typical of the mid-fifth century trireme. The maximum length would be about 125 feet, with a beam of about 20 feet, and she would lie low in the water, with roughly 8 feet of freeboard above the waterline and a draft of 3 feet. This meant that they were shallow enough to be beached easily and hauled over rollers, if necessary. The three banks of oars, however we decide to interpret their actual construction, were made up of 27 oarsmen, known as *thalamites*, with their oars projecting from ports only about 2 feet above the waterline; above them, 27 *zeugites*; and, above them, 31 *thranites*. This meant that there were 85 oarsmen a side, which, with the two steersmen, who also had oars, as we saw in earlier ships, added up to a total of 172. The trireme would be capable of traveling at 7 knots, if all three banks were used.

So much seems generally accepted, but we must now consider the two main theories about the actual seating of the oarsmen. Landström and others support the theory of "zenzile" rowing, which means that the thwarts were placed at an angle, each running obliquely from the center line of the ship. Two oarsmen sat side by side on the upper thwart with their oars running out through ports on the outrigger. The man on the lower thwart would be able to swing between the two men above him, and, as has been said, his oar port would be in the hull of the ship below the outrigger and very little above the level of the water. These men would handle the middle and top banks of oars, and it would seem that there were two banks of oars, because the inner man would have a longer oar and its port would be a little forward and higher up than the outer oarsman's. From the outside, this would look as though there were three banks of oars, though there were, in fact, only two. The weakness of this theory is that it presupposes a certain construction for which there is no positive evidence.

Professor Casson, on the other hand, thinks that there certainly were three rows of benches and that each oarsman in the upper rows would sit a little forward of the corresponding oarsman in the row below. He argues that in rough weather, the thalamites, on the lowest thwarts, would not be used and that the zeugites and thranites alone would propel the ship, with their oars hitting the water at a much sharper angle. He says, too, that except for the oars used in the extreme bow and stern positions, where the side of the hull curved in, all the other oars would be of the same length, which would have simplified the stocking of spares considerably. Contemporary dockyard records state that each ship carried thirty spares.

We know that the ship's company numbered 200, which was made up of 5 officers and 25 petty officers and other hands in addition to the 170 oarsmen. There were also some marines, consisting of about a dozen archers and some bowmen. The chief executive officer was the *kybernetes*, or helmsman, who, among his other duties, navigated the ship. The captain, or *trierarchos*, was, like the admiral above him, a political appointment. He was a rich man who could afford to fit out and command a trireme for the period of a year. The *proreus*, or bow officer, looked after the hull and the ship's gear, supervised anchoring and beaching, and maintained the roster of lookout men. The other two officers were the *keleustes*, who was responsible for the oarsmen, and the *pentekontarchos*, who was the junior officer on board and perhaps equivalent to the captain's secretary today.

These triremes were undoubtedly expensive to maintain both in men and in matériel and, because of their lightness, must have needed frequent refits, especially if they ran into bad weather. Also, they had little room for the stowage of food and other equipment and so needed bases from which to operate. Their sails, too, would require constant attention, for each trireme had a large square sail for cruising; it was frequently left on shore or replaced by a much smaller boat-sail for which there would be just enough stowage room on board under the thwarts when the oarsmen took over in action.

By the time of the Peloponnesian War, in the last third of the fifth century B.C., the tactical use of the trireme had developed enormously; so much so, that Thucydides can make a special point of saying that one of the earliest engagements in the war, one which up to that time was, he says, the greatest sea fight between Greek states, was "of a somewhat old-fashioned kind," since the protagonists were "still behindhand in naval matters."[13] This was the clash between Corcyra and Corinth off the southern tip of Corfu, and Thucydides goes on to say that it was "more like a battle on land than a naval engagement." In fact, he records, "both sides relied more for victory on the marines who were on the decks and who fought a regular pitched battle there while the ships remained motionless." He adds, "No one attempted the maneuver of breaking through the line." This particular maneuver, the *diekplous*, was possibly of Phoenician origin and had certainly been tried out by them at the battle of Artemisium a few weeks before Salamis. It involved a sudden dash forward on a given signal, the consequent piercing of the enemy line, and then left and right wheels to attack the enemy's unprotected rear. It required, however, the element of surprise, initial speed, and, above all, considerable coordination, or else it could be countered by the formation of the enemy's fleet into a "hedgehog," with bows pointing outward and sterns to the center of a circle, a countermeasure that Themistocles successfully brought off at Artemisium.

The other main tactical maneuver was the *periplous*, which was the turning of one or other flank to take the enemy's line in the stern. This could be avoided either by an extension of the line, though this could be overdone and lead the enemy to try the breakthrough or, if the fight were taking place near land, by keeping one flank close to the shore. Again, if numbers were distinctly uneven, the fleet with the numerical superiority could divide up into two lines so that the second line could deal with enemy ships that broke through the first. The Athenians did this successfully off the Arginusae islands in 406 B.C., their last success, as it turned out, in the Peloponnesian War.

In the fourth century B.C., it seems that the bireme came back into favor, possibly because of the difficulties experienced in manning the trireme and indeed of training the crews up to a sufficiently high standard to ensure the efficient handling of the ship. The fragmentary pedestal of the Winged Victory of Samothrace, now in the Louvre, which shows clearly the existence of an outrigger with the openings of two oar ports, is generally thought to be an accurate representation of the bow of a bireme. It may commemorate the victory won by Demetrius Poliorcetes over Ptolemy in 306 B.C., or it may belong to the middle of the third century and be a dedication set up by Antigonus Gonatas after one of his victories against Egypt off Cos or Andros. In either case, it shows that the *thalamite* bank of oars had been dispensed with completely.

Other developments, however, were afoot much earlier in the fourth century B.C. The unscrupulous but resourceful Dionysius, tyrant of Syracuse, experimented with the idea of having more men to the oar, and this is probably the correct interpretation of the otherwise fantastic quadriremes and quinqueremes. In the late fourth and early third centuries, the rivalries between the successors of Alexander and their immediate descendants extended to the bid for sea power. Antigonus, who inherited Macedonia, and his son Demetrius Poliorcetes built fleets that had ships requiring crews of eighteen hundred men. Demetrius' son, Antigonus Gonatas, continued this race into the third generation, but his eighteen-banked vessel was countered by Ptolemy III's "twenties" and "thirties." Ptolemy IV gave instructions for a "forty" to be laid down in about 200 B.C. that was more than 400 feet in length with a beam of 50 feet, and required four thousand oarsmen, though in fact she was never used. The supercraft were perhaps the logical outcome of any sort of "arms race," and, except for Ptolemy IV's "forty," they were tested in action. Unfortunately, little is known about them in detail, though a "sixteen" was found in a Macedonian dockyard by the Romans in 168 B.C. It seems likely that they would have had sails on a mainmast, on a mizzen, and on the bowsprit.

The introduction of catapults for hurling darts and of stone-throwing ballistae, two inventions that are both attributed to Demetrius Poliorcetes, led to the appreciation of range as a tactical factor of importance. Yet smaller vessels were still content to rely on ramming, and the larger of them, with their bows and beaks heavily reinforced, did not avoid the head-on collision and indeed seem to have welcomed the close-packed melee. Temporary wooden turrets were set up in the bows and sterns to give the marines vantage points from which to shoot down onto the enemy decks.

Looking back on the history of these rivalries, we can see that, for a period of about a century, the two great powers, Macedon and Egypt, canceled each other out in their attempts to win the supremacy of the eastern Mediterranean. It is hardly surprising, though, that other communities rose to positions of naval prominence. Such a one was Rhodes, a small community that by the end of the third century B.C. virtually held the balance of power. Her aim was to secure the safety of the seas for the merchant ships upon which her livelihood depended— it was never to extend her political influence.

Her requirements, then, were swift, effective warships to deal with pirates as well as the great powers, and she built up a small fleet of probably not more than forty vessels, no numerical match for Ptolemy's three hundred, but nullifying his advantage by her concentration on good training for her citizen-sailors—they were not conscripted slaves—and sound administration. The careers of two of her officers, Alexidamus and Polycles, recorded on stone and still extant, are an interesting example of this point. Rhodes' resourceful methods can be seen in the way in which some of her ships escaped from a tight corner by slinging containers of blazing fire onto poles that projected from their bows, thus anticipating by many centuries the invention of "Greek fire," which will be described later on.

An assiduous student at all times, Rome learned a great deal about the arts of shipbuilding from the Greeks she conquered. Her people were not naturally maritime in the way that the Greeks had been, but once she found herself in control of the south of the Italian peninsula, she had penetrated into a Carthaginian area of development, and she was soon to see that the western Mediterranean was virtually a Carthaginian lake.

The first Punic War broke out in 264 B.C. over the possession of Sicily, and when in 260 B.C. the Carthaginians sent a squadron to cruise around the island and terrorize the coastal towns into submission, the Romans realized that they must have a fleet of their own. Accordingly, though with some initial reluctance, the Senate agreed to the construction of a hundred quinqueremes and twenty triremes, which were built in a very short time by shipwrights from the Greek towns of southern Italy. Luckily, a Carthaginian quinquereme had been washed ashore at the outbreak of war and could be used as a model.

While the ships were being built, the crews were trained to row on a scaffolding of skeleton benches at given words of command. At some point, either at this early stage or perhaps when the flotilla had mustered in the harbor of Syracuse, so fateful to Athens nearly two hundred years earlier, it was decided to equip each ship with a hinged gangway, lowered by a pulley from the masthead. These gangways, which were about 36 feet long and 4 feet wide, had a grappling spike, known as a *corvus*, at the outward end to enable the boarding parties to land easily; for it was on the marines that the Romans chiefly depended and not on purely naval tactics, and their numbers had, accordingly, been stepped up from the original 40 to 120.

The Romans were very successful to start with, and Gaius Duilius destroyed or captured forty-four Carthaginian ships and ten thousand men off Mylae at the northeastern end of the north coast of Sicily. This was followed by further successes elsewhere, including the capture of Corsica during the next few years. An overbold attempt to attack Africa itself, with only an imperfect knowledge of battle conditions in bad weather, led to setbacks, and the war dragged on until Lutatius Catulus' victory near the Aegates Islands off the western end of Sicily.

All this is important because it is the beginning of the long period that led Rome to see herself as a maritime power. She had emerged, perhaps to her surprise, as mistress of the western Mediterranean at the end of the first Punic War; she was soon to become involved in the east too. In 201 B.C., the Rhodians invited her to intervene on their behalf against Philip of Macedon, who had bribed the Cretan pirates to attack them, and this was Rome's entry into the world of the Levant. More particularly, it was the beginning of a long tussle with the eastern Mediterranean pirate. This menace reached its height in the second quarter of the first century B.C., largely because the Romans did not see the necessity for developing an efficient system of patrolling those waters. Some of Rome's enemies, such as Mithridates of Pontus, had encouraged pirates to venture into the Adriatic and even further west; and on one occasion, shipping was burned by them at Ostia, the port of Rome herself. With regular bases and arsenals in Crete and elsewhere, they were more than a match for the halfhearted efforts to check them, and eventually they even became a threat to the corn vessels returning to Rome from the Black Sea.

At last, in 67 B.C., Pompey was nominated to take up a three-year commission to deal with this menace in the whole Mediterranean basin, with full proconsular powers to operate up to fifty miles inland from the coastline at any point and in any province. The vast force, including five hundred ships, which he was authorized to raise and his division of the Mediterranean into thirteen districts show that Rome now realized the need for proper planning and a systematic clearing of the seas. Its successful outcome also shows that Rome had learned at long last the necessity of having a standing fleet if she was to become a real maritime power.

The navy that remained in existence after the pirate threat had been dislodged played an important part in the civil wars with which the whole structure of republican Rome was brought down. Perhaps a glance at the Battle of Actium in September of 31 B.C., which gave Octavian the full control of the Mediterranean and made him able, as Augustus Caesar, to establish the principate, will enable us to see, among other things, how fateful the loss of initiative can be in sea warfare. This battle, described centuries later by Bacon as one that decided the empire of the world, was an early example of the maxim, proved true on many occasions in later history, that smaller ships, if well commanded, will defeat larger ships that have no such advantage.

Agrippa, Octavian's chief naval commander, had won the *corona classica*, the golden crown embellished with miniature beaks of ships, for defeating the younger Pompey in Sicily five years earlier. He seems, too, to have invented new types of grappling irons and such devices as collapsible wooden towers. On this occasion, however, his skill was shown in what today would be called a shrewd appreciation. Actium is the promontory on the south side of the narrow entry into the Ambracian Gulf, a large, almost landlocked lagoon on the northwest coast of Greece. Agrippa saw the need to be on the spot quickly, and he must have crossed the southern Adriatic sooner than was expected, for this alone would explain Antony's amazing inertia. Again, he saw the need of securing bases in Greece, which not merely would support his own forces but would deny the enemy this advantage. In consequence, he drove Antony from his headquarters in the town now known as Patras, at the western end of the Gulf of Corinth, and seized Methone, at the tip of the westernmost prong of Peloponnesus, thus giving himself two places from which he could operate to harass the supply route from Egypt. He also secured the island of Leucas, just south of the Ambracian Gulf. Above all, Agrippa was determined that his smaller fleet should not be caught in the narrow straits around the Ionian Islands, so he kept to the open sea, where there was room to maneuver and avoid Antony's ships, which, though larger, were considerably slowed down by the clumsy timber structures fitted to their hulls as antiramming devices. Agrippa's great advantage was that his ships were nimbler than his adversary's, so his aim was to ram the enemy oars rather than the ships themselves, knowing that the oars were too heavy to be quickly shipped.

Antony's sudden defection, whether it was premeditated flight or not, with its undoubted demoralizing effect on his fleet, is no concern of ours here, but a detail from the later stages of the battles must be mentioned. This was the obviously planned use by Agrippa of fire: oiled and blazing tow was wound around arrows that were then fired at the enemy at close quarters. Also, rafts laden with easily combustible materials were set on fire and directed at the enemy.

There is an interesting relief carving from the Temple of Fortune at Praeneste, and now in the Vatican Museum, which shows one of the heavy ships that fought at Actium. She may have only two banks of oars, but she could also be a trireme, as the toothéd pattern in the relief below the gunwale might be the tips of the uppermost bank of oars, shipped but protruding through the outrigger. In any case, it is probably that each oar would be manned by several oarsmen, so she could easily be a quinquereme or even something grander. She is clearly *kataphraktos*, that is, protected by decking above and along the sides, and we can see a forward spar for the *artemon*, or bowsprit sail, and, immediately aft, a turret painted to give the effect of stone but probably of wood and possibly even collapsible. On the whole, however, the pictorial evidence of Roman warships generally is disappointing, as the details are indistinct, making it hard to decide whether they differed greatly from the Greek.

One of the two ships hauled up from Lake Nemi in the Alban Hills southeast of Rome after the water had been drained off in 1932 was certainly a warship, with a recognizable bow and ram, but her most interesting aspect is the light her discovery threw on the very skillful construction of the hull, making it quite clear that the Romans could have built ships large enough to require fifteen men or more to each oar. Unfortunately, the ship and her companion merchantman were destroyed during the Second World War, and it seems unlikely that we shall ever know why such large vessels were to be found in such an unlikely place.

After Actium, Roman supremacy in the Mediterranean lasted for 250 years. The sea was divided into sectors, and we know that the headquarters for the western area were at Misenum near Naples, with a patrolling force of fifty ships and ten thousand men. The prefecture of the Misene fleet, however, was not so much a military as an administrative appointment, otherwise the elder Pliny would never have held it. The eastern headquarters were at Ravenna, which was then connected with the Adriatic by a network of lagoons. There was a minor base at Forum Julii, the modern Fréjus near Cannes, and there were smaller provincial squadrons at Alexandria, in the Black Sea later on, in the English Channel, and elsewhere. The ships were manned by slaves of all nationalities, and the completion of a regular engagement of twenty-six years led to the grant of full citizenship.

The significant fact is that these fleets were "in being" at all, for the Romans, as has been said, were not by nature nautical-minded. They saw the function of their fleet as limited to patrolling and clearing the seas of pirates and the very occasional support of a land expedition. Moreover, coins and carvings show very little development in the ships apart from minor and decorative embellishments. There was, however, one original type of ship, the Liburnian, which might almost be called a destroyer, used for convoy protection. She was light and therefore speedy and easily handled. She seems to have been invented by a pirate tribe living on the Illyrian coast, though the name was used later to describe almost any warship. She was originally single-banked, but later she was made heavier with a second bank of oars, as can be seen in a lively and attractive mosaic now in the Palazzo Barberini at Palestrina dating back to about the beginning of the Christian era.

During the period of eleven hundred years in which the center of the Roman Empire was at Constantinople, there is little development that need delay us. The *raison d'être* of a fleet was still the pirate menace, but to this was added the Saracen raider. The Byzantine fleet, in consequence, consisted of light cruising vessels, and among these some new types are to be noticed. The *dromon,* "runner," with two banks of oars, one hundred in all, and sometimes as much as 150 feet in length, was low in the water and often narrow in the beam, though this could vary, as in some cases two or three men could sit at the upper oars. She had a forecastle and, at one stage, another amidships, used as fighting towers for the marines, and the catapults could throw half a ton of lead about 750 yards. We can see, therefore, a beginning, though still a very tentative one, of sea fighting from a distance. These vessels had two, and sometimes three, masts, and a small triangular sail was used, very like the lateen, which was kept in position even in action, unlike the square sail and its mast in almost all the other warships we have been discussing.

There seems to have been a smaller and lighter version of this ship called the Pamphylian Chelander, and there was also a reconnaissance vessel, the *galea,* which might be described as a frigate. She was also small and light, but she was armed strongly enough to enable her to fight for the information she was seeking.

Finally, no account of the Byzantine warship and her period would be complete without mention of "Greek fire." Gibbon refers to "the novelty, the terrors and the real efficacy" of this secret weapon, which the Byzantine Romans managed to conceal from their Islamic invaders.[14] It seems to have been made up of liquid bitumen, or naphtha, which was a light and inflammable oil mixed with sulfur, and the pitch extracted from coniferous trees. Water increased its efficacy, and it could only be quenched with sand, vinegar, or urine. In ships it was usually blown laterally through long copper tubes placed in the bows and, as Gibbon says, "fancifully shaped into the mouths of savage monsters" to increase the terror. There seems also to have been a small hand version that was used by the marines on board with great effect. These flame-throwers were used successfully during the sieges of Constantinople in the first quarter of the eighth century, but the invention is said to be much earlier, even if we do not believe that it was revealed by an angel to the great Constantine himself. Though its effect must have been devastating at close quarters, Gibbon is right in saying that it did not bring about that revolution in tactics that the discovery of gunpowder, that "scientific or casual compound of nitre, sulphur and charcoal," was to lo in the fourteenth century.

NOTES

[1]For the views of Thucydides on early Greek History, see Book I, chaps. 1–22.
[2]See the *Iliad,* Book II, ll. 493–759.
[3]See the *Odyssey,* Book V, ll. 244–261.
[4]*Ibid.,* Book XIV, ll. 191 ff.
[5]*Ibid.,* Book IV, ll. 81–85.
[6]See Herodotus, Book I, chap. 163.
[7]*Ibid.,* chap. 166.
[8]See Thucydides, Book I, chap. 14.
[9]See Björn Landström, *The Ship,* p. 36.
[10]See Thucydides, Book I, chap. 13.
[11]Aeschylus, *Persae,* translated by Gilbert Murray, ll. 359–438. Cf. Herodotus, Book VIII, chaps. 66–96.
[12]See Lionel Casson, *The Ancient Mariners.*
[13]See Thucydides, Book I, chap. 49.
[14]See Edward Gibbon, *Decline and Fall of the Roman Empire,* chap. 52.

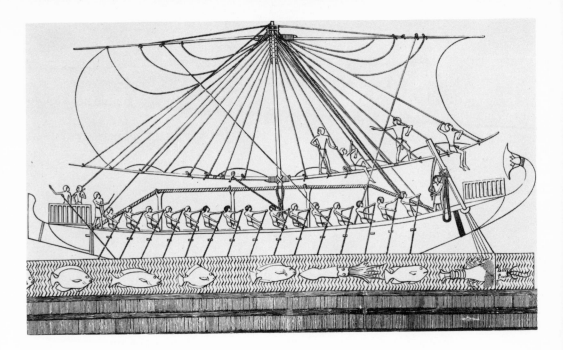

Drawing from a relief carving in the Temple of Deir el Bahari at Thebes
(*c.* 1600 B.C.) showing an Egyptian ship of Queen Hatshepsut's expedition
to Punt. The two steering oars in the stern with their tillers and the mast
with its square sail athwartships (though it is represented as fore and aft by
convention) mark a considerable advance on Pharaoh Sahu-Re's ships.
Science Museum, London

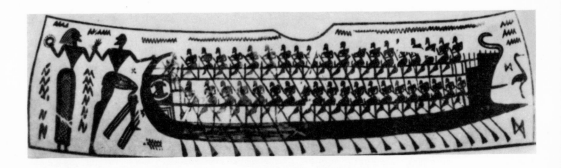

Early Greek penteconter, or fifty-oared galley (*c.* 800–700 B.C.). The vessel
appears to be two-banked, but this is because the artist wished to include
both port and starboard oarsmen but had not yet overcome the problems of
perspective. From a bowl in the British Museum, London. *Science Museum, London*

(*Above*) Drawing of an Egyptian seagoing ship (*c.* 2600 B.C.) from a relief carving in the pyramid at Abu Sir representing Pharaoh Sahu-Re's expedition against the coasts of Syria. Note the bipod mast in the lowered position and the twisted rope stretched over several queen posts to take the strain off bow and stern. *Science Museum, London*

(*Left*) A Greek merchantman pursued by a pirate galley (from a cup *c.* 540–500 B.C.). The pursuing ship is a *hemiolia,* a "one and a halfer," specially constructed for running down merchant vessels. Half the oarsmen, those in the afterpart of the ship, could secure their oars, thus enabling the mast to be lowered onto their vacated thwarts. These men would then be ready to board the victim. *British Museum, London*

WAR GALLEY of VIIᵗʰ CENTURY B.C.

אניה קרב בנויה ע׳י מספנה פניקית

FIGHTING SHIP BUILT BY
PHOENICIAN SHIPWRIGHTS

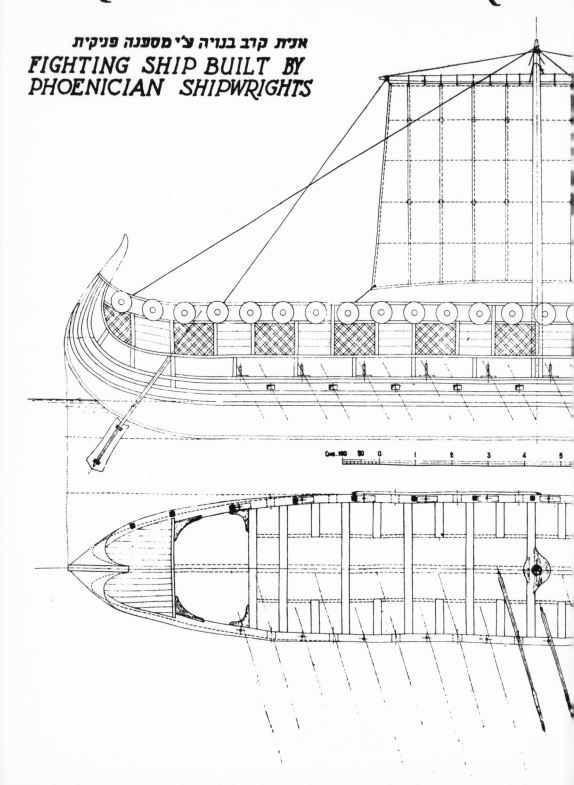

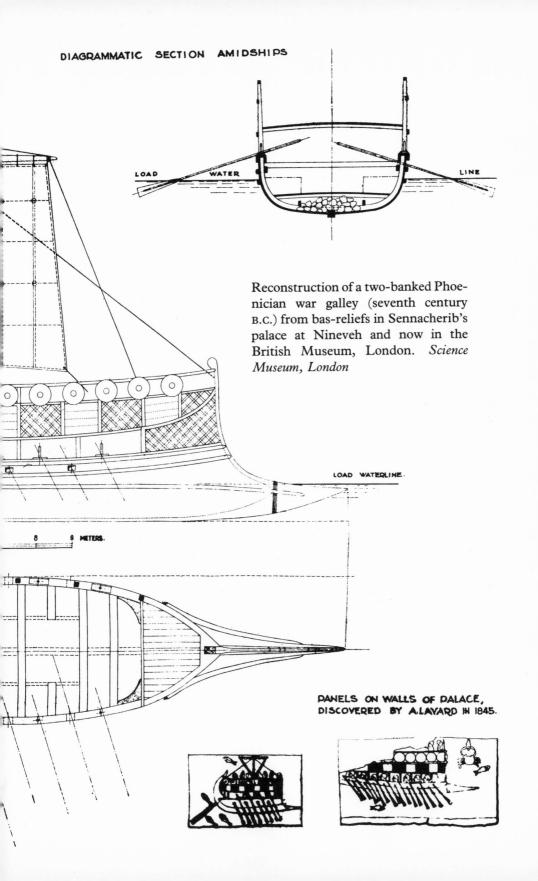

LOAD   WATER   LINE

Reconstruction of a two-banked Phoe-
nician war galley (seventh century
B.C.) from bas-reliefs in Sennacherib's
palace at Nineveh and now in the
British Museum, London. *Science
Museum, London*

LOAD WATERLINE.

8   9 METERS.

PANELS ON WALLS OF PALACE,
DISCOVERED BY A. LAYARD IN 1845.

Relief carving of a Roman warship at the Battle of Actium (31 B.C.) from the Temple of Fortune at Praeneste and now in the Vatican Museum, Rome. Note that the oars in the upper bank are shipped with only their tips visible. The spar for a bowsprit sail, the decking, and the turret are other interesting features. *Science Museum, London*

(Left) Greek cup (probably early fifth century B.C.) showing four galleys. *British Museum, London*

Conjectural model of a Greek galley (*c.* 500 B.C.), port quarter, based on the best existing contemporary representations of the parts of a galley. The trireme usually pulled 170 oars arranged in three banks—31(top), 27, 27—on each side. Her length would be about 150 feet, and the necessary longitudinal strength was obtained by "wales," or belts, round the outside of the hull, which also reinforced the ram. There is considerable controversy about the actual position of the oarsmen, but this model is constructed on the theory that though the men on the top and middle banks were on the same level, the oars of the former pivoted on the outrigger, while those of the latter, who were sitting farther inboard, rested on the gunwale. *Science Museum, London*

Prow of the Oseberg ship showing the detailed carving in "the only known major work of decorative art of the period." This elaborate and beautiful work suggests that the ship was not strictly a fighting ship, but it is clear that Viking warships would be built on these lines. *Universitatets Oldsaksamling, Oslo*

II

The Viking Ship

THE point has already been made that in early days there was very little distinction between an actual warship and any other type of ship. The intentions of the men on board and the weapons they carried were the factors that decided the issue. At any moment, a vessel apparently involved in the peaceful occupation of trade or exploration might find herself challenged, and so, if she chose to retaliate, she became a warship.

This must have been as true of the Norsemen as it was of the Egyptians or the early Greeks, and for this reason the fragments of all types of ships that have miraculously survived to be uncovered by the modern archaeologist's spade are of importance. They tell us something of the supreme mastery over ships these Scandinavian peoples had, and we need not, in considering the vessels of the early centuries of the Christian era, concern ourselves with the separation of these magnificent ships into the categories of war and peace to appreciate this point.

The Viking era covers the period A.D. 800–1300, but there are some relics belonging to earlier centuries that deserve mention. The boat dug up at Nydam in Schleswig in 1863, and now in the Gottorp Museum, can be dated to the first half of the fourth century. She was a large and open rowing boat with high, incurving stem-and-stern posts but with no provision for a mast and sails and no proper keel. She was clinker-built, with the overlapping oak planks riveted together with iron nails, and in this she was exhibiting a feature that was characteristic of all Norse shipbuilding throughout the Middle Ages.

The Hjortspring boat, found preserved in a bog at Als in south Jutland, can be dated to about A.D. 300 also. With her were dug up a great quantity of weapons, so she would seem to have been buried as a victory offering, and therefore must have been a warship in all probability. Like the earliest Scandinavian skin boats with their wooden ribs, known to have existed from rock carvings found in northern Norway, and, after them, the log boats from further south, the boat from Hjortspring was essentially frail. All these boats were therefore too vulnerable for use on the open sea but were admirably suited for inshore travel in the fjords and bays of the Norwegian coast: they would be maneuverable and able, too, to carry comparatively large crews, since the space on board was not limited by a mast or the stowage of sailing gear.

As long as these Norse ships were only required to operate close to the shore and in home waters, the need for sails was not felt. This explains why the evolution of the sail during the sixth to eighth centuries was comparatively late in northern European waters. We know from Tacitus that when Civilis reviewed the fleet off the Rhine delta in A.D. 70, the men were allowed to use their cloaks as sails, yet as late as A.D. 560 Procopius recorded that the English depended only on oars, a point that is borne out by the royal ship found in England at Sutton Hoo, not far from Ipswich, which can be dated to the middle years of the seventh century.

Yet in spite of these finds and others, especially the ship excavated at a Gokstad farm near Sandefjord, which we shall discuss later on, the sources are meager. Pictorial art generally, as seen in coins and seals and in carvings in churches and elsewhere, shows, as we might expect, that the ship was an integral part of Norse life; yet it is disappointing that we find ourselves relying more or less entirely on the references in the sagas for our information. For though these references are plentiful, they are suspect for a number of reasons—for the exigencies of meter, for example, or because, written years after the event, there may be a certain amount of hindsight employed or evidence of the use of propagandist retouching.

Nevertheless, it is in these skaldic writings that the Norse delight in the sea emerges, and phrases such as that in which a ship is said "to butt the waves with her bows like a goat of the sea" create in our minds a picture which is both arresting and likely to be accurate.

At the beginning of the Viking period, the technical problem seems to have been how to get full strength into a keel. A large boat excavated in 1920 at Kvalsund and dated around 600 is the earliest known Norse vessel to have a keel, and she also has, for the first time, a rudder actually attached to the ship's side, aft of the starboard gunwale, with a tiller fixed at right angles to it.

"Longship" is the generic term for the Viking warship, and she must now be considered in some detail. Her narrowness was all the more noticeable because of her length, and, though there were many variations, it seems safe to say that the Gokstad ship, mentioned above, shows the longship in her early stages. The importance therefore of this ship is considerable.

Strictly speaking, the Gokstad ship that was found well preserved in a 15-foot-high mound of blue clay when excavated in 1880 is not large enough to qualify as a warship. She belongs rather to the category of the *karfi*, a word which derives from the Byzantine Greek term for the Roman vessels used on rivers and therefore light enough to be dragged past rapids comparatively easily. The largest of these vessels had thirty-two oarsmen, sixteen on each side, and this is the size of the Gokstad ship. Such vessels were not built for warfare or for long sea voyages, but the Gokstad ship, with her beam of 16 feet and her freeboard of nearly 6 feet, was probably more seaworthy than many of them.

The construction of the ship is a tribute to the skill of the Norse marine architects. Her keel, bows, and stern were each made of one solid piece of timber, and the sixteen strakes of her planking are riveted together, calked with tarred ropes, and lashed to ribs by means of thick "cleats" in order to give the ship the necessary elasticity in a heavy sea. The "mastfish," so called because of its shape, contained a 40-foot mast made of pine, and there were sixteen pairs of oars, though no thwarts, so perhaps the oarsmen sat on their sea chests. The mast carried a square sail, varying between 16 and 17½ feet, which may have been gaily colored, like the sails depicted in the Bayeux Tapestry, or striped or checkered perhaps, a detail mentioned frequently by the skalds and unlikely to be wrong.

The ship was built in about 900, and with her distinct keel and fixed starboard rudder with a tiller, she does seem to represent an advanced stage in the evolution of Norse shipbuilding and is a long way from the early rowing boats. All that could happen in the future was that the ships would become larger, as we shall see presently. The most characteristic feature of Norse ships, apart from the high bows and stern, which had removable dragons' heads on them, is to be seen in the Gokstad ship—the overlapping shields, thirty-two of them on each side, which were hung externally along the length of the uppermost strakes and were painted black and yellow. A stock phrase in the sagas frequently calls attention to this, but it should be pointed out that this had nothing to do with defense and was merely a method of identifying the ship when in harbor. A replica of this ship commanded by Captain Magnus Andersen crossed the Atlantic in 1893 for the Chicago World's Fair, commemorating the four hundredth anniversary of the discovery of America. The journey was accomplished in twenty-eight days.

The Oseberg ship, the showpiece of the Viking ship finds, was also found in a burial mound. Her importance is that with her beautifully carved prow and stern and splendid workmanship throughout, she is the only known major work of decorative art of the period, and as Gustav Vigeland, the sculptor, has said, is worthy to be cast in bronze and set up in Oslo as a national monument. She is a hundred years older than the Gokstad ship, which would place her about 800, and Professor Shetelig (see Bibliography) thinks that she was an old ship specially refurbished for the burial at Oseberg. At all events, it seems certain that both ships were genuine and were not merely mock-ups put together for particular ceremonial occasions.

Yet, as was said earlier, the Gokstad ship and certainly the ship found at Oseberg were not really warships at all, for the longship proper would have been larger, having at least thirty oars, that is, fifteen thwarts. Nevertheless, they were the prototypes, and there can be little doubt that they provide us with much valuable information about Viking ship construction; and we can see before our eyes, in little, as it were, the warships themselves.

These longships vary slightly, but we should be able to accept the general features described by the skalds, as most of them were bound to be knowledgeable about nautical matters, and even if they were not, they would certainly be writing for a public that was. General accuracy would therefore seem essential, if only to avoid incurring ridicule. In details, however, the descriptions by the skalds are probably useless and should be taken with considerable pinches of salt.

Professor Brøgger (see Bibliography) makes the point that by about the year 1000, the Viking longships can be fairly precisely categorized into three groups: the great ships, those with between twenty and thirty thwarts, and those with fewer than twenty. He also states that the measure of a ship was the number of spaces between the crossbeams— in other words, how many *rums*, or rooms, it had. Each room corresponded to a pair of oars, with a thwart or seat to each oar, as can be seen from direct references in the sagas. This designation by rooms and thwarts persisted throughout the Middle Ages and even afterward.

Yet, on the whole, it seems that the largest ships, those with thirty-seven or more rooms, were too clumsy, and their very construction proved too difficult to be worthwhile; at all events, there were probably never very many of them, to judge from the comprehensive list given by Professor Brøgger. At first the longships were not really designed as warships, as they were not likely to meet any serious opposition from any western European country, but later on they seem to have been built as high as possible to enable the crew to shoot down onto the enemy when the ships had come to close quarters. Also, their height would prevent even the most determined enemy from boarding. We are told that King Haakon's *Kross-suden* (the *Holy Cross*), which was built at Orust in the winter of 1252–1253, had her gunwale level with the tent ridge of a ship of thirty-five rooms, which implies that she was a considerably larger vessel herself.

Let us now consider some of the ships in the first two classes. Professor Brøgger thinks that the name *dreki*, "dragons," was applied only to ships with more than thirty rooms and that such ships must have existed before 900, though they were built at specially troublesome periods in Norse history after that date. At first, great landowners like Raud the Strong built and owned such ships, but later it seems as though the building of the largest ones was reserved to the Crown. The Northerners were probably the first in the field, for we know that Olav Tryggvason, who imagined his *Tranin* (the *Crane*) of thirty rooms to be the "proudest ship yet built," was greatly impressed by Raud's *Ormrinn Skanni* (*Short Serpent*) and went so far as to take her away with him after having rather brutally disposed of her owner. This was in 999, and a tradition was established that lasted for several centuries, starting with Tryggvason's thirty-four room *Ormrinn Langi* (*Long Serpent*), built almost immediately for that king's expedition against Wendland.

We know quite a lot about the building of the *Long Serpent*, and even the name of one of the most important craftsmen has survived. This was Torberg, who introduced a radical alteration in the construction of the stern-and-stem posts, which, though revolutionary, convinced the king of Torberg's wisdom and led to his appointment as master builder for the whole ship and earned him the nickname of *shavhogg*, that is, "he who cuts smoothly with the ax." Though the *Long Serpent's* measurements were carefully kept as a guide for the future, the ship herself did not last long. Sven Forkbeard defeated Tryggvason at the Battle of Svolde in 1000 and so gained control over almost the whole of Norway. The skald Snorre has written that the *Long Serpent* "of all the ships in Norway was the best made and at the greatest cost," but this phrase is too frequently used elsewhere to be particularly convincing in this context.

Half a century later, another great ship was built with thirty-five rooms. This was Harald Hardrada's *Buza*, built in the winter of 1061–1062 for his expedition against Denmark and constructed on the measurements of Tryggvason's *Long Serpent*. Professor Brøgger quotes the skald who wrote of the part this ship played in battle and how, as her long hull lay on the water, the serpent's mane gleamed against the deck and how, when she was rowed away, she looked like the flutter of an eagle's wings.

Toward the end of the twelfth century, King Sverre came to realize that his only hope of retaining power was to build up a fleet, so once again a great warship was built, the *Mariasuden*, as well as a number of smaller ones. The *Mariasuden* was not really a success, though she acquitted herself well in the one action in which she took part. She was "no fair ship," because she was "pieced together," records the saga with commendable frankness.

Another half century later, three large ships were built for King Haakon's Danish and Scottish expeditions between the years 1252 and 1263. The last of these to be built, the *Kristsuden*, had as many as thirty-seven rooms. This was the king's flagship, and in her his body was brought back from the Orkneys in 1264.

These large ships, however, were expensive to build and difficult to handle in the exigencies of war, so they were exceptional rather than normal; and the middle class of ships, those between twenty and thirty rooms, and especially those of around twenty-five, proved the most valuable. Luckily a good deal is known about them, much more than about the third class, the ships with fifteen to twenty rooms, though these too had an important part to play in war.

In the middle class, there was the first *Olavssuden*, built by Erlingr Skakki the Wryneck, with twenty-five rooms. In action she proved that maneuverability was the deciding factor, not the number, or size even, of ships. In the battle off Nordnes in 1181, King Sverre, who had captured the *Olavssuden* from King Magnus two years earlier, was victorious, with half the number of ships his adversary had; but Magnus had the last word that same year when he defeated Sverre in the Battle of Nidaros and captured the whole of his fleet, thirty-three ships altogether, including the *Olavssuden*.

Another ship in this class, the *Goldenbreast*, with twenty rooms, must have been exceptionally well built, as she is mentioned in the sagas over a period of nearly sixty years. The sagas are likely to be less reliable when we consider them as sources for the actual sea battles, but there are some points that seem certain. The repeated references to the lowering of the mast during battle show that battles were not fought under sail, and no engagement would take place in the open sea if it could be avoided. Rather, they fought in enclosed waters, in the inshore reaches of the fjords and on the lee sides of islands. Professor Brøgger reminds us that the first sea fight was thought to be in Hafrsfjord, which could only be reached through a narrow channel.

Thus it seems safe to say that the battles were comparatively small affairs, never involving anything like the number of ships mentioned in the sagas as taking part. It seems, too, that the low-lying longship, with her accompanying speed and maneuverability, would outdo the cumbersome great ships like the *Mariasuden*. After about 1240, there seem to be fewer battles in Norwegian waters, and the records are more concerned with the musters for overseas expeditions. Yet surely here again the numbers are often grossly exaggerated: it seems most unlikely that Canute invaded England with six hundred ships. Harald Hardrada's two hundred in 1066, a figure which excluded the smaller craft and the supply vessels, may, however, be about the right one.

Viking ship found in 1904 in a burial mound at Oseberg near Tønsberg,
Norway, and now preserved in Oslo. Built about A.D. 900, she is 70 feet long
and 17 feet in the beam and is less sturdy than the ship found at Gokstad
(see page 40). Her fifteen pairs of oars were found intact and are 7 feet
shorter than those of the Gokstad ship. *Universitatets Oldsaksamling, Oslo*

Drawing of Harold's ship from the Bayeux Tapestry (c. 1080), which is identical with those used by the Norsemen at this period. Colored aquatint by J. Basire, after C. A. Stothard, plate VI, published 1819–1823. *National Maritime Museum, Greenwich*

William the Conqueror's ships, colored aquatint by J. A. Atkinson, after C. Hamilton Seaforth, published 1811. The ships are based on the evidence provided by the Bayeux Tapestry, in which both Norman and English ships are similar. *National Maritime Museum, Greenwich*

Starboard quarter of the Viking longship (*c.* A.D. 900) excavated at Gokstad near Sandfjord, Norway, in 1880 and now preserved in Oslo. This very seaworthy vessel is 76 feet from stem to stern, is 17 feet in the beam, and has a freeboard of nearly 6 feet. She would have sixteen pairs of oars. Note the fixed rudder, the distinct keel, and her clinker-built hull with its sixteen strakes and stout ribs. *Science Museum, London*

Crusading round ships at the conquest of Constantinople (1203), from a fifteenth century miniature. Note the superimposed fore- and aftercastles. *Bibliothèque Nationale, Paris*

III

The English Warship Before 1600

WHEN we consider the beginnings of a specifically English warship, two factors should be borne in mind: first, the very concept of a fighting fleet is foreign to the English medieval mind; and, second, but following on closely from the first point, the evolution of the fighting ship herself is, on the whole, slow. It is not till the early sixteenth century that a ship was actually built for war. Certainly, before then, ordinary merchant ships could be converted into warships by the addition of temporary superstructures and by supplementing the normal crew with "fighting" officers and men—points which we shall return to presently—but there was no such thing as a permanent warship before the Tudors.

If this is so, it is hardly surprising that the modern functions of a navy were also absent. Perhaps, though, there were exceptions, for Alfred seems to have been the pioneer in carrying out the active defense of his country when he met the Danes at sea instead of waiting for them to land. This offensive action was possible, and not just foolhardy, because Alfred modified the ships to his own specifications. They would have been very like those of the Norsemen, but they are described in the chronicles as being "full twice as long" as any earlier English ship and swifter, steadier, and higher in the water. Dr. and Mrs. R. C. Anderson state that these vessels were constructed "so as it seemed to him they would be most efficient,"[1] a direct reference to intentional improvement in design to meet a given situation.

[43]

Again, King Harold seems to have been aware of the need to defend Britain when he lay off the Isle of Wight during the summer of 1066 keeping an eye on William's movements. It was merely unfortunate that the logistics of "keeping a fleet in being" at that time were inadequate; the strategy itself was impeccable.

The Bayeux Tapestry, really an embroidery, is an important document for our purposes. Though it is not now thought that it was worked by Matilda, William the Conqueror's queen, it can reasonably be dated to within about twenty years of the events it so vividly describes. A problem, however, is to decide how much importance can be placed on the details of the ships. If we bear in mind the likelihood of minor errors caused by feminine ignorance and the vagaries of the embroiderer's needle, we should also remember that the general appearance of the ships is more likely to be right than wrong. Therefore, since the vessels are only very slightly different from the Gokstad boat, a difference that might be due to the sewing, it seems that there was virtually no change in ship construction during the two hundred years the Norsemen spent in France. They were not likely to have been shorter in length, as at first suggests itself, because of the convention of enlarging the men on board, as can be seen in Egyptian art and on Greek vases. Again, at least one ship on each side has sixteen oar ports visible,[2] the exact number of the Gokstad ship.

A difference is that in the Saxon ships there are no oar ports amidships, while the Normans have a continuous row along the uppermost strake. Other features are the carved figureheads on the high bows and sterns, which were detached on landing, the steering paddle aft on the starboard quarter, and the square sail. All the ships depicted are striped in appearance, which must be the convention to show that they were clinker-built, as we would expect. One scene shows a mast being lowered before landing, and in another there are shrouds to the mast, as well as a stay and backstay; so it would seem that by this time, they were making use of a wind blowing at right angles to their course by giving additional support to the mast. Of course, it is possible that the Oseberg and Gokstad ships may have had them too, but there is no surviving evidence to prove the point.

In general, then, the typical ship of the late eleventh to the end of the thirteenth century would have been single-masted, square-rigged, and clinker-built, a recognizable descendant of the Viking longship. As time went by, however, and oars gave way to sail as the main method of propulsion, the length of these ships decreased from about five times the beam to three times, and this was to remain fairly constant for several centuries. Further improvements came in about the year 1200, owing to the penetration into the Mediterranean world by the Normans and the experience gained there; and perhaps the Third Crusade, which began in 1189, had its effect too on both French and English. The Northerners would have found that though their own ships were tougher than those they met there, they were less sophisticated because they were lacking in so many refinements.

Few would disagree with Dr. Anderson when he writes that the stern rudder, the deep-draft hull, and the bowsprit were the features which transformed the Viking ship into the real sailer that could take advantage of any wind, and it is these that must be considered now in some detail.

Contemporary seals are a valuable source here, but their shape and the tendency to stylize or even distort the ships for decorative reasons can be misleading. It seems likely that the ports entitled to have such seals would depict on them their larger and more important vessels—in fact, exactly those ships that would be used for war; and it is because of this that the seals become such a valuable source.

However distorted the ships may have become to fit the circular demands of the seal, the fore- and aftercastles are clearly to be seen on them. In some, such as the seal of Sandwich, which is dated 1238, these structures, which were platforms for the soldiers at first, look very temporary; but by the end of the century, they seem to have become integral parts of the ships, as can be seen in the Dover seal of 1284 and even more so in that of Poole, which is dated 1325. The stern rudder, which is so definite a feature in the Poole seal, is first seen in the seal of Ipswich, 1200, though the scholars who use the evidence of a panel on a font in Winchester Cathedral to push the first appearance of this feature back to 1180 may be correct: the font is certainly thought to come from the Low Countries, and the idea of the stern rudder may well have originated there.

The adaptation of these ships to the circumstances of war and the use the kings of England made of them, such as it was, are of great interest. In the first instance, a king could supplement the few vessels he might own with several hired from private individuals for the duration of his campaign. Later it was thought easier to hire from corporate bodies of shipowners, and it was in this way that the Cinque Ports, originally Hastings, Romney, Hythe, Dover, and Sandwich, came into existence. These five ports agreed to provide fifty-seven ships, each carrying a master and twenty men, for fifteen days annually in return for certain privileges, which included relief from tolls. Further ships could be provided in return for further privileges. Their charter is dated 1278. The geographical position of these "head" ports and their "limbs" on a dangerous and, at that time, indented coast gave them a considerable bargaining counter, especially after the loss of Normandy; so much so, that the king could easily find that he had surrendered too much sovereignty to them and that they were tending to monopolize trade in the Channel. Thus there came a return to the private contractor, usually a well-established merchant like William Cannynge from Bristol, whose vessels even traded with Iceland and who equipped a whole expedition for Edward IV.

The other way in which the medieval king could raise a fleet was to place an embargo on all his subjects' ships, a maritime equivalent of the *levée en masse* on land, and compel them, or some of them, to muster at the Tower of London, where they would receive their orders and undergo such modification as was necessary to turn them into warships. This could entail little more than the addition of the fore- and after-, or summer-, castles mentioned above, which would enable the soldiers to shoot down onto the decks of lower enemy ships, if the occasion arose. Another more important process that took place at the rendezvous at the Tower was the allocation to each ship of a captain and his lieutenant, who brought with them a group of fighting men, probably their own feudal retainers. All these were quite distinct from the standing officers who helped to make up the normal crew of a merchantman. They included the master, who was responsible to the owner for the ship; the boatswain, whose duty it was to look after the masts, yards, and sails; the carpenter, whose importance in the days of wooden ships is obvious; and the cook, as well as a number of others. The line of demarcation between the specially imported fighting officers and the experienced officers permanently attached to a merchantman must often have been largely theoretical, if we are to judge from the pen picture

Chaucer gives us of the shipman who joined the other Canterbury pilgrims at the Tabard. They all must have been tough and ready to cope with any eventuality arising in that disputed territory between legitimate trade and downright piracy. Above all, however, the masters of these merchantmen-turned-warships brought with them their invaluable knowledge of coasts, shoals, and currents and their experience of handling ships in all weathers.

Before we turn to the emergence of the fully rigged ship that is to hold the stage for so long, we must look at the evidence that exists for the way in which these ships were used in war. Here the essential point is that there was no real naval policy before the Tudors. Edward III called himself "Lord of the Sea" after 1350, but this did not amount to very much: it merely accentuated the fact that he owned territory on both sides of the English Channel and expected to be able to transport himself and his armies and their supplies across the narrows as well. The navy, collected together in one of the ways mentioned above, was thought to be a mere troop-carrying organization. It was prepared to fight on the way, if need be, but once its load had been deposited onshore, there seems to have been no question of its keeping to the sea. The earliest recorded sea fight was at Damme in Flanders, between Bruges and the open sea. This was in 1213, and it can only be called a sea fight in that the English, under the command of William Longéspee, anchored their ships some way offshore, reached the land in their boats, and destroyed those enemy ships they found lying on the beach. This was really little more than a raid, as was the incident three years later when Hubert de Burgh and a fleet from the Cinque Ports attacked some French ships, under Eustace the Monk, off Dover.

More than a century later, a more sophisticated battle took place off Sluys. This was in the year 1340, and it was a retaliatory action on the part of Edward III for damage done by the French two years earlier. Though the English king was outnumbered by four to one, according to the account in Froissart's chronicles, a skillful ruse brought the French out into the open sea, and there followed a "sore battle": "archers and crossbows began to shoot, and men of arms approached and fought hand to hand; and the better to come together they had great hooks and grappers [sic] of iron, to cast out of one ship into another, and so tied them fast together."

This would be the typical sea battle in the days before the use of guns completely revolutionized naval tactics. In fact, as a modern historian has put it, "the object of a sea-fight in those days was to ram or scuttle your enemy, or to manoeuvre him into shallow water with your galleys (*sc.* oared vessels) and throw him out of action at the mercy of the sea or to get alongside and disable his tack and tackle, cut his halliards and cordage with shearhooks mounted on long poles and then grapple and board at the waist for a hand-to-hand encounter."[3]

In August, 1350, there was a brief encounter between Edward III's ships and those of the King of Castile in the English Channel off Winchelsea. This was a haphazard affair, not part of any formulated strategy; it is known as Les Espagnols-sur-Mer and was merely another example of land tactics employed, successfully as it turned out, at sea. A battle fought off La Rochelle in June, 1372 gives us an example of an English fleet failing in its role of providing armed transport, which must have been the navy's main duty in the centuries before the Tudors. On this occasion, the Castilians, in alliance with France, overwhelmed the lighter English ships by dropping iron bars and heavy stones from the greater height of their own ships. This defeat lost the English the control of the seas they had won at Sluys, though they had hardly appreciated the point, and led to a considerable diminution of their French territories.

These engagements are enough to show us that the round ship, the merchant ship that could be quickly adapted for war, did not really answer the purpose on those rare occasions when it came to offensive action at sea. Geography ruled out the efficacy of any specific warship, such as the Mediterranean galley, which was equipped with a ram and was easily maneuvered by a crew of trained oarsmen. There is, in fact, good reason to believe that English ships were specially constructed to stand up to the sou'westerlies blowing in from the Atlantic and to operate in waters that would reduce the galley to impotence. The compromise that did work was one that combined a round, less easily maneuverable ship with steep sides, and therefore suitable for the English seas, with the requirements of a merchant ship—plenty of stowage space, seaworthiness, and general toughness in construction. On the whole, this dual-purpose ship justified her existence; indeed, she had to, as most English kings before the fifteenth century could not have afforded the luxury of special warships.

In the early fifteenth century, a new element was to be seen for the first time since Alfred's reign. This was the notion of the defense of England, and, though tentative at first, it was later to become a permanent feature of English naval strategy and a justification for improvements in ship design. Indeed, eventually it led to the construction of specific warships under the early Tudors. It is difficult to date the actual beginning of this notion, but a valuable source for its early development can be seen in *The Libelle of Englyshe Polycye*, a poem on the use of sea power, now attributed with some confidence to Adam de Moleyns, Bishop of Chichester and for a time Keeper of the Privy Seal. This poem can be dated to the end of 1436, and it is interesting to note that the only incident in Edward III's long reign to be given any space is that king's siege of Calais in 1346–1347. It relates how Edward

> made a sige royall
> and wanne the toune, and in especiall
> the see was kepte and thereof he was lorde.[4]

It was to commemorate this occasion that Edward's magnificent nobles were struck with their depiction of the one-masted round ship of the day, complete with high and elaborately decorated castles, stern rudder, and a likeness of the king himself, a gigantic figure personifying perhaps the might of England and certainly displaying to advantage on his shield the lilies of France. The nobles were to be the grounds for trouble later, apparently, as the Duke of Burgundy had similar coins struck in Flanders.

Unfortunately for us, the author considered Edward's naval victories to be so recent, and therefore common knowledge, that he did not tell how it actually came about that in Edward's time

> was no navey in the see
> that myght wythstonde the power of hys mageste.[5]

Toward the end of the poem, there is a short passage that may make us wonder whether Shakespeare was, after all, so anachronistic when he put into the mouth of John of Gaunt the famous words about the silver sea serving England "in the office of a wall or as a moat defensive to a house." Shakespeare has been accused of attributing late Tudor attitudes of mind to the Plantagenets in his histories, yet in the *Libelle*, written 150 years before his time, are these words that create the self-same image:

> Kepe than the see abought in speciall,
> Whiche of England is the rounde wall,
> As though England were lykened to a cite
> And the wall environ were the see.
> Kepe than the see that is the wall of England
> And than is England kepte by Goddes hande[6]

In the reign of Henry V the war with France flared up again, and the king came to possess fourteen large ships, all presumably very much larger and more stoutly built than ordinary merchantmen, though they were basically the same in appearance. He also had twenty-four smaller ships of his own. Of the larger ones, we know that the *Holy Ghost* (760 tons) was built at Southampton by a shipwright called William Soper in 1414 and that the *Trinity Royal* (540 tons) carried Henry to France in August, 1415. Both ships, however, were considerably smaller than the *Jesus*, which displaced 1,000 tons. The *Holy Ghost* had six guns, and at least one of the others, the *George*, three; so, for the first time, guns were being used on shipboard, though traditionally the first gun was placed in an English ship in 1406, and the ship in question was the *Christopher of the Tower*, so called because in Crown employment.

Most of Henry's ships were sold at his death to pay his debts—a grim proof, if one were needed, that they were his personal property and not the beginnings of a national fleet. It is this, no doubt, which inspired the author of the *Libelle* to such flights of eulogy for the late king, whom he may well have known personally. Henry is depicted as being wise and farseeing, endowed with all the qualities, a very paragon of all the virtues—even likely, if he had lived, to have initiated an enduring policy of building up sea power:

> And if he had to this tyme lyved here
> He had bene prince named wythouten pere;
> His grete shippes shoulde have bene put in preffe
> Unto the ende that he mente of in cheffe.
> For doute it not but that he wolde have be
> Lorde and Master aboute the rounde see,
> And kepte it sure, to stoppe oure enmyes hens.[7]

In northern Europe, there seems little likelihood that many ships had a second mast before the year 1400, even though in the Mediterranean the lateen-rigged two-master was common enough before that date. The great increase in size in Henry V's ships, already mentioned, gives us the reason for the introduction of the second mast, and it seems clear that it was a direct importation from the Mediterranean, where the *artemon*, lying forward of the mainmast on which a headsail could be set, had for a long time been almost a second mast in embryo.

As early as 1418, this second mast can be found in Henry V's *Grâce Dieu*, a ship with a hull about 100 feet long; and though there is some doubt about the nature of this "mesan," whether it was the aftermast, later called a "mizzen" by the English, or a foremast, in the French sense of *misaine*, the important point surely is that here is a second mast appearing in northern waters for the first time. A stall end from St. Nicholas' chapel at King's Lynn and dated to about 1419 shows a two-masted ship with a much sharper bow. She is also square-rigged on the mainmast and lateen-rigged on the mizzenmast.

Very soon the one additional mast led to another, and so the three-masted ship came into existence. Here, too, a precedent can be found in the Mediterranean. Richard I sank a large three-masted ship during the Third Crusade; but from the context in which this incident is described, it seems to have been the exception rather than the normal rule. During the next two centuries, there is no mention of three-masted ships either in the Mediterranean or in the north. Indeed, even though it is logical to suppose that the greater ships of Henry V—especially perhaps the one he started to build at Bayonne in 1419, for this ship was 186 feet from stem to stern—might have been three-masted, there is no satisfactory evidence of the third mast before the middle of the fifteenth century. Once introduced, however, rapid strides forward must have been made, since by the end of the century, ships were no longer dependent on fair winds only—indeed, the feats of mariners speak for themselves: by that time, Columbus had discovered America, Vasco da Gama had opened up the trade routes to the Orient, and Diaz had doubled the Cape of Good Hope.

The ship begun at Bayonne, mentioned above, was probably of the type known as a carrack, a development of the northern one-masted cargo vessel and in her prime in the fifteenth century. The type was further refined in the Mediterranean. We know that several Genoese carracks had been captured in 1416 and 1417, so it is reasonable to say that this type of vessel was becoming the standard fully rigged ship everywhere and, indeed, was to be the model on which warships were planned later on. The first dated three-masted ship is to be seen on a seal of Louis of Bourbon of the year 1466; but in a manuscript belonging to Lord Hastings, now thought to be not later than 1450, some charmingly realistic three-masted ships can be seen.

The warships that were being built in the very first years of King Henry VII's reign were not really very different from the normal round ships, the essentially cargo-carrying vessels of the later Middle ages that we have been discussing. But for the first time for the greater part of a century, they were permanent "king's ships" and were, in fact, intended to be the nucleus of a larger fleet that could be mustered in one or other of the traditional ways. Henry VII, who in Bacon's well-known phrase "could not endure to see trade sick," was in the habit of lending his warships to merchants for their longer voyages to the Levant. Such voyages had become regular features in the programs of the more enterprising merchant syndicates, such as that of Southampton, and we can imagine that the presence of great armed ships would greatly increase the chances of a safe return. The *Mary of the Tower* undertook such journeys in 1486 and 1491, and another of Henry's ships, the *Sovereign*, in 1494, 1497, and 1504.

We know something of the details of one of these ships, the earliest of her kind in England. The *Regent*, built in 1487, had four masts and carried topsails and even a topgallant sail on her mainmast, but she was still designed for "in-fighting" and not "off-fighting." She had guns sited on each side of her high castles and on the upper deck; but in spite of their number and variety, they would mostly have been small, breech-loading "serpentines" and as such would hardly qualify as other than man-killers. A sister ship, the *Sovereign*, was built in the same year, and these two ships seem to have been the first occupants of the earliest dry dock recorded in England, that constructed in 1496 at Portsmouth by Robert Brygandine. Henry VII's two other principal ships, the *Sweep-stake* and the *Mary Fortune*, were built ten years later. They were much smaller ships; they were three-masted and seem really to have been oared galleasses—forerunners, in fact, of Henry VIII's galleasses of 1546, which will be mentioned later. The exact arrangement of their oars is hard to determine, but it is likely that they were biremes, that is, with their oars in pairs, as in the Venetian galleys and as, indeed, had been the practice in the first English galleys two centuries earlier.

Henry VIII inherited seven warships from his father, including the four mentioned above. He set about rebuilding the *Sovereign* at once and in the first five years of his reign added a further twenty-four to his fleet. One or two of these ships and others built at the end of his reign will be selected for comment, but in general it is true to say that his early ships would differ little from their fifteenth century forbears in appearance.

Henry VIII's really important innovation was the introduction of proper ordnance into these ships. This led to a further, even more important, change that was brought about by the unsuitability of having such heavy guns sited on the high poops and forecastles. This was the construction of gunports—at first, low down in the waist of the ship and, later, along the full broadside. From this time forward, the visible appearance of a ship showed whether she was a warship or a merchant vessel. This innovation also brought about the end of close-fighting and led eventually to line-ahead tactics. Also, from then on, the hitherto purely administrative sailors became fighters, taking over this task from the soldiers imported for fighting duties.

Henry VIII's *Mary Rose* is traditionally the first ship to have had gunports constructed on her broadside, and the date is said to be 1513. She had five muzzle-loading brass curtals, or short-barreled cannon, weighing about 3,000 pounds each. Some very good specimens of the brass cannon belonging to the *Mary Rose* were recovered in 1836 from her wreck off Spithead and are now in the Tower of London and elsewhere.

The reconstructed *Sovereign* had only four curtals, but she had three demicurtals and three brass culverins as well, and now that these different types of ordnance have been mentioned, it seems appropriate to examine briefly the whole nature of the early Tudor gun.

In this aspect of the warship, Henry VIII's reign brought about something of a major revolution. At the beginning of the century, naval guns, and indeed most other guns, were made up of a number of wrought-iron bars welded together so as to form a tube, which was reinforced by several thick iron hoops shrunk over it. An open trough into which the powder-loaded chamber could be firmly fixed was fitted at the breech. Naturally, these guns varied considerably; and, indeed, standardization, even within the same class, was still a long way in the future. The smaller guns that threw shot of only 1 or 2 pounds' weight were mounted on swivels so that they could be elevated or depressed, but this was not possible for the larger iron guns. The powder charges were small for safety reasons, so the range these guns could fire and the impact the shot made on arrival were negligible.

Henry's brass or bronze muzzle-loading guns, introduced at the very beginning of his reign, became, with very few alterations, the generally accepted guns for the next 250 years. Cast-iron guns were introduced from Mechlin, as we shall see, but only very slowly did they replace the heavier brass guns; and for the lighter calibers, brass was used till well on into the nineteenth century.

Unfortunately, we do not know why, when, or how the muzzle-loading "great gun" from Mechlin was put into Henry's ships, but we know that guns from the foundry of Hans Poppenruyter were sent over on approval in 1543 and were tried out against some buildings in Houndsditch that had been cleared for the purpose. The successful outcome of this test led eventually to the innovation of cutting gunports low down in an increasingly pronounced "tumblehome" in ships, this last an innovation too, designed to bring the heavy ordnance nearer to the center line so as to prevent the ship from becoming top-heavy.

The evolution of the gun in England (for very soon English gun founders were encouraged by the king to rival the Flemish master) was through two types, the cannon and the culverin. The first threw a heavy iron shot of about 50 pounds, but there was a smaller version, a demicannon, which could throw a 32-pound shot, and this seems to have become very commonly used in English ships. The second type, the culverin, was a longer and stronger gun that could fire a smaller shot a greater distance. It was perhaps as much as 13 feet long. Once again, there were many smaller variants—with such fascinating names as demiculverins, sakers, minions, falcons, falconets, and robinets—which fired shots from 9 pounds down to 1 pound. All these culverin-type guns were probably designed in the first place to fire over the bow or stern of a ship, as their length would seem excessive on the broadside; but the gun had proved so satisfactory by the time of the Armada that about 95 per cent of the English ships were so armed. Gradually, the length was cut down, and the culverin became the ancestor of the seventeenth and eighteenth century ship gun.

Nothing has been said so far about the range these culverins could achieve. There are difficulties about this, as contemporary writers give the figures in "paces," a distance that varied a great deal according to the system being used. Professor M. A. Lewis, the great expert on Tudor guns, believes that the "point-blank" range would be about 330 yards and the "random" about 1 ¼ miles, though he warns his readers that these distances would have to be doubled if the Roman custom of regarding a pace as a double step were followed.[8] At any rate, using the short pace, the comparative ranges for cannon would have been about 280 yards and 1 mile.

There is no doubt that the introduction of these comparatively heavy guns into ships hastened the change from clinker-building to carvel-building. The overlapping planks of the former method were an unsatisfactory surface for cutting gunports in; and in any case, this method of construction must have been less strong than the flush-fitting planks in the carvel-built ship. Clinker-building seems to have come to an end by 1523.

Another development was the change from the rounded stern to the square, which can be seen clearly in the well-known painting by Volpe in the Royal Collection at Hampton Court Palace which shows Henry's departure for the Field of the Cloth of Gold in 1520. This picture shows, too, that low-placed ports for two stern-chaser guns had been cut in these square sterns, and this added firepower was, no doubt, the reason for this structural alteration.

Before we leave Henry VIII, some account must be given of his best-known warship, the *Henry Grâce à Dieu,* or *Great Harry.* This carrack-built four-master of 1,000 tons was begun in 1512, "hallowed" at Erith in 1514, rebuilt in 1540, and finally destroyed by fire at Woolwich in 1553. She may have been inspired by the startlingly impressive *Great Michael,* built a little earlier by a Frenchman for the King of Scotland, thus epitomizing one of England's greatest fears at that time—a Franco-Scottish alliance. The *Great Harry* did not, however, differ noticeably from the other great ships of the period. Like them, she had four masts, and, as was already becoming normal in larger ships, she was fitted with topgallant masts and sails on her fore- and mainmasts; a topsail and topgallant sail above the lateen on the main mizzen; and a topsail on the aftermost mast, the bonaventure mizzen. She may have been designed and built by Robert Brygandine, the Clerk of the Ships himself, under the supervision of William Bond. Oppenheim records that 56 tons of iron, 565 stones of oakum, and 1,711 pounds of flax were used for her.

Her original complement of guns, 186 in number, would have been mostly carried high in the castles, for ships were built "loftie" at this time, thus making her look squat and clumsy. When she was rebuilt, however, she had two rows of gunports, with two nearly complete tiers of guns, though their number was reduced to 122, most of which were iron-cast. An interesting inventory of her "stuff, tackle and apparel" (printed as an appendix in Oppenheim's *The Administration of the Royal Navy*) includes a detailed list of the ordnance, artillery, and "habillamentes for warr" delivered into the charge of the master and pursers.[9]

According to the *Letters and Papers of Henry VIII*,[10] the main guns were distributed as follows:

	Forecastle	Waist	By the rudder	Lower deck	Second deck	Total
Iron serpentines	33	29	7	20	33	122
Brass serpentines	1				3	4
Stone guns	4				18	22
Great guns of iron		4			2	6
Great spanish pieces		2				2
Brass falcons					6	6
Brass culverins					2	2
Brass curtals					1	1
Vice pieces of brass					4	4
Great stone guns of iron					2	2
Slings of iron					1	1
"Fryre pieces"					1	1
Totals	38	35	7	20	73	173

SOURCE: *Letters and Papers of Henry VIII*, vol. i, 4968, quoted in M. Oppenheim, *The Administration of the Royal Navy*, p. 380.

From the same documents, we find that before she was launched, the following schedule was laid down for her: 400 sailors, 260 soldiers, 40 gunners, 2,000 bows, 5,000 bowstrings, 4,000 sheaves of arrows, 1,500 morris-pikes, 2,000 stakes to defend the archers in the field, 5 lasts, that is, 10 tons, of gunpowder, and 500 suits of armor.[11] Though interesting, these numbers should not be accepted either as actual or, indeed, as a scale based on needs proved by experience. The provisions of the men would have been the responsibility of various individuals. Though we do not know who provided the complement for the *Henry,* we know that the 350 soldiers for the *Gabriel Royal,* the Genoese carrack bought in 1509, were made up of the personal retinue of her captain and of those of such men as Sir Thomas Courtenay, Sir William Cornwall, the Bishop of Exeter, Lord Arundel, and Lord Stourton.[12]

Ships such as the *Henry Grâce à Dieu* were not carved and gilded in the way fashionable a century later, but their streamers, those forerunners of the pennant, and flags must have added a gay and impressive touch. The *Henry's* two mainmast streamers were 40 and 51 yards long, respectively; that on the foremast was 36 yards, and that on the mizzen 28 yards. There were, in addition, twenty-eight banners wrought with gold and silver with silk fringes, ten flags of St. George, and seven more banners of buckram.

Unfortunately, there is no representation of this ship as she was originally built, though there are two of her after she had been reconstructed and was in fact an entirely new and up-to-date ship.

The painting at Hampton Court by Volpe, often wrongly attributed to Holbein, has for long been thought to represent Henry VIII embarking for France in 1520 in the *Henry Grâce à Dieu.* It is now generally accepted that that ship was not in use, since she drew too much water to enter either Dover or Calais harbor. However, the picture is important in that the artist must have represented the great ships present on that famous occasion reasonably accurately, though perhaps he added fittings to some that belonged to others; perhaps, indeed, he included genuine details that belonged to the absent *Henry.* The well-known print made by Allen in 1767, and so often reproduced as the *Great Harry,* is certainly later and may even be the *Ark Royal,* the ship Queen Elizabeth bought from Sir Walter Raleigh in 1587, which was to become Howard of Effingham's flagship.

The generally held picture of the English navy in the second half of the sixteenth century is distorted by a number of false images. To take one only, it is often thought that because the Armada failed in its object and the British Isles did not become a Spanish dependency, therefore the English fleet had been building up under the guidance of a benevolent and prescient queen for this inevitable trial of strength. It is forgotten that the war lasted another fifteen years after the defeat of the Armada and that peace was not declared until both the rival sovereigns were dead.

There is, indeed, a certain ambivalence in Queen Elizabeth's attitude toward her navy. On the one hand, she seems to have appreciated, as even Henry VIII had not, that a fleet should be used offensively and that it was a desirable practice, and one that should become increasingly normal, to engage an enemy out at sea rather than let him take the initiative and attempt a landing first. Beyond that, her understanding of naval strategy did not go, nor does she seem to have understood very much about naval tactics.

Though, by her standards, Elizabeth was generous in the amount of money she allowed to be allocated to the building up of the navy, she did not follow any very consistent plan; and she relied, too much perhaps, on the ambitions of her seamen, many of whom were little more than pirates: it was lucky for her that she was served by them so well. For the sake of profit, she was prepared to support trading expeditions but not to authorize them. In 1561, for example, she hired four of her ships to Sir William Chester for a voyage to Africa in return for a third share of the profits; and two years later, she loaned the *Jesus of Lübeck* to Dudley in return for £500 in cash. This high-charged ship had been bought by Henry VIII from Hamburg in 1544, and she was to be loaned out again in 1568, with five others, to Hawkins for his third, and "troublesome," voyage, which lead to her loss to the Spaniards in the harbor of San Juan de Ulúa, one of the only two warships to be lost to Spain during the whole reign—the other was the *Revenge*, as we shall see later.

On the credit side, however, it must be seen that during the last half of the century, a new and effective warship was being evolved in England; and she was so successful that she became the standard warship, with comparatively few structural changes till the introduction of steam.

What, then, was she like, this new Elizabethan warship, which we can begin, as the reign progresses, to call the first ship of the line? In the first place, she was far more seaworthy than her predecessors of anything like comparable size had ever been. This was partly due to improved techniques in construction but partly also to the wider horizons seafaring men were beginning to have. Ships were expected to be more efficient because they had farther to go—it was as simple as that. The age of discovery, that period of intensive maritime activity, meant to the Englishman, to merchant and mariner alike, that there was a greater incentive than ever before for making his ship efficient, handy to maneuver, seaworthy, and comfortable to live in for long periods.

The growth in trade, a parallel movement to the opening up of the world, again accentuated the need for efficient ships, and when we recall the activities of the Turkey (later the Levant) Company ships, which were able to beat off eleven Spanish galleys and frigates in open fight, we can see that the border line between war and trade was still not a very clear one.

The improvement in navigational instruments and in the methods of navigation itself is another important aspect of the second half of the sixteenth century. Men like John Davis, the inventor of the double quadrant and other instruments; William Borough, one of the first hydrographers; and the mathematicians John Dee and Robert Recorde deserve mention alongside the better-known names, because they were able to do something to improve the art of navigational training. This had been instinctive rather than taught, so that no establishment existed in England at all similar to the Portuguese school for navigators.

In actual appearance, the warships were lower in the water than they were in the first half of the century and had long projecting beaks. The forecastle, itself much lower than before, was well back from the stem. The afterworks were less exaggerated too, and the stern was cut square, a feature we noticed in some of the later ships of Henry VIII's reign. There were partial decks at different levels to accommodate the guns, which we shall discuss in more detail later. This seems to have been mainly owing to the desire to include as many guns as possible without cutting ports through the wales, the timber strips that gave added strength to the hull. Gradually, the length of ships increased until it became standardized, with a keel length of three times the beam, as we know from a paper signed by William Borough, the Comptroller of the Navy.[13] But larger ships seem to have been longer still toward the end of the reign, perhaps nearly five times as long as they were broad.

The first true galleon was the *Foresight* (300 tons), built in 1570, the year after Hawkins became Treasurer of the Navy. It was natural that with a man of his great practical experience at the head of affairs, new types of ship to suit contemporary requirements would be constructed. The type that found the most favor was the middleweight galleon, such as the famous *Revenge*, built at Woolwich in 1577, a ship considered by Drake to be the finest fighting "galley" of his day and "low and snug in the water like a galiasse," according to a contemporary description. It is worth noting that any low-lying and low-waisted vessel might be called a "galley" or "galiasse" at this period. The *Revenge* class, as Hawkins' ships might be termed, had finer lines than the old carracks, were medium in size, lying much lower in the water, and were no longer built "loftie." They had, however, a comparatively heavy battery of guns, and it was this feature that proved so effective against the Spanish.

Though she displaced only 500 tons, the *Revenge* had, as was still usual, a broadside of thirty-four mixed guns, ranging from 9- to 32-pounders, as well as a number of the obsolescent sakers. She was a four-master, with topmasts that could be struck in accordance with Hawkins' improved method, which was said to be "a wonderful ease to great ships." The *Revenge* achieved fame as Drake's flagship, when he was second-in-command to Howard of Effingham against the Armada, and also, thanks perhaps to Tennyson's poem, at the moment of her ending, when Sir Richard Grenville found himself fighting single-handed against the might of Spain at Flores in the Azores.

It cannot be denied that the English ships of Queen Elizabeth's reign were small, when we study the tonnage records, and there is a strong case for criticizing the queen for failing to make more use of her extremely favorable position in the early years of her reign. She had no serious rivals near at hand, as France, divided by religious wars during most of the second half of the century, hardly had a navy at all, and the United Provinces had not yet emerged as a maritime power. Yet in spite of great naval activity of a kind throughout the reign—75 ships were added to the total of just over 30 that Elizabeth inherited—very few of them were large warships; indeed, only 29 ships of 100 tons and above were added during the reign, and of these only 21 were suitable for long voyages. It has been noted that Elizabeth, who inherited 22 effective warships of 100 tons and upward in 1558, handed over to her successor only 29 similar ships in 1603.

Luckily for England, a navy was hardly considered a national commitment in Spain. Admittedly, there were galley establishments at Barcelona and elsewhere, but otherwise there were no royal dockyards. Only 3 ships in Santa Cruz's fleet in 1583 and only 25 of the 130 that sailed in the Armada five years later belonged to the Crown. Indeed, as late as 1601, the Duke of Medina Sidonia complained that "the King should build the vessels he required and not ruin private individuals." There was no Spanish admiralty, and ships were obtained by different methods of contract, either with towns or with individuals who had agreed to serve as admirals, bringing so many ships with them.

Contemporary pictures of the Elizabethan warships are scarce, though there are some particularly valuable records. Of these, an unsigned and undated manuscript, now in the Pepysian Library at Magdalene College, Cambridge, is of great interest. Pepys called it *Fragments of Ancient English Shipwrightry,* and there seems little doubt that the document was the work of Matthew Baker, the famous shipwright, and was written about 1586. It shows scale drawings, plans, cross sections, and elevations of ships in general—the earliest examples of such things we have—though not of particular vessels. Nevertheless, the proportions are so nearly those of a number of the royal ships known from other sources that Baker's drafts must have been the basis of ships that were actually built. These and the drawings of Thomas Pettyt, especially one of Calais harbor just before the death of Henry VIII, are interesting contrasts to the more stylized ships in Anthony Anthony's Roll of 1546, where the great height of the ships above the waterline must be exaggerated. In the 1560's, Pieter Brueghel the Elder drew a series of Flemish, Dutch, and Spanish warships that corroborate Pettyt's details and cannot have been very different from their English equivalents. To judge from the admirable ship in his *Fall of Icarus,* Brueghel must have been a good observer, and for this reason and because he spent most of his life at the great port of Antwerp, his work is important.

It is strange that though Drake's famous *Golden Hind* was preserved in dry dock at Deptford for so long, little pictorial record of her has survived; in fact, the small sketch in the margin of Hondius' map of the voyage, published in 1594, seems to be the only one.

Matthew Baker's drawings help considerably when we come to consider the decoration of Elizabethan ships. He used the accepted methods of the period, which were much the same as those of Henry VIII's reign, if the picture by Volpe mentioned earlier can be accepted as accurate in this matter. The hulls were unpainted; but above the top wale, all the upperworks were displayed in vivid and contrasting colors. White and green, the Tudor livery colors, were popular, though not exclusively so; and the patterns might be geometrical, or they might be sham architectural features such as pillars or arches.[14] There was not yet, however, a great deal of carving, except in the actual figureheads. The royal arms on the stern would be blazoned in the correct heraldic colors but would not necessarily be carved. The *White Bear*, rebuilt in 1598–1599 after thirty-four years of service, did have £172 spent on carving and £205 on painting and gilding; and in the same year, the *Elizabeth* had £180 spent on her ornamentation. But these figures seem exceptional when we look at the more modest sums of £20 and £30 spent on other ships. A contemporary proudly claimed that the navy "wanteth neither goodly, great nor beautiful ships who of mould are so clean made beneath, of proportion so fine above, of sail so swift, the ports . . . so well devised, with the ordnance so well placed, that none of any other region may seem comparable unto them."[15]

As in Henry VIII's reign, flags, banners, and streamers were worn, and their different colors must have looked attractive, especially in a combination of wind and sunshine. "Sarcenets of divers colours" were used for them, but it is interesting to note that the Cadiz fleet of 1596 had distinguishing colors for its four squadrons, the earliest known example of what later became common practice.[16]

Before we leave Elizabeth, two further subjects must be considered: the development in naval ordnance during her reign and the new tactical use to which warships could be put. Both are subjects of considerable complexity, but neither can be treated in a great deal of detail here. They also overlap each other to a certain extent.

Perhaps the most unexpected convert to the importance of ordnance in any future naval war was the Spanish king himself. It is significant that between 1586, when the projected plans for an Armada were being prepared, and 1588, when the actual Armada set sail, Philip cut down his galleys drastically from forty to four. The galley, apart from her long-distance and oceangoing weaknesses, which will be noted in a later chapter, was a ship-ramming weapon, and her complement of only one ship-killing gun was clearly unlikely to be effective against the twenty-eight ship-killing guns, firing broadside, that were becoming the normal firepower of an English man-of-war.

Drake's dramatic success against the galleys in Cadiz harbor, where everything should have favored galley warfare, provided the moment of truth, and Philip did not fail to apply the lesson he learned. The result was that of the 130 ships that sailed, 73 were fighting units, the great majority of them of the sailing ship–galleon type. This figure can be broken down into 24 royal ships (10 Portuguese royal galleons, 10 galleons of the Indian Guard, and 4 great ships of the *flota* of New Spain), the sailing element of the projected Armada, which now became the spearhead of the fleet; 41 improvised merchant ships; 4 Portuguese galleys, which failed to reach England at all; and 4 Neapolitan galleasses, those compromise vessels, as they might be termed, between the rejected galley and the great sailing ship, now so wholeheartedly accepted as the fighting ship of the day.

Accompanying this reappraisal of his ships, Philip rather more than doubled the 1586 number of guns. He also allocated more guns to individual ships, even up to forty a vessel, thus making them much more comparable in this respect with the best-armed English warships. The visible effect of Drake's guns at Cadiz and the advice of such trusted and influential men as de Leyva and de Valdez, as well as the reports from his spies, made it clear that English tactics would be to try to turn any sea battle into a gun battle. This essentially correct appreciation seems to have obliterated the traditional Spanish aristocrat's dislike of the gun, that "ignoble arm," as he called it, which reminds us of the French attitude toward the English crossbow during the Hundred Years' War.

Having conquered their disdain for the gun, the Spanish believed that the best artillery would be the heavy-battery pieces, the cannon or demicannon that fired round shot from 60 down to 30 pounds in weight but could not throw very far because of the shortness of their length of bore. They also favored the short cannon-perrier, the *pedrero*, which threw a shot of 24 pounds an even shorter distance and was already obsolescent in England because of its limited range. Historians have been misled for a long time about the Spanish gun, but Professor Lewis, who has studied the whole problem of the Armada guns in great detail and is the acknowledged expert,[17] has proved that the heavy guns were much more considerable than was previously thought and that Philip, learning from experience, increased their size as well as their number between the years 1586 and 1588. In fact, the Spanish ships carried three times as many cannon types as the English did and nearly eight times the number of the perrier types.[18] Professor Lewis also believes that the English cannon types were the smallest of their class, whereas over half of the Spanish guns were full cannons, the heaviest-shotted then used in ships anywhere.

Thus, in sheer weight, the Spanish guns were superior to the English; but when we take into consideration the factor of range, the picture is very different. For in the days when it was true to say that the longer a gun, the greater its range, there came a point when a barrel could not be lengthened if it was to remain workable in a comparatively small and narrow-beamed ship. This meant that the maximum range of an English gun was that of the 14-foot culverin, which had a bore of just over 5 inches and fired a shot of about 17 pounds. Any heavier shot than this would mean a decrease in range.

Professor Lewis has come to the conclusion that there was something like parity between England and Spain in the category of full culverins only. Above this type of gun, the Spanish, concentrating on weight, had a far greater number of guns; below it, the English had the preponderance in 9-pounder demiculverins, 5-pounder sakers, and 4-pounder minions, and these weapons had range. Thus the Spanish had the means of hurling a greater quantity of heavy shot, but they could not hurl it as far as the English could hurl their lighter shot.

As we pass to the subject of naval tactics, a word must be said about the English warships themselves: 34 of them were royal ships, which included 21 first-line vessels only; but a great many other vessels of varying sizes must be added, so that we find 197 different ships' names in the lists. Though it may have been true, as Raleigh said, that the Spanish ships had more "majesty," meaning, it is supposed, that they looked greater, it seems that the real fighting elements of the two fleets were far more equal to each other in size than was thought.

A confusing factor has been the discrepancy between English and Spanish tonnage, which is now accepted, with the result that Frobisher's

Triumph of 1,100 English tons must have been the largest vessel on either side and that the English royal ships were larger than the Spanish. Howard certainly had no ship to match *La Ragazona* among the auxiliary vessels that served him as temporary warships, but he had 40 ships among them capable of hitting the Spanish hard. In fact, as Professor Lewis has written, each fleet had between 60 and 70 fighting units, including rather more than 20 actual men-of-war each.

This is not the place to examine the details of the Armada campaign, which the Spanish called "the Enterprize of England," but a few useful lessons can be learned from it about the changing nature of naval warfare. Though King Philip had come to appreciate the importance of the gun, as we have seen, he did not rely on it solely; in fact, he retained on board the full complement of soldiers that had been fixed for the 1586 project.

An interesting document, quoted by Lewis in *The Spanish Armada*, gives Philip's instructions to his new commander in chief, for the Duke of Medina Sidonia had succeeded the far greater Marquis of Santa Cruz, whose death early in 1588 was the first, and by no means the least, blow that Spain was to suffer.[19] "The enemy's object," wrote the king, "will be to fight at long distance in consequence of his advantage in artillery. ... The aim of our men ... must be to bring him to close quarters and grapple with him." The directive included a description of the way in which the enemy would employ his artillery "in order to deliver his fire low" and sink his opponent's ship; and, as Professor Lewis writes, here was the fundamental principle behind English tactics, which was to last as long as the sailing ship herself. The intention was to fire on the downward roll right into the hull and sink the ship or, failing that, to subject the crew to flying splinters or worse and thereby induce surrender. The Spanish and, later on, the French believed in firing on the upward roll, because this would mean destroying the motive power of the enemy vessel—the masts, sails, and yards.

Thus we see that by 1588, English naval commanders relied on broadsides of potentially ship-killing guns in much improved sailing ships. We have already noted the arguments for weight of shot on the one hand and length of range on the other. The English favored the latter, because they knew they could keep out of the enemy's way through their better technique of sailing; they knew also that they must avoid close-fighting, which would allow the Spanish battering pieces and grappling hooks to come into play and so enable their great superiority in soldiers—more than 18 to 1—to make its presence felt.

A contemporary narrative, that of the Florentine Petruccio Ubaldino, then living in England, which was drawn up for Drake and is dated April, 1589, illustrates this point. In the passage dealing with the fighting on July 22, 1588, the writer says that the battle was "fought always within half musket shot, a fact which was very advantageous to the English, whose ships were exceedingly handy . . . [and who] made no attempt to board but hurled their shot at the enemy with due consideration, always trying to hit the hulls and the rigging of the enemy ships which, being far higher out of the water, could not make such useful play with their artillery on the English ships." Ubaldino need not be taken as a particularly accurate or knowledgeable recorder of these stirring events—and, indeed, he is guilty of a number of errors of fact—but it is interesting to see that this point of tactics struck him as worthy of note.[20]

The six days of fighting in the English Channel during the last week of July, 1588, culminated in the novelty of a night action, the sending in of fire ships by the English, and a last and violent fight when the Armada had already been driven to the leeward of Dunkirk. Finally, there was the intervention of the weather in favor of England, which should not be allowed to conceal some important facts. In the first place, Spanish seamanship must have been of a high standard, for, after all, more than half of the ships that fled up the North Sea eventually reached home—no mean feat of navigation—and most of them were men-of-war. Secondly, the action in the Channel had given the new English warship her baptism of fire and had proved that the techniques of broadside fire at short range, of line-ahead formation, and of concentration on the enemy's weathermost ships were worth persevering with, tactical considerations that were to prove their value again and again during the next two centuries.

NOTES

[1]Romola and R. C. Anderson, *The Sailing-Ship*, p. 78.
[2]See Eric Maclagan, *The Bayeux Tapestry*, plates 5 and 42.
[3]G. J. Marcus, *A Naval History of England*, p. 17.

[4] Sir George Warner (ed.), *The Libelle of Englyshe Polycye*, ll. 998–1,000.

[5] *Ibid.*, ll. 1,002–1,003.

[6] *Ibid.*, ll. 1,092–1,097.

[7] *Ibid.*, ll. 1,054–1,060.

[8] See M. A. Lewis, *The Navy of Britain*, p. 426.

[9] M. Oppenheim, *The Administration of the Royal Navy*, pp. 372 ff.

[10] See J. S. Brewer (ed.), *Letters and Papers of Henry VIII*, Master of the Rolls, London, vol. i, 4968.

[11] *Ibid.*, vol. i, 4379.

[12] *Ibid.*, vol. i, 3977.

[13] See *State Papers* (Domestic), vol. 253, 110, quoted in Oppenheim, *op. cit.*, p. 126.

[14] See G. S. Laird Clowes, *Sailing Ships: Their History and Development*, pt. i, p. 54.

[15] See James Montgomery, *Additional Manuscripts 20,043 Treatise Concerning the Navy of England*, f. 6, quoted in Oppenheim, *op. cit.*, p. 132.

[16] See *Pipe Office Accounts*, 2232.

[17] See Michael Lewis, *Armada Guns* and articles in *The Mariner's Mirror*, 1942, vol. xxviii and 1943, vol. xxix.

[18] See Michael Lewis, *The Spanish Armada*, p. 75.

[19] *Ibid.*, p. 73.

[20] See G. P. B. Naish (ed.), *The Naval Miscellany, Vol. IV, The Narrative of P. Ubaldino*, Navy Records Society, London, 1952, vol. xcii, p. 66.

English ships of the period 1375–1425, reconstruction based on Froissart's *Chronicles*, from a colored aquatint by J. A. Atkinson and Havell, after Charles Hamilton Seaforth, published 1812. *National Maritime Museum, Greenwich*

(Right) Drawing of a carrack, or armed merchantman, by a Flemish artist who signs himself W.A. (*c.* 1480). Note the two forecastle decks with an awning over them. There is a deck above the quarterdeck aft of the mizzenmast, and though hard to detect, the muzzles of five guns protrude just below it. There would be five more on the opposite side, and there is a small gun on the mizzen top. Note also the grapnel at the end of the bowsprit. *National Maritime Museum, Greenwich*

(Above) The first *Ark Royal*, Howard of Effingham's flagship in 1588. She was built the previous year by Richard Chapman for Sir Walter Raleigh, who sold her to Queen Elizabeth. From a line engraving by C. J. Visscher. *National Maritime Museum, Greenwich*

(Top left) Line engraving of a Dutch man-of-war at anchor in harbor, from a set of engravings by Frans Huys, after Pieter Brueghel, mid-sixteenth century. *National Maritime Museum, Greenwich*

(Bottom left) Line engraving of a large English ship, port bow view, probably after Hendrik Cornelisz Vroom (1566–1640). *National Maritime Museum, Greenwich*

(*Above*) Four-masted Dutch ship of 1597, a detail from the oil painting by Hendrik Cornelisz Vroom. *Rijksmuseum, Amsterdam*

An incident in the battle off Manila on December 14, 1600, when the Dutch were attacked by the Spanish. The Dutch under Van Noort had just captured a Japanese vessel, which can be seen with its matted sails on the left. From De Bry's *Voyages,* published *c.* 1600. *National Maritime Museum, Greenwich*

Schlacht for Manille.

fol. 88

Netherlands warship (mid-sixteenth century), from a line engraving by
Frans Huys, after Pieter Brueghel. *Science Museum, London*

IV

Galleys, Galleasses, and Galleons

T HE galley, in essence, was a moderate-sized vessel used in the Mediterranean as a warship, and her main features were a ram bow and oars as the principal means of propulsion, though she carried sails as well. She was, in fact, the direct descendant of the old *navis longa* of the Romans, and when we consider that she was recognizably the same ship right up to the time when Venice capitulated to Napoleon at the very end of the eighteenth century, we can see that this type of ship had a very long history. There were, of course, changes during this period, but they were largely questions of detail concerning the grouping and manning of the oars; they were, in fact, adaptations of an accepted design rather than attempts to replace one vessel by something entirely different.

The sea conditions in the Mediterranean made Venice what she was, so it is right that we should start with the republic's galleys, where the sources are plentiful, especially as these vessels can be taken as typical of the Mediterranean galley generally, whether from Genoa, Naples, or Malta—or, indeed, from elsewhere. The first mention of the Venetian galley is as far back as the ninth century, for the earliest doges were well aware of the importance of building up a fleet. The triple threat of the nearby mainland landowners, of the Arabs, and of the pirates from the Dalmatian islands made it clear that their continued independence required constant vigilance.

Early successes such as the capture of Ravenna in 740, then in the hands of the Lombards, gave her confidence in herself and her methods and, more tangibly, supremacy in the Adriatic. Fifty years later, Venice had contributed to the overthrowal of the two-hundred-year dominion of the Lombards; and in 810, Charlemagne recognized her right to exist as an independent republic. It was not, however, until the fifteenth century that distinction between actual warships and merchant vessels was made; but at least a century before that, the standard galley had emerged, and it is this vessel that we must now consider in a little detail. The fourteenth and fifteenth century galley can be described as *alla sensile*, that is, designed in the simple fashion, which means that the oars were grouped in threes, with one man to each oar. This system was derived from the old biremes and was in general use by the middle of the fourteenth century. After the middle of the sixteenth century, the phrase *al scaloccio* is used, which means that the oars were spaced out singly along the sides and that each oar was manned by a number of men, usually five but occasionally by as many as seven.

To return to the earlier type, it is regrettable that there are no accurate contemporary representations and that those that do exist admit of several interpretations. Modern experts, however, think that the close grouping of oars at one level must have been reinvented, so to speak, between the years 1000 and 1200 and that such an arrangement was not just a continuation of the old method seen in the Greek triremes, which had never died out completely.

The Venetians had a number of galleys, but they can be classified into two main types: the *galea sottile*, or slender galley, designed for war and first mentioned in a decree of 1494, and the *galea pesante*, or heavy galley, used as a transport, though also suitable for offensive action if an emergency arose. Both types can be subdivided even further: the *sottile* had smaller versions of herself, all with slight variations themselves, such as the *galeotte, fuste, panfini, brigantini, saettie, felucche,* and *mezzagalee*; while the *pesante* included such variations as the *galea taride, galeazze, galeoni,* and *galeoncino,* some of which will be dealt with later on.

The light fighting galley, the *galea sottile*, is much better documented. She was carvel-built, was long and narrow, had very little sheer, and she does not seem to have grown very much in size during the passing of the centuries. The oarsmen's thwarts, or rather benches, were not continuous across the width of the galley, but were divided by a narrow gangway called a *corsia*, and they ran at an angle to the sides so as to enable the different lengths of oar to be worked harmoniously. There was a castle constructed amidships to shelter the archers, and the outside of the vessel would often be padded with leather so as to protect it from catching fire. There seem to have been six "rooms" below the deck in the sixteenth century galleys, though it might be more accurate to call some of them little more than small storerooms. Only one, the *camera della poppa*, had any seating in it, and it was reserved for the "captain, the officers of the poop, for the passengers and people of consideration, for their weapons and their goods."[1]

The other rooms included the *camera di mezzo*, in which the sails, some of the rigging, passengers' luggage, and ammunition were kept. Toward the prow, there was a raised space called a *rembata*, consisting of two stands connected by a bridge. On this platform, or castle, were placed the artillery, and it also served as a barrier across the widest part of the beam and so would perhaps check an enemy from easily gaining control of the galley once he had boarded and entered.

Mention must be made, too, of the band, which seems to have been an important part of the ship's company. Its instruments usually consisted of a drum, two trumpets, two timbrels, and a number of *naccherista*. Its psychological effect on the spirits of the crew was important, but it also provided a system of signals and calls to duty and so ensured efficiency and precision of action from all on board.

The commander of the galley, the *sopracomito*, was usually a man of noble birth, but he was paid by the republic for his services. A decree of July 13, 1294, ordained that the richest Venetian families should equip the galleys in proportion to their wealth, and sometimes the galleys carried the names of these families. The crew also was paid at first, and it was considered a great honor to row in the state galleys; it was not till about the year 1549 that they were manned by slaves. Another interesting fact is that there was a system whereby youths between the ages of ten and thirteen were taught the rudiments of seamanship. They were selected by a captain and appointed to serve in the galleys, rather like the King's Letter Boys in the English navy in Pepys's time.

Before we discuss the armament carried by these Venetian galleys, some further points must be noted. The first is that the stern rudder had displaced the rudders on the quarters before 1500, though at first both types of rudder were often used, especially in fighting galleys. The stern rudder appeared first in northwestern Europe in the early thirteenth century. It was called *timon bavonescho* by the Venetians, so perhaps it reached Venice from Bayonne, along with the one-masted square rig that we know they acquired in 1303.

A second point is that the sails in Venetian galleys, and probably in Mediterranean galleys generally, were lateens and remained so to the end. This fact has caused some surprise to sailing experts, because it would seem that the narrow galley could hardly make the best use of the lateen's strong feature, the ability it gave to sail into the wind.

Next we must return to the galley which was said to be oared *al scaloccio*. The principle here, as was said above, was that several men worked on the same oar. The origin of the term is uncertain, though it may derive from *scala*, a ladder, since the arrangement of the crosspieces joining the handgrips to the oar between each pair of men may have suggested such an object. The first reference to this arrangement is in 1534, when long oars suitable for three men were ordered for trials. Apparently three-man oars proved less successful than three separate oars, but there was a marked increase in efficiency when five men were allocated to an oar, and this seems to have become the normal number for *remo di scaloccio*, though flagships often had even more men to the oar.

The size of some of these flagships was quite remarkable; sometimes they reached a length of more than 150 feet, with thirty banks of oars on each side instead of the more usual twenty-five. Some were quad-riremes; that is, they had four men to the oar. And we know that Vettore Fausto built a quinquereme as early as 1529. This vessel was 158 feet long by 20 feet wide, and the experiment was not repeated, though she was highly thought of and may even have been the flagship of Marc'antonio Colonna when he commanded the twelve galleys lent by Venice to the Pope in 1570. By that time, she must have been very much out of date, but no doubt her magnificent and stately appearance, quite apart from the craftsmanship in her construction, kept her afloat so long.

Lastly, the armament of these galleys deserves mention. In the *galea sottile*, space was a considerable problem. A great quantity of stones was needed for the catapults in the fourteenth century, and we know from decrees just how many boatloads could be carried in each galley. The crew had crossbows, as well as other types of bows of different sizes, though all were made of iron. They had scimitars, "knives for wounding," and a gruesome-looking beechwood lance, 15 feet long, with a third of its length, the lower part, bristling with blades. Its point was made of an iron peak covered with hooks. Other weapons were devised for damaging the oars of enemy ships, and there were various types of grappling iron.

The actual presence of proper guns on board the galleys cannot have been until at least 1450. It seems unlikely that the literary sources in the early fifteenth century, which mention so many details so meticulously yet are silent about ordnance, could have missed such an obvious feature if it had been present. Once introduced, the arrangement of the guns seems to have been standardized and to have remained so throughout the remainder of the galley's history. This was the placing of them well forward, so that, in fact, they really continued the function of the ram, that is, end-on attack, which was already two thousand years old. The main gun, the *corsier*, so-called because it was on the line of the *corsia* or fore-and-aft gangway, was placed at first in a fixed carriage, with no means of elevation or training onto a target. Later, it would have a recoiling carriage. This gun was flanked by two pairs of smaller guns, all on fixed mountings and also forward-firing, the heavier pair inboard of the lighter pair. An interesting list of the guns needed for a Florentine galley in 1574 has survived; it mentions one 50-pounder *cannone*, two 10-pounder *sagri* (sakers), two 4-pounder *mezzi sagri*, and finally eight 4-pounder breech-loading *smerigli*, all of which, except the last category, would be mounted forward. Pantero Pantera, writing in 1614, has given valuable detailed information about the guns in the sixteenth century Venetian galleys; and from contemporaries of his, we learn that gradually all the forward-firing guns were mounted on recoiling carriages. This was certainly true too of the French galleys before the end of the seventeenth century.

The last occasion on which Mediterranean galleys took a serious part in any fighting was at the battle of Matapan in 1717. Venice, Malta, Tuscany, and the Papal States provided the galleys, but they do not seem to have affected the issue very much. The first half of the eighteenth century saw the end of the galley service in Tuscany, Naples, and France, but Venice and the Knights of Malta and the Pope used their galleys till they capitulated to Napoleon at the end of the century. Even then, the half galley, or smaller version of the *galea al scaloccio*, persisted a little longer; and two, built for the papal fleet, even acquitted themselves respectably in 1798 at the Battle of the Nile. Five French half galleys were built—in imitation of them, in all probability—but were captured, though they were returned to France in 1814, the year in which two other smaller galleys of this class were launched for the Sardinians, "the last representatives," as Anderson has said, "of a family which can be traced back for at least 2,500 years."[2]

It would be wearisome to attempt any detailed and comprehensive account of the way in which the Mediterranean galleys were used in war, but it is instructive as well as interesting to study a few isolated naval occasions to see whether we can learn anything about galley tactics. The magnificent paintings by Tintoretto and others give us some insight into the noble yet formidable appearance of these vessels, and they present almost too eloquent a picture of the confusion and turmoil in which the battles must have been fought. Details, for instance, from *The Apotheosis of the Battle of Lepanto* by Veronese in the Doge's Palace and Andrea Vicentino's picture of the same battle in the same building corroborate these impressions of confusion, though, of course, the naval historian should beware against the dangers of interpreting the artistic grouping of the vessels too literally in terms of contemporary tactics. Yet what we can see of the details of the ships, such as their flags and pennons, the hooplike structures erected over the aftercastles and the ferocious rams, must surely be authentic. Guesswork, however inspired, would hardly have escaped the critical notice of such nautical-minded people as the Venetians or the Genoese.

The first episode to be selected belongs to the last quarter of the eleventh century, when the Normans were making a fair bid for supremacy in the southern parts of the Italian peninsula. After they had added the control of Apulia and Calabria to that of most of Sicily, Venice viewed further encroachments into the Adriatic, which she considered to be her own sphere of influence, with some consternation. Her action to meet the situation was typical, since she saw the problem as not merely a military but an economic one as well.

Consequently, her treaty with Emperor Alexius Comnenus, signed in 1081, was very much in her own favor. It brought Venice's relations with Constantinople much closer and gave her valuable concessions in certain markets there, enabling her, in fact, to establish an absolute monopoly, since she was freed from paying the heavy duties imposed on all other foreign merchants. In return, however, Venice undertook to aid the Greeks, to fight against the Normans led by the indomitable Guiscard, and to arm every available vessel. This became necessary when Duke Robert Guiscard followed up his conquest of Corfu by besieging Durazzo further up the Dalmatian coast.

The Venetian fleet consisted of fourteen galleys, nine transport ships, and thirty-six other vessels and was commanded by Doge Selvo himself. The engagement which took place followed a night spent in feverish preparations, since the Venetians had discovered that they were numerically inferior to their enemy and would have to rely on strategy if they were to be victorious. They therefore lashed their largest transport ships together with stout cables so as to make a floating rampart, semicircular in shape to lessen the likelihood of unexpected attack. Also, the masts of these ships were fitted with movable stands, each capable of taking two or three bowmen or slingers and their ammunition.

When the Normans attacked, on the assumption that this "field of ships," as Princess Anna Comnena has described it, could be easily broken up, they found that they had miscalculated. The Venetians showered down fire, stones, and missiles of all sorts onto the low-lying Norman ships from their higher galleys.

This success, though it brought only temporary relief, was not, however, repeated when the same plan was adopted during the campaign at the end of the next year. On this occasion, the heaviest ships were again tied together and once again ordered to advance in a semicircle, with the lighter galleys on the wings. Unfortunately, lack of ballast made the ships heel over on the shock of impact, and this, together with other vicissitudes, led to the Venetians' defeat and the reconquest of Corfu by Duke Robert, though disease, the tempestuous seas, and the duke's death a year or so later robbed the Normans of any lasting gain.

Nearly two centuries later, the Genoese admiral, Lanfranco Borborino, tried out the same plan. This was in the year 1266, when Venice herself was only able to man four galleys for the task of driving the

Genoese out of the areas the Venetians claimed as their own. Giacomo Dandolo, the Venetian commander, had, however, the support of Crete and other Venetian colonies and, with a force of fifteen galleys, brought the Genoese to battle off Trapani in Sicily. Borborino entrenched himself behind a group of linked galleys, and this time Venice had the greatest difficulty in breaking through the enemy line. She did succeed, however, in detaching three Genoese galleys, and this led to the complete and utter defeat of Genoa and the complete loss of her fleet.

No account of Mediterranean galley warfare, however slight, should omit the best-known battle of all. Lepanto, fought off the west coast of Greece in 1571, is rightly considered to be a decisive battle, perhaps even a turning point in European history, since it is certain that if the Turks had defeated the Christians, they would have had access to the riches of Venice, they might have cut off Spain from Austria irrevocably, and they would have had a fair chance of establishing themselves in the western Mediterranean and in western Europe too. The fact that none of these things happened because the Christian League was victorious, in spite of many conflicts of loyalty and an alliance that can at best be described as uneasy, is important. Some historians think that it gave Spain a false sense of security, making her feel that her ships were modern enough to deal with any foreseeable emergency, whereas her whole outward-looking economy, so dependent on her overseas colonies, should have led her to improve her fleet—a lesson she was to learn too late when the "cold war" with England gave way to open hostilities in the late 1580's.

Though we are concerned only with the way in which galleys were handled, the circumstances of Lepanto are of particular interest. Pope Pius V's Christian League, ratified in May, 1571, was remarkable in that it brought together at all such unwilling allies as Spain and the Venetian republic. Indeed, the unsatisfactory nature of the alliance was accentuated by the fact that Philip II did not see an attack on Turkey as an essential part of his particular *Weltanschauung*, though to Venice her losses to the Turks in the Aegean and in Cyprus and their attacks much nearer home on her Dalmatian possessions made some sort of concerted action vital if she was to survive at all.

A concourse of the allies was planned to take place at Messina in the summer of 1571, and Sebastiano Veniero, the commander of the

Venetian fleet, found himself in difficulties even at this stage. His ships were in two divisions, one, under Marco Querini and Antonio Canale, off Crete, and the other, his own, off Corfu. Yet the Turkish fleet was in the entrance to the Adriatic. However, as it turned out, his instructions to the two divisions to proceed separately to the rendezvous were carried out, and the palpable danger of a divided force was remedied without disaster.

Don John of Austria, the youthful and rather ebullient commander in chief, did not hurry to the rendezvous at Messina. He seems to have enjoyed a royal progress, with all its attendant festivities, and while he was being feted at Genoa and Naples, time was slipping by. Once he did arrive, however, Veniero had no difficulty in persuading him, "the last and lingering troubadour," as G. K. Chesterton calls him, to take his military command seriously.

A combined force of just over 200 galleys, 30 other ships, 6 Venetian galleasses, 28,000 soldiers, 12,000 sailors, and 43,000 oarsmen set sail across the Ionian Sea for Cephalonia. Inevitably, there are discrepancies in the numbers, but the array was certainly a formidable one. The Venetian contingent, however, was in a low state of morale and was considerably undermanned. Whatever the reason for this, whether it was owing, as Pantera thought, "to the avarice of the ministers in buying and distributing bad food" or to some other cause, the decision to bring the galleys up to strength by introducing Spaniards and Italians into them did not improve matters. Indeed, the knowledge that this was being done so as to lessen the risk of desertion by whole ships produced the worst sort of results, as the riots on board several ships when the fleet reached the Albanian coast prove.

The battle began at dawn on October 7 and lasted till nearly midnight, when the imminence of a storm made disengagement imperative. But by that time, the issue was in no doubt: the Christian cause had prevailed. The Turks had slightly more galleys than their enemy, but they had fewer of the larger ones and no equivalent of the huge Venetian galleasses. Both sides adopted the well-tried practice of advancing with their ships in three closely compacted squadrons. Don John commanded the blue squadron in the center, which numbered about sixty ships—again there are discrepancies about the numbers—and was flanked by the green squadron of between fifty and sixty ships, under Giannandrea

Doria, on his right and by Agostino Barbarigo's yellow squadron of fifty-five galleys on his left. Within the squadrons, the galleys were ordered to row as close together as possible without fouling their oars, so as to prevent a determined enemy from forcing his way between the ships. The six galleasses, which so proved their worth in the later stages of the battle that they remained an important part of the Venetian fleet for 150 years, were intended to cover the line of advance, about a mile ahead, two to each squadron. They took a long time to take up their correct positions, but the plan proved effective in the end.

The Turkish fleet also advanced in three squadrons but in a crescent-shaped line and, until noon, had the advantage of a following wind. When battle was actually joined, they found that they had under-estimated the strength of the enemy and were considerably disorganized by the fire from the Venetian galleasses, though their own mobility enabled them to row beyond the range of the guns of these rather cumbersome vessels. The clashes between the Christian left and center squadrons and their opponents must have embodied all the confusion and clamor so marvelously portrayed in Vicentino's painting or in the almost equally vivid picture by an unknown artist in the Maritime Museum at Greenwich. We are told that Ali Pasha's flagship, with its heavier spur, rammed Don John's galley with such force that it penetrated to the fourth bench, thus implying that this *galea al scaloccio* had at least four men to the oar. Doria, with the green squadron on the right, seemed a doubtful security risk at one time, as he broke the line and allowed the Turks to sail between himself and his commander in chief. Later, however, he was able to rejoin the main force, though his inefficiency, or perhaps disloyalty, may have taken something away from the completeness of the victory.

The battle was the last of its kind to be fought on such a scale. It must have been fought with great violence, but it did not lack its lighter moments. An example of this is the celebrated interchange of oranges and lemons when no other form of ammunition was available, if we can believe the account of Gerolamo Diedo.

The casualties in ships and men are, as we have seen so often before, under dispute, but it is certain that the Turkish losses included more than a hundred galleys and that thereafter they were never again to be in a serious position to take the initiative at sea.

GALLEYS, GALLEASSES, AND GALLEONS   [85]

The term "galley" was also used in the late thirteenth century and onward to describe certain English vessels built for fighting and propelled by oars but not fitted with rams. There are, however, some difficulties in interpretation, because the documentary evidence is not too easy to understand. These sources include the building accounts for the construction of eight of the twenty galleys ordered by the king from certain ports, but it is uncertain whether all the ships mentioned were actually built or, if built, measured up to the specified standards. These building accounts and certain inventories for individual ships, such as *La Phelipe*, built in 1336, cover a period of about eighty years from 1294, when King Edward I ordered the twenty ships mentioned above, and from them it seems possible to draw certain conclusions about these English galleys.

They were certainly different from the Mediterranean galleys we have been looking at, for they were square-rigged and clinker-built. They probably had an average of fifty oars on each side, and these would be arranged in groups of two, *alla sensile*; but there are many problems still to be solved concerning their size, because of uncertainty over the actual length of an ell in different parts of Europe, and concerning the arrangement of the oars, especially as oars of different lengths are known to have existed. Again, there is no mention of such features as oar ports, which must have been universal by this time, as we know they were to be found as far back as 900 in the Gokstad and Oseberg ships and, two centuries later, in the Bayeux Tapestry.

Historians have often asked how this essentially Mediterranean type of vessel found its way into northern European waters, and it may be that the French galley fleet based in the Seine provides the answer. Though the descent from the Norse longship must not be forgotten, these galleys were certainly Mediterranean in type and, according to De La Roncière, were repaired by southern workmen who understood carvel-building and were "brought at great expense" from Genoa, Marseilles, and elsewhere.

At all events, these galleys do not seem to have been really popular in England, otherwise there would have been more of them. Perhaps the normal weather conditions, especially the long Atlantic swell, were unsuitable for them, or perhaps the handling of a very long ship, with its many closely grouped oars, proved too difficult in untrained hands under such conditions. The galley, however, did reappear toward the end of Henry VIII's reign and again in the first years of the seventeenth century. In one of Anthony Anthony's rolls of ships in the British Museum, there is among his drawings of galleasses a picture of the *Galley Subtylle* of 1544, which is, except for one feature, just like the normal Mediterranean fighting galley of that period. The difference is that the oars are not grouped in threes but are evenly spaced out—in fact, this is a very early example of the *al scaloccio* arrangement, and it is all the more interesting in that it should be found in an English ship, though it should be noted that she was built by Italian shipwrights.

Four galleys were built for Queen Elizabeth I in 1601–1602. Their names were *Superlativa, Gallarita, Advantagia,* and *Volatilla,* thus betraying their southern ancestry; and no doubt they were something of an anachronism by that time, and, indeed, they were described as "decayed and unserviceable" less than twenty years later.

Very little is known about these last true galleys to be built in England, but they were rowed by about 240 men each, perhaps arranged four men to the oar and thirty oars on each side. After them, oars played an increasingly subordinate part to sails, though a number of hybrid vessels came into existence that were far removed from the Viking long-ships in which their origin lay. They merged, as it were, into the eighteenth century concept of the frigate, which will be considered later on. The existence of some of them is attested to only by models and sketches, while others that were actually built, such as the ten *Lion's Whelps* of 1627, those supposedly "nimble and forcible" ships, proved a failure because they were too heavily armed for their size and too slow under oars or sail to overhaul the type of ship they were intended to fight against.

Of the hybrid vessels, the *Charles Gally* and the *James Gally,* both built in 1679, were based on the designs of French ships from Toulon, according to Pepys. Like the galleasses in Henry VIII's reign, they had a row of guns above their twenty oars on each side.

To show how difficult it is to be sure that we have reached the end of a chapter when dealing with a class of warship, it must be noted that one last southern galley, built at Pisa in 1671 for service at Tangier, then still an English commitment, did exist in the English navy. She was called the *Mary Gally* and was built as a thirty-four-gun ship, though she was rebuilt with forty nearly half a century later.

At the time that her importance was declining in the Mediterranean, the galley reappears in the Baltic. Three years before the last Mediterranean galley action was fought off Cape Matapan in 1717, the first Baltic galley action was fought out near Hango. Oared vessels were used by both Sweden and Russia when the possession of Finland, with its rocky, island-girt coast, was repeatedly contended for between them. The geographical considerations made some sort of a rowing fleet essential, and this was quickly seen by Peter the Great, who built a great many galleys, though they must have varied in size and military value. The first one, built in Holland in 1695, reached the river Don flotilla via Archangel and Moscow and served as the pattern for twenty-two others. The model of her in the Rijksmuseum in Amsterdam shows that she had only sixteen oars a side and so was very much smaller than the Mediterranean galleys of the period. His later galleys were, however, much longer and narrower.

Yet in spite of Peter's quick appreciation of a new situation, Kort Adeler, who had personally experienced galley warfare in the Mediterranean, had introduced the southern galley into Scandinavian waters as early as 1664, when he had become Admiral Lieutenant of Denmark. This was the *Friderich*, known to us, it is now thought with confidence, from the ivory model in the Rosenborg Museum in Copenhagen. Eight more were soon built, and others followed, gradually increasing in size.

Sweden was slower off the mark, not really seeing the importance of armed, oared warships in the defense of rocky coasts until the Russian advances in this direction showed that an opportunity had been lost. Yet even she had tried to copy a *Turkske galej* at Gothenburg as early as 1665—the shipwright was an Englishman named Sheldon. Her real galley program began in 1712; and in spite of early losses, she had a flotilla of thirty by 1719. An important lesson learned from the long war with Russia was that a galley fleet was essential, and so, between the end of the war with Peter the Great in 1721 and the outbreak of the next in 1741, a serious attempt was made to remedy the deficiency. A fact-finding commission was sent to the Mediterranean, which was followed by an ambitious building program; but it was not fully carried out, and Sweden started this next war with a mere twenty galleys, which were inferior to those in the Mediterranean in a number of ways.

Soon after the Swedish navy had become part of the army in 1756, traditional galley building was discontinued, and three completely new types of oared vessel, designed by Chapman, the distinguished naval architect, appeared. These were the *turuma*, the *udema* and the *pojama*, so called after three Finnish provinces. Of them, the *udema* was the most original, since she had her main guns on the middle line in traversing carriages so that they could fire on either broadside. A weakness was that her eighteen pairs of oars were worked on the same deck and so could not be used when the guns were firing. Later in the century, other types emerged with varying success, such as the *hemema*, which had her oar ports in pairs in between her guns.

The Russian reply to these experiments was not immediate. She was still building galleys as late as 1796, some of which were noteworthy for having a heavy gun firing aft over the rudder as well as three firing forward. *Shebeks, half-shebeks,* and other small oared vessels began to make a tentative appearance in the last decade of the eighteenth century and seem to have been some sort of answer to the Swedish *hemema*, though they were smaller. The capture of two *hememas* at Sveaborg in 1808 enabled the Russians to copy this type of vessel more exactly.

Lastly, gun sloops and gun yawls (*kanonslupar* and *kanonjollar* in Swedish) were produced in great numbers and were used in all Scandinavian waters till oared propulsion was replaced by steam. Even though they continued to build galleys long after the Swedes, the Russians were the first to make experiments in gunboats. In the 1760's and 1770's they built "double sloops," 70 feet long by 14 feet wide, with eight guns and ten pairs of oars.

These Russian experiments were, however, superseded by Chapman's gunboats, built for the Swedes after 1775. The first type, the gun sloop, had a heavy gun at each end on a moving carriage, and by 1789 this had become a 24-pounder. Similarly, as the years went by, the dimensions increased till they reached 66 feet by 14 feet. There were fourteen or fifteen pairs of oars and two lateen-rigged masts. The second type, the gun yawl, had one 24-pounder aft in a fixed carriage, and her double-ended structure enabled her to be propelled almost equally easily stern first as bow first, thus eliminating the weakness of of having to turn within the range of enemy fire.

The Russians retaliated with various types of *Kanonskia lodki*, to give the term they used for all classes of oared gunboats. The larger ones usually carried two heavy guns. The last rowing gunboats were built by the Russians in 1854, and the engagement off Aabo that year was, surely, the last occasion on which oared ships fired their guns.

The persistence of Denmark in experimenting with small oared gunboats well on into the nineteenth century, as well as her successful production of at least two *kanonjoller*, does suggest, as Anderson has written, that the Baltic gunboat, the last stage in the long history of the galley, might easily have become "as nearly a standardised type as the Mediterranean galley had been in her day" had it not been for the coming of steam.

The term "galleass" causes difficulties in interpretation because it is used very loosely once it is applied to ships outside the Mediterranean. We have seen that the Venetian galleys could be subdivided into two main classes, the *galea sottile*, or slender warship, and the *galea pesante*, or heavy transport vessel, suitable nevertheless for offensive use if the occasion arose. This second group was further subdivided, and among the variations to be found in it was the *galeazza*, a descriptive term that was to travel far from the confines of the Venetian fleet. We saw, too, that six great galleasses acquitted themselves with distinction at the battle of Lepanto and became thereafter an integral part of the Venetian conception of a fleet.

In the English fleet, however, in the middle years of the sixteenth century, the galleass-type ship was something different. After suffering a minor defeat at the hands of the French in the enclosed waters of Spithead in 1545, Henry VIII tried to devise a new warship that would combine the free movement that oars alone gave with far greater sail power than existed at the time in the Mediterranean galley. Thus his galleasses were really hybrids, combining the mobility of the galley with the sail power of the round ship. It is uncertain whether ships in this category, such as Henry's *Anne Gallant*, were ever actually propelled by oars, but perhaps they were on one occasion at least, in the action off Shoreham on August 15, 1545. Lord Lisle's despatch to the king after that rather inconclusive engagement recorded that the "oared pieces" on the windward wing, so placed to prevent the French galleys from attacking the heavy ships of the main "battle" group, "did their part well." Among them, the *Anne Gallant*, the *Grand Mistress*, and the *Greyhound* are singled out for priase, along "with all your Highness's shallops and rowing pieces," though it is hard to be sure from this phrase whether the named ships were actually "rowing pieces" themselves or not.

It has been said that in this battle, there was a reversion to the old idea of land fighting, with the oared vessels taking the place of the cavalry, while the infantry, so to speak, was the heavy sailing ships. A modern touch must, however, be noted: it is that perhaps this was the first occasion on which a broadside was actually fired from an English ship. One phrase from Lisle's despatch certainly suggests this interpretation.

Two of Henry VIII's ships deserve mention in some detail, as they seem to belong to this category, and they may help to pin down in our minds a clearer picture of the northern galleass.

The first is the *Great Galley,* launched in the presence of the Venetian ambassador in 1515, who also partook of a banquet on board. In his letters, she is referred to as a galleass, without any further comment about the arrangement of her oars. From the same source, we can learn something of her details. She had 120 oars and 207 guns and carried her heavy guns on a deck above the oarsmen, two firing forward and five firing aft on either side. The disposition of her oars raises the usual problems, as she had 160 oarsmen, but Anderson has argued that she must have had 80 one-man oars and 40 two-men oars, which could make forty groups of three, with two men on the longest oar in each group and one on each of the others. Her dimensions are less easy to be sure about, as we do not know whether the figure of 800 tons at which she was rated refers to her burden or to her "tons and tonnage," a rather larger figure than the former. With her deck "like a great plain" and her four masts— three of which had tops and topmasts—and the mainmast a top of its own and a mast above, she could set nine sails and must have been an impressive ship.

The *Great Galley* was a spectacular step forward in ship design and may well have been the last clinker-built ship in England. She first went to sea in 1522 but was obviously considered unsatisfactory, as she was rebuilt "carvelwise" the following year. Eventually, in 1536–1537, she was rebuilt again as an ordinary sailing man-of-war and was renamed *Great Bark.*

The second ship to be mentioned is the *Bull,* which was built in 1546, after the inconclusive fights against the French, mentioned earlier. There is a drawing of her in one of Anthony Anthony's rolls in the British Museum that shows a broadside of six heavy guns above twenty-two oar ports on one level. The oars must have been manned by two men each, as we know that the crew consisted of a hundred men in addition to the twenty gunners. The *Bull* was rebuilt in 1570 and was still in existence when the 1591 list of ships was compiled, the earliest list so far known that gives dimensions. From it, we learn that she was rated at 200 tons, had a keel length of 80 feet, and had a beam of 22 feet. Other ships of this type existed, and we know something of them, but it is thought that enough has been written to give a fair impression of the English galleass.

The Spanish galleass was also a hybrid and, in the long run, gave way to the large ship relying on sail alone. Naval historians have noted that this was the one serious attempt by Spain to devise a warship that would still retain the important feature of the galley—its mobility—but that would have, in addition, much more effective firepower. The result was that a broadside of reasonably heavy guns in the English style made its appearance in a ship that was really too lightly built for such a thing. And there was the problem that we have met before: where to place the main gun deck—above or below the rowing deck? Some of these hybrid galleasses did well enough on Santa Cruz's expedition to the Azores in 1583 for four Neapolitan galleasses to be included in the Armada in 1588, and, in spite of all the hazards, one of these returned to Spain.

At about the same time as Venice was experimenting with the galleass, a similar evolution was going ahead in the galley fleets of Naples and Florence; and about a century later, the Turkish *mahona*, which was used in the long Cretan war, seems to have evolved from an oared merchantman.

Experts think that all these early fighting galleasses averaged 157 feet in length, that is, about the length of the galley during the hundred years of its history from the middle of the fifteenth century. The beam, however, gradually increased by about a third. The oars were arranged *al scaloccio*, though contemporary evidence at first seems conflicting. Some attractive drawings of Florentine galleasses by Baccio del Banco (1604–1656) now in the Uffizi show other features: they seem heavy in comparison with the galleys in the same pictures; they have broadside guns and a square-rigged foremast, with three lateen-rigged masts abaft. The term *bastardelle*, that is, a diminutive form of the *bastarda*, or extra-large galley, is used to describe them.

The main guns in these Mediterranean galleasses were carried well forward, and though we know nothing about the actual armament of the six Venetian galleasses at Lepanto, we do know that the Neapolitans in the Armada carried 29 or 30 guns and 60 smaller pieces and that at least four of these could fire forward. In the seventeenth and eighteenth centuries, there are difficulties in interpretation again that need not concern us here, especially as very few galleasses were, in fact, built in all—even in the Venetian fleet, where they were in use for as long as 150 years, there were never more than seven in service at any one time. It is doubtful, too, whether there were any French galleasses at all, in spite of the famous model of *La Réale* in the Musée de Marine, for this marvelous piece of craftsmanship may simply have been a model for a ship that was never built, a theory suggested by such features as the position of her oars.

The third general term for ships in the sixteenth century must now be considered. The word "galleon" derives from *galea* undoubtedly, but there seems to have been no likelihood that she was ever an oared vessel; so, lacking this essential galley feature, she must be seen as something quite distinct. This last fact also differentiates her from the galleass, which was oared, though sometimes, as was mentioned above, the oars may not have been used.

Anderson's definition of the galleon has received general acceptance. "The galleon," he has written,[3] "was a sailing ship—usually four-masted —with the ordinary ship-rig of the time but with a hull built to some extent on galley lines, long for its beam, rather straight and flat, and with a beak-head low down like a galley's instead of the overhanging forecastle of the ship." The new galleon in fact superseded the "great ship," such as Henry VIII's *Henry Grâce à Dieu*, and was more like his last galleasses, though without the oarage.

The great Portuguese ship, the *São João*, built in 1534, is described as a galleon, though again we must remember that contemporaries might loosely have called such a ship a galley or even a galleass. We know something of her appearance from tapestries woven to celebrate the attack on Tunis in 1535, and now in Madrid, and also from a set of paintings in the Alhambra, some drawings of which Anderson has included in his *The Sailing Ship*. The impression that these give is one of an efficient, up-to-date four-masted fighting ship, far removed from the mental picture we may have of the "stately Spanish galleon" of the well-known poem. In fact, though they certainly were to develop the galleon later in the sixteenth century, the Spanish were among the last to experiment with this type of ship; it is strange, therefore, that the galleon should be almost indelibly associated with them.

NOTES

[1]Pantero Pantera, *L'Armata navale*, Spada, Rome, 1614, chap. iv, p. 45.
[2]R. C. Anderson, *Oared Fighting Ships*, p. 73.
[3]Romola and R. C. Anderson, *The Sailing-Ship*, p. 126.

Maltese and Turkish galleys in action, first half of sixteenth century.
National Maritime Museum, Greenwich

"The Galie Subtile," from Anthony Anthony's Roll (1546), in the British Museum. This vessel differed from the Mediterranean galley only in that the oars were spaced out and not grouped in threes. She provides an early example of the *al scaloccio* arrangement and was built for Henry VIII by Italian shipwrights. *Science Museum, London*

"The Fall of Phaethon" (mid-sixteenth century), line engraving, after Pieter Brueghel, of a man-of-war followed by two galleys. *National Maritime Museum, Greenwich*

Model of Elizabethan galleon (*c.* 1600) based on measurements, elevations, and scale plans contained in contemporary manuscripts, including Matthew Baker's *Fragments of Ancient English Shipwrightry* (1586), now in the Pepysian Library at Magdalene College, Cambridge. The galleon-built ship of this period had the forecastle set well back and a long beak. Four-masted rig was customary for larger warships. Note that square topsails were not yet introduced, but topgallant masts and sails on the two forward masts were coming in and are therefore included in the model. The sternworks are lower and less clumsy than those found earlier in the Tudor period. *Science Museum, London*

Model of Dutch man-of-war (*c.* 1665), stern view. *Science Museum, London*

V

Northwestern European Warships in the Seventeenth Century

T HE warships of the seventeenth century in England looked very different from those of the Tudor period. They were elaborately carved and gilded instead of being painted in bright and contrasting colors, and there were changes in the rigging, such as the introduction of square mizzen topsails and a spritsail topsail. Structurally, however, a ship such as the *Royal Prince* of 1610 was very like the big ships of the Armada period. She had the same distinct "sheer," the same square "tuck" at the stern, and the same long, low-set beak. From the original manuscript of *The Survey of the Navy* of 1618, now in the Public Records Office in London, which perhaps marked the beginning of an awareness of the importance of maritime ascendancy after a period of dangerous inactivity, we can learn a great deal about the changes in masts and sails then introduced, but little can be learned, unfortunately, about the actual design of the ships. It is not till the middle years of the century that we are on firmer ground in this respect.

Pictures and drawings by members of the Van de Velde family, beginning in the late 1640's and continuing into the 1670's—by which time the father and son had been appointed marine painters to King Charles II—and even later, are among the most valuable records of this period, since these men not only were first-class artists on any reckoning, but also were knowledgeable and accurate in the details of the ships they portrayed. Another valuable source of information was the practice of making scale models of the larger warships at the time when the ships were laid down. Many of these have survived, and one of the most impressive is that of the 100-gun *Prince* of 1670, which can be seen in the Science Museum in South Kensington, London.

Samuel Pepys's contribution to our knowledge of the ships of the period is also important. As Clerk of the Acts, he joined the Navy Board, and later he became Secretary of the Admiralty; and in these appointments, he did much to regularize the administration of the navy. Luckily for later generations, he was also an antiquarian and an enthusiastic collector of books, which are still preserved at Magdalene College, Cambridge. Among these are Anthony Deane's *Doctrine of Naval Architecture* and *Mr. Dummer's Draughts of the Body of an English Man-of-War*. In the first of these, we find a series of drafts and a set of mast and rigging plans for each of the six rates of ships in the fleet. The draft of the third-rate is the earliest example of such a thing preserved in England that is complete enough to give the form of the ship fully. *Mr. Dummer's Draughts* contain sectional views and deck plans of a first-rate of about 1680 that show little difference from the methods used a century later.

The activities of the more persistent barnacles and sea worms, especially the *teredo navalis,* and the accumulation on a ship's bottom of various kinds of seaweeds posed problems. In late Tudor times, Sir John Hawkins' remedy was to apply a layer of felt made of mixed hair and tar to the underwater timbers of a ship and then nail to it a sheathing of elm boards. This was really the only successful method, though it gave an extra drag on the ship's "way," and it was generally used until copper sheathing was introduced in the eighteenth century. In the Restoration period, however, sheets of lead fastened with copper nails were used; and later on, a system known as "studding" was introduced by which broad-headed nails were hammered close together and covered with a mixture of tallow and resin. There were several drawbacks, such as the electrolytic action set up by salt water, which corroded the nails, and lead sheathing was abandoned.

The next experiment was to use thin copper plates as sheathing. This was officially adopted in the Royal Navy in 1783, but not before the loss of the *Royal George* had shown that even copper sheathing availed little if the timbers to which it was fastened were rotten. A supporter of coppering was Rodney, who was sure that its efficacy was proved by the speed with which those of his ships that were coppered gave chase in the "Moonlight Battle" in 1780. It is interesting to note that as early as 1708, the navy was inquiring into copper sheathing, though, in fact, it was considered too expensive and slow a process to be justifiable at that time.[1]

We must now consider one of the most important aspects of development in the English warship. This is the rating of the ships and the growing awareness that the line of battle should be composed of equally matched vessels unencumbered by weaker ones. As we shall see in a later chapter, Anson's reforms in the middle of the eighteenth century are more important, but it is worth noting that the idea was already crystallizing in the seventeenth.

Even in James I's reign, there had been three or four different "ranks" of ships; but under the Commonwealth, a system of rating seems to have been introduced that was made more definite, at least officially, after the Restoration. First-rates had 100 guns, but the *Sovereign of the Seas* was the only ship in this category till 1660; second-rates had 52 guns; third-rates, 46; and fourth-, fifth-, and sixth-rates had 40, 24, and 18, respectively. The tendency had been to concentrate on the middle-sized warship of between 30 and 60 guns, but the lessons of the Dutch Wars showed that the smaller ships were not really suitable for the line of battle, and the big three-deckers came in to stay. By 1685, the rating was as follows: first, 100 guns; second, 80; third, 70; fourth, 54; fifth, 32; and sixth, 18. Gradually, this official rating was abandoned, and ships of the line were known by their gun establishment; for example, the 74 was the standard third-rate. The first- and second-rates—with their extra deck, which provided more accommodation—were frequently used as flagships.

These details should not, however, give the impression that there was any really recognizable system of rating even by the end of the reign of Charles II; but in retrospect, it seems that this was probably how contemporary administrators thought of the ships. A more definite improvement seems to have been the standardization of gun batteries in the first three rates; that is to say, each deck had guns of the same weight and caliber on it. Earlier, in the *Sovereign of the Seas*, for instance, the guns were mixed. The old names persisted, and we hear that the *Prince* of 1670 had cannons and culverins still, as well as the sakers and other smaller pieces. Toward the end of the seventeenth century, guns were described by their weight and the 32-pounder became the standard lower-deck gun in a man-of-war.

In 1607, the Venetian ambassador reported to his master that there were only thirty-seven warships belonging to the King of England and that, even of this small number, many of the ships were "old and rotten and barely fit for service." Ten years later the situation was even worse: the number had dwindled to twenty-seven. The long war with Spain had come to an end in 1603 with the death of Elizabeth, and soon after, privateering had been declared illegal. However, pirates and privateers increased their activities, showing how easy it was for a maritime nation to lose its grip. Throughout the first half of the seventeenth century, pirate craft from the Barbary coast of North Africa became more and more bold, penetrating into British waters and even crossing the Atlantic. Lundy Island was captured in 1625; and a few years later, the Irish coastal town of Baltimore in County Cork was raided and two hundred of its inhabitants were removed and sold into slavery, an exploit that was repeated at Penzance in 1640. The British government seems to have been able to do little about this menace, though Sir Lionel Cranfield's commission, set up in 1618 to inquire into the condition of the navy, and the appointment of Sir William Monson as Admiral of the Narrow Seas were steps in the right direction, but not very effective ones.

In shipbuilding, the improvements that were due to Sir John Hawkins—the increased length and the decrease in height above the water—did not automatically lead to faster and more reliable ships. There was still a tendency toward overloading, and there was still something amateurish about the way in which the designers and builders applied themselves to their tasks. Captain George Waymouth saw this and complained that there never was any uniformity, since "you could never see two ships builded of the like proportion by the best and most skilful shipwrights . . . because they trust rather to their judgement than their art, and to their eyes than their scale and compass."[2] More pertinently, he considered that these ships were too high out of the water; but, to offset his criticism, it must be remembered that the late Tudor ships had done all that had been asked of them.

Raleigh's opinion, however, may be more important; at any rate, it is of considerable interest. In his *Observations on the Navy*, he said that there were six things required in a man-of-war: "she should be strongly built, swift, stout-sided, carry out her guns in all weathers, lie-to in a gale easily, and let stay well." King James's ships did not do any of these things, he continued, because they were "overfestered and clogged with great ordnance."

Perhaps the weak point was really in the administration. Nottingham remained Lord Admiral till 1618, a post he held for thirty-three years. He had been born in the 1530's and had, in fact, seen the whole early development of the idea of a national navy and must have contributed something toward its establishment and the traditions of seamanship and leadership that it has retained ever since. But he remained in office too long, and his judgment had become clouded, as can be seen in the trust he put in such men as Sir Robert Mansell, who is now thought to have been a poor seaman and a bad and dishonest administrator.

One of James I's ships must be mentioned in detail, because this ship, the *Prince Royal* of 1,200 tons, was the largest ship to be built up to that time. Her keel was laid down in October, 1608, but right from the start there was controversy. Phineas Pett was bitterly attacked by other shipwrights, including Matthew Baker—by now, at the age of seventy-nine, the *doyen* of his craft—and Waymouth, whom Pett disliked particularly. These men "pry'd up and down . . . belching out nothing but disgraces, despiteful speeches, and base, opprobrious terms," though Pett is glad to be able to note that "God put a hook into their nostrils" and that they themselves fell into the pit they had dug for him.[3]

These personal antipathies were extended to official inquiries about the standard of the work, and the king himself agreed to visit the ship in Woolwich dockyard in May, 1609, and see for himself. Pett was vindicated, though the charges leveled against him of making a showpiece and not a warship were never disproved by the test of active service. However, the *Prince Royal* was launched in 1610, and she was the first three-decker in the English navy, in the sense that she had her guns on three different levels; though really, perhaps, she should be described as having two full batteries and an upper deck armed. Her original armament consisted of 56 guns, but she was rebuilt to 90.

Her most distinctive feature was her decoration, which was something new in a warship. Painting and gilding by Peake and Isaacson cost £868, and the four upper strakes were embellished with badges, coats of arms, and "mastheads," which can be seen in all their Jacobean exuberance in Vroom's painting. Her carving, which cost £441, included fourteen "great lions' heads" for the round ports.

During the last six years of James I's reign, the newly appointed Navy Commissioners took matters in hand, and a plan to build two new warships a year was agreed on. In 1624, James's last navy list included the *Prince* and three other ships described as "first rank," fourteen "second rank," nine "third rank," and four "fourth rank," but they were most of them in very poor condition, and the king can hardly be absolved from the charge of having neglected to maintain this important part of his inheritance.

If James I's reign added little to the development of the warship, it was nevertheless a period of great maritime activity. Exploration, overseas trading, and colonization sum this up, and the English were to find in the Dutch competent and energetic rivals in each one of these enterprises, a point to which we shall return later when we consider the Anglo-Dutch Wars in the second half of the century. It is in this context of growing rivalry—the French, under Richelieu, were also building up a navy—that the developments in the English fleet in the 1630's should be seen, though it is doubtful whether Charles I can personally take very much of the credit for them.

The inefficiencies in administration that had chiefly caused the expedition to France initiated by Buckingham to be so disastrous did not cease with his death, but the decision to issue writs for ship money would seem to have been a wise one. In the first instance, toward the end of 1634, the writs were sent to ports and maritime counties only, asking them "to maintain a proportion of shipping for the safeguard of the Narrow Seas . . . which is very needful, for the French have prepared a fleet, and challenge a dominion in the seas, where anciently they durst not fish for gurnets without licence."[4]

London's squadron was ready by the end of the year, and though inferior in some ways to the king's ships, they were nevertheless described as "ships of good countenance." During 1635, the numbers of royal ships were to be increased, and King Charles was talking in terms of increasing his authority "to the ancient style and lustre." In the autumn, emboldened by the success of this new policy, the king decided to extend ship money to the inland counties and issued writs for the establishment of a fleet of forty-five ships. This fleet hardly justified itself during 1636, but it did convince Charles that a strong fleet was necessary, and the plans for the 1637 fleet were even more ambitious. It was to consist of fifty-five ships and was no doubt meant to be an important factor in his negotiations with France, which demanded a sufficiently strong fleet in the Channel to attack Spanish merchant shipping.

Richelieu, however, thwarted these plans, knowing of the English king's weak financial position, and the result was again unsatisfactory. The Earl of Northumberland gladly gave up his command of this fleet in the autumn of 1637, for it had had little to do, and it had certainly done nothing to reduce Richelieu to a more amenable frame of mind. In 1638, Northumberland was appointed Lord High Admiral; and on several occasions during the summer of that year, the king inspected the *Sovereign of the Seas*, the most recent addition to his fleet and direct fruit of the much-hated ship money.

It is with some relief that we can turn from the inefficiency and maladministration of naval affairs in those days to a consideration of this famous ship. We know her best from John Payne's magnificent contemporary engraving, with its elegant verses in which "this Britain's Argo" is thought to be the eighth wonder of the world. But there is also the painting of her in the Maritime Museum at Greenwich, ascribed to the elder Van de Velde, with her admirably gilded stern carvings, her handsome lantern, and her neatly balanced yards. In the foreground on the right side of the picture is Peter Pett, who collaborated with his father in building her and probably took the leading part in the work.

The *Sovereign of the Seas'* keel was laid at Woolwich in the presence of Charles I on January 16, 1636, and she was launched in October, 1637. The expenditure on her was considerable, not to say extravagant, though it is possible that a high percentage of the figure can be attributed to the absence of adequate control over the master shipwrights, who were apt to be dishonest in their estimates, especially where ornamentation was involved. At all events, she was a "great ship," the first real three-decker of a hundred guns, a three-master, and she displaced about 1,500 tons. Her ornamentation was the work of the royal master carver, Gerard Christmas, after drawings by Van Dyck; and with her glittering figurehead of Edgar the Peaceful riding down seven enemy kings, flanked by heraldic animals and royal monograms, she must have well earned the title of "the Golden Devil" that the Dutch bestowed on her.

In spite of doubts expressed in several quarters, she survived sixty years before she was accidentally burned in 1696, though by then her rig had been reduced and much of her upperwork had been cut down. The doubts just mentioned are interesting because they throw light on contemporary views on the size of warships. The Masters of Trinity House felt so strongly about the venture that in August, 1634, presumably as soon as the project of building such a ship became public, they wrote a letter of protest to Sir John Coke, the king's principal secretary. Their argument was, first, that a ship of such proportions, such "strange and large dimensions," could not be of use nor fit for service anywhere because there would be no harbor large enough for her, except in the Isle of Wight, so that the "wild sea alone must be her port"; secondly, that her anchors and cables would not be manageable; and thirdly, that three tiers of ordnance would endanger "the quality of the ship." And, indeed, they thought that "neither can the art or wit of man build a ship well conditioned and fit for service with three tiers of ordnance," recalling the sinking of the *Mary Rose* in Henry VIII's reign.

Modern criticism might be rather different. We may well think it ill-advised of Charles to have put, so to speak, all his eggs in one basket. It would have been wiser to have built several ships of, say, fifty guns at a cost of £5,500 to £6,500 each instead of this one great and lavish ship, which we are told cost £40,833. 8s. 1½d., exclusive of her guns.[5]

After the death of Charles I, in the years of the Commonwealth and Protectorate, there was a dramatic expansion of England's maritime power, all the more surprising because the country had suffered considerably during the Civil Wars and, as Oppenheim says, there was no past experience to justify the decision to spend such vast sums of money on supporting a great navy. Under Cromwell, ships were ordered by tens, and in 1654, for instance, we are told that twenty-two men-of-war left the slips, as well as other lesser vessels. Cromwell saw that it was necessary to have a reserve in the Downs ready for any emergency, but he also saw the wisdom of having permanent squadrons in the Mediterranean and off the West Indies.

From these decisions, brought about almost accidentally but also because Prince Rupert was still at large with a sizable fleet, came the emergence of England once more as a European power to be reckoned with. Robert Blake's personal contribution to all this was considerable both as an administrator and as a daring leader, and his activities in the Mediterranean and the Channel and his last exploit at Santa Cruz in 1657 show how well the Lord Protector was served at sea. Oppenheim prints a list of 207 new vessels added to the navy during the eleven years of the interregnum[6] and observes that 121 of these ships were still on the active list in 1660. There were also a number of ships from the old navy, some of which had altered names; the *Prince Royal*, for example, became the *Resolution*, and the *Charles*, the *Liberty*.

Though improvements in shipbuilding were introduced during this period, they were not revolutionary and were largely concerned with reducing the height of the hull above water and lengthening the keel, both intended to lessen the pitching, a chronic weakness, to give a steadier gun platform and to make the ships more weatherly. Apart from these, there was little attempt to improve the sails and rigging generally, and the actual sail area remained small for the tonnage of these ships. At first, as we might expect, the austerity of the age led to the reduction of decoration in ships, and the use of gilding ceased altogether for some years and the amount of money to be spent on carving was strictly limited. Later, there was a relaxation, and we discover that Richard Isaacson was allowed £240 to gild and paint two second-rates. Though decoration was frowned on by the Navy Commissioners as undignified, a certain latitude was allowed for figureheads: that of the *Naseby* consisted of a representation of Cromwell himself on horseback "trampling upon six nations."

The seven northern provinces of the Spanish Netherlands successfully flouted the authority of Spain in the second half of the sixteenth century and became known as the United Provinces. Later, because of the leadership of the House of Orange-Nassau and the supremacy of the province of Holland, that province's name was given to the whole country. Her inhabitants must always have been aware of the importance of the sea in their lives, and by the end of the sixteenth century she had already become an overseas power. This was because the seizure of the Portuguese crown by Philip of Spain meant that Lisbon was no longer open to the Dutch, and they were compelled to build ships of their own seaworthy enough to survive the long journeys to the East Indies and back. We know little of the four ships that set off thither in 1595, but the fact that they went, and that three of them returned more than two years later, is important because it marked the real beginning of a brilliantly successful experiment in imperial ascendancy that was based, above all, on an up-to-date and efficient concept of shipbuilding and seamanship.

By the second half of the seventeenth century, when they came to blows with England on three separate occasions, the Dutch had evolved a man-of-war that had two gun decks and was shallow of draft. This type of vessel, as opposed to the heavier three-decker that was being built in England and France, was the most suitable for the river estuaries and the shallow waters around their islands; but it seems certain that their lighter construction canceled out their maneuverability when it came to any engagement with enemy guns. In appearance, Dutch ships differed little from English or French ships of the period, but they were less elaborately ornamented, had plain sides, and as the century passed, their beak heads curved upward more and more.

Inevitably, the two maritime nations, England and the United Provinces, found themselves rivals and then enemies. The three Anglo-Dutch Wars of 1652–1654, 1665–1667 and 1672–1674 were of brief duration, but they were fought with an unflagging intensity; and the fact that the opponents were so evenly matched and were fighting each other in similar types of ship and were, on the whole, accustomed to similar geographical and climatic conditions gives them an added interest and importance. Again, these wars are more fully documented than many previous wars have been, and the pictorial records that have survived, very many of them from the hands of the talented members of the Van de Velde family, give us a vivid idea of the ships and the conditions under which they fought. "The trade of the world is too small for us two, therefore one must down," a Dutch sea captain told Pepys before the outbreak of the second war, and this reason would seem to be true of the first and third wars as well.

Andrew Marvell's well-known and uncharacteristically abusive poem *The Character of Holland,* published in 1653, was the result of war fever, or perhaps it had a propagandist intention in order to win over public opinion in England, which may not have been very enthusiastic for the war. In it, he was guilty of belittling a tenacious and lively enemy with such phrases as

> Holland, that scarce deserves the name of land,
> As but th' off-scouring of the British sand;
> And so much earth as was contributed
> By English pilots when they heav'd the lead;
> Or what by the ocean's slow alluvion fell
> Of ship-wrackt cockle and the muscle-shell,

Which culminate in the majestically rude taunt that

> This indigested vomit of the sea
> Fell to the Dutch by just propriety.

The author of *Hudibras* was hardly kinder; but in the following lines he introduces the authentic grounds for the quarrel that were not ideological but economic:

> A country that draws fifty foot of water
> In which men live as in a hold of nature,
> They dwell in ships, like swarms of rats, and prey
> Upon the goods all nations' fleets convey.

We are not concerned with the details of the wars here, but there are some tactical and other considerations that deserve mention even in the briefest account. Both sides seem to have had unmanageably large fleets that were made up of too many unsuitable ships, such as merchantmen—sometimes, perhaps, as many as a quarter of the total—and this must have influenced the English decision to introduce a uniform line-of-battle ship. A mixture of ships proved unsatisfactory because it tended to weaken the control of the commanders and turned battles into a series of disconnected melees sooner than might otherwise have happened. Alongside the desire for uniformity in ships in the line of battle—and here, as we shall see in the next chapter, we find the origin of the word "battleship"—was a stress on "formalism" in the actual conduct of a battle. The elaboration of fighting instructions came about and was indeed to bring with it serious drawbacks during the next century and a quarter.

Having made these few general remarks, it seems proper that we should now consider the handling of warships in action during the middle years of the century.

Though, on the whole, there had been few opportunities for the practical testing of their theory, those concerned with the development of naval tactics in the first half of the seventeenth century had come to accept the view that it was unwise to fire at extreme range. Instead, the view expounded by Sir Richard Hawkins, the last great Elizabethan seaman, who lived on into the 1630's, gained acceptance: that ships should close to a range where the smallest gun could be effective and that this should be done from to windward, if there could be choice. In 1625, Lord Wimbledon actually issued "Fighting Instructions," the first of a long series, for the Cadiz expedition of that year; but they were, on the whole, vague, though they did contain the first reference to *fleet* line ahead. It is noteworthy, too, that in them the colors red (for the admiral's squadron), blue (for the vice admiral's), and white (for the rear admiral's) were first laid down for the squadron flags; though by the time of the first Dutch War, the last two colors had been reversed, and this revised order was to remain in force till 1864, by which time the white ensign had been universally adopted by the Royal Navy. Another interesting point is the forthright view of Admiral Sir William Monson, who did not believe in too rigid formations. He did not think that heavy men-of-war should ever be subjected to precise movements —a view that was sensible but, in the event, very wide of the mark, owing to the seamanship shown by masters, boatswains, and others in the handling of their ships even in the most adverse conditions.

If we take the three Dutch Wars together, we can see a gradual crystallizing of naval tactics and, at the same time, the beginnings of a great tactical controversy, which was by no means resolved by the time the third war ended. To start with, there is no doubt that the innovation of real line-ahead formation belongs to the first war and was an English invention. Its official recognition can, indeed, be dated to March 29, 1653, and is found in the third Fighting Instruction issued by the Generals at Sea, Blake, Deane, and Monk, and by a more experienced seaman than any of them, William Penn. This instruction reads: "As soon as they shall see the general engage . . . then each squadron shall take the best advantage they can with the enemy next to them: and in order thereunto all the ships of every squadron shall endeavour to keep in line with the Chief . . . ." The need for this instruction seems to have been the near-disaster off Portland a few weeks beforehand, when the independent and uncoordinated activities of the squadrons almost led to their annihilation. It was tried out with success in June, 1653, off the Gabbard Bank, in an action in which the Dutch were still not really confident in the efficacy of the gun and hankered after the time-honored but now outlawed practice of boarding and entering. In fact, the Dutch plan was to fight with their ships in clumps, as it were, so as to prevent any single ship becoming isolated when damaged. Professor Lewis argues that the tactical formation of line ahead must have been tried out before the Instruction was introduced and not after, and, indeed, there is evidence that it may have been used in the very first action of the war.

The next stage is the adoption of close-hauled line ahead, that is, sailing six compass points into the wind. This can be inferred from a phrase in an eyewitness's account of an episode in the first battle of the Texel, in which Tromp lost his life, and recorded in Père Hoste's *Evolutions navales*. This witness clearly stated that the English ships were drawn up in full line ahead and "on a line which stretched more than four leagues, north-north east and south-south west, the wind being north-west." This became a definite instruction in 1665 during the second Dutch War, after it had been successfully tried out in the later stages of the first war. Another stage in these tactical developments was the adoption of the fixed distance of half a cable, that is, one hundred yards, between ships, an interval again officially adopted in 1665, though obviously tried out earlier. This improved the rather haphazard "follow-the-leader" method of approaching the enemy and engaging him, which showed little economy of effort because it did not allow all the ships in a squadron to fire at the same target at the same time.

The tactical controversy mentioned earlier was between the two rival schools of thought about the extent to which line-ahead tactics should be used. Put simply, there was the "formalist" view, upheld by seamen of the caliber of James, Duke of York, and Penn, who believed in the importance of rules and orderliness, even to the extent of stifling individual initiative; then there was the "melee" point of view, with Prince Rupert and Monk as its protagonists. They believed in the orderly approach but in engaging the enemy immediately on arrival within close enough range, without relying on concerted tactical maneuvers, accepting the inevitable shift of control from commander in chief to subordinate in the heat of battle and exploiting any unexpected advantage as soon as it presented itself. The formalists insisted on the conterminous line of battle, which in theory, though it hardly ever turned out to be so in practice, meant that the windward fleet in close-hauled line-ahead formation would ensure that its leading ship was exactly opposite the enemy's leading ship and that the remainder of the line would space itself out so that the complete van was opposite the enemy's van, the center opposite the enemy's center, and the rear opposite the enemy's rear. Normally, these maneuvers would take place long before the two opposing fleets were within fighting distance of each other, and both schools of thought believed in the maxim that it was more advantageous to engage at as close range as possible.

Thus, to join battle, the ships of the windward fleet turned eight points of the compass toward the enemy, if his ships were actually stationary, and advanced in line-abreast formation until the enemy was in range of their weakest guns, when they would turn back onto their original line-ahead direction. Then each ship would engage her opposite number at a given signal and at the same time, and this was thought to be the real justification for the whole maneuver, the concentration of gunfire on the enemy at a given moment. This presupposed, as Professor Lewis has observed, "a surprising degree of compliancy"[7] on the enemy's part, and we can only note that the Duke of York really did expect him so to behave. Article 17 of his Instructions issued at the beginning of the third war shows this: "None of the ships of his majesty's fleet," it reads, "shall pursue any small number of the enemy's ships before the main body of their fleet shall be disabled or run"; in other words, if an enemy ship dropped away to leeward, she was not to be rounded up and destroyed.

The second and third wars show the veering of naval opinion backward and forward between these two points of view. The first encounter in the second war, off Lowestoft in June, 1665, can be seen as formalist. The Duke of York retained control, but he was criticized for indulging in too much maneuvering and too little fighting, so much so that the king removed him from his command, and Prince Rupert and Monk, now Duke of Albemarle, took over. In the Four Days' Battle, however, in June, 1666, things went wrong, and the advocates of the melee found themselves in difficulties. Even though de Ruyter drew off his ships first, Albemarle was criticized by Pepys and others with some justification, for his losses had been far heavier than those of the Dutch, though it is fair to add that he showed his characteristic powers of resilience a few weeks later and won a decisive victory in the so-called St. James's Day Battle.

In the third war, the Duke of York was again in command and so, therefore, were the formalists. The Fighting Instructions committed to writing the theory of the conterminous line examined above, but they also included the order for "dividing the enemy from to leeward" which should not, however, be interpreted as a concentration on part of the enemy's line, a meleeist principle, for the line was to be preserved intact even in the inevitable close action that was bound to follow any breakthrough. Perhaps it was merely an attempt to enable at least part of the fleet to gain and exploit the windward position. But whatever the formalist theories behind these fighting instructions, James was unable to carry them out at the battle of Solebay on May 28, 1672. It was even impossible to establish a formal line, so Sandwich, commanding the rear squadron, decided to put about and come in behind the Dutch, though even such melee tactics did not prove entirely successful.

Mention must be made of the Dutch handling of fire ships. Each flagship had several of these vessels under her lee, and they were used at suitable moments to destroy an immobilized enemy ship. The Dutch used specially constructed vessels, paying great attention to the loading of them and to such details as a means of escape for their crews. De Ruyter's great success at Solebay was the burning of Sandwich's flagship, the *Royal James*, 100 guns, one of the five English first-rates then in existence and, according to Evelyn, "one of the best men-of-war that ever spread canvas on the sea." The English fire ships were more amateurish in comparison and often required a certain amount of first aid to make them effective. This can be seen from an entry in the journal of George Legge, then captain of the *Royal Katherine* and later to become Earl of Dartmouth. He relates that the *Truelove* fire ship was sent "to wait upon our ship in time of service" but was found to have neither foremast nor fore-topmast and her fireworks were "most of them damnified with water, whereupon I, not knowing how soon we might engage the enemy, went on board the fireship myself . . . and . . . ordered my carpenter to make her a foremast and fore topmast of my studding sail booms. . . . Likewise I ordered my gunner to go aboard and to carry a barrel of powder to new prime all the fireworks again . . . for the better doing of execution."[8]

As has been said already, the standard of English and Dutch professionalism increased greatly during this third quarter of the seventeenth century. Though it is probably true to say that the English had better ships and had appreciated the logic of the naval gun more shrewdly, nothing should be allowed to obscure the ability and daring of the Dutch leaders. Maarten Harpertszoon Tromp, whose last words when he was mortally wounded by an English bullet off Ter Heide in 1653 were, "I am finished; keep up your courage," takes a high place in any catalog of distinguished Dutchmen in their golden century. James, Duke of York, told Pepys that he was "the greatest seaman that ever was in the world for governing of a military fleet," and perhaps his only rival was his pupil Michiel Adrianszoon de Ruyter. Both men were simple in their bearing and in their personal habits, and they seem to have been courteous and just in their dealings with their fellow men. We are told how Tromp was satisfied with a mere pickled herring for his breakfast and how he was "not terryfying or rough, like the children of Neptune usually become from the boisterousness of the sea," while de Ruyter struck a contemporary Englishman as a man to be "recommended to posterity as an ornament of his age, the darling of the seas, and the delight and honour of his country." Yet this same man was discovered by a visitor who had come on board to congratulate him on the evening of the last day of the famous Four Days' Battle in 1666 sweeping out his cabin and feeding his chickens.

Before we leave the Anglo-Dutch Wars, a less-sophisticated eye-witness of those far-off, hotly contested battles should be allowed to speak for himself. Edward Barlow spent the whole of the second war in the *Monk* frigate, 58 guns, "a ship," he records, "which deserves to be set in a ring of gold for the good services she had done . . . and she shall have my good word so long as she is a ship." This is what he had to say about the fleet movements that led up to the Battle of St. James's Day in July, 1666:

"So . . . our General [Albemarle] having had good commendations from His Majesty and the Duke [of York], wishing him good success, he loosed his foretopsail and fired a gun as a sign to weigh our anchors. And having a south-west wind and fair weather, we weighed our anchors and set sail from the buoy of the Nore. . . . So being under sail, having a fleet of eighty-five ships in all, well manned, yet we had some cowardly commanders . . . who were more fit to go commanders in some dung-boat than in a good King's ship. . . . And coming down that tide into the Swin, we came to an anchor and rode there that night. And the next morning we weighed our anchors and came down to the buoy of the Gunfleet. And espying the Hollanders' fleet and they seeing us, they weighed their anchors and plied the wind further from the shore, and we plying after them. But we came again to our anchors that night and weighed again the next day; but the wind being easterly and they to windward, so that we could not come near them in two or three days, they were not willing to come near us, thinking they were too near our shore. So coming to an anchor that night and the next day weighing again, we espied the Hollanders' fleet to leeward of us, for they not coming to an anchor, the wind and tide had driven them to leeward of our fleet, which was to our advantage.

"So preparing all our fleet ready and putting them in a posture to fight, putting the Vice-Admiral of the White, [Sir Thomas Tideyman] the *Royal Katherine*, the headmost ship, and all the White squadron to be headmost; and next to them our General's squadron, the Red, our General having the *Royal Sovereign* as his second, being the best ship in England, yet carried no flag, reckoning herself an ordinary squadron, bearing only a flagstaff on the main topgallant masthead with a blood-red pennant or streamer flying upon it, signifying the Admiral of England, being commanded by one Captain Lockes, a man of approved valour and good success, having in her a thousand seamen and soldiers, and a hundred and two pieces of ordnance.

"So having all things ready and being up to the Hollanders' fleet, and both fleets, having about ninety sail, stretching themselves in equal length that they might all engage at once to try who were the best men, and our General sailing right against their General, being both in the middle of their fleets, about nine o'clock of the morning of Wednesday, being St. James' Day, the 25th July in the year 1666, the Vice-Admiral of the White began the fight. And our General, hoisting up the bloody flag at his fore topmasthead, the fight began on both sides extremely hot and fierce, the noise of the cannon roaring in the seas like claps of thunder, which were heard in England all over Kent."[9]

How inaccurate it is to think of France as a really united country in the early years of the seventeenth century can be seen when we consider her position in terms of naval power. Though her coastlines are considerably longer than her land frontiers, very few stretches of them and none of the main ports belonged to the Crown; and what central naval authority there might have been had devolved into the hands of the governors of Brittany, Provence, and Guienne, who called themselves admirals but saw themselves rather as independent and local rulers than as representatives of the French king. The Lord High Admiral of France extended his official influence only over the Channel and the North Sea, but the gentle Henri de Montmorency, who held this office at the time when Richelieu came to power, was hardly likely to make his presence felt, especially as there was no such thing as a French fighting fleet.

As early as 1625, Richelieu saw that France should become a naval power, looking at first to the Mediterranean coast and seeing that the raids of the Barbary pirates were a continual threat and appreciating that Spain, an even nearer threat, could only be defeated on the sea. He saw, too, that French warships and the succor they might bring might persuade Spain's Mediterranean dependencies, such as Sicily and Naples, to turn to France, to her ultimate advantage. Consequently, he ordered five warships from the United Provinces, which were delivered in 1626 and which included the *Saint Louis*, a two-decker of sixty guns. These were to be models from which French shipwrights could build up the fleet.

Richelieu made himself *Surintendant général de la navigation et commerce* and soon after abolished the title of admiral so as to remove from those members of the nobility who possessed it even this titular authority. He also bought from their owners such ports as Le Havre, Honfleur, and Brouage, then a small harbor north of the estuary of the Gironde, for bases for the new fleet. Richelieu's *Ordonnance de la marine*, which set in motion these changes, received impetus from the revolt of La Rochelle, aided, though ineffectively, as it turned out, by England: it was plain that an organized navy was essential.

The naval program promulgated in 1629 set out to create a navy of fifty warships and the necessary auxiliary craft. Every port in the country that could boast a shipyard was to build at least one, and arsenals were to be established, though at first cannon cast in the United Provinces were bought in. By the late 1630's there were thirty-eight ships in the new Atlantic fleet—twelve of them more than 500 tons —divided into three squadrons, those of Normandy, Brittany, and Guienne; and France was even able to build a ship in 1638 in answer to the imposing *Sovereign of the Seas*, launched the year before. This was the *Couronne* of seventy-two guns, built at La Roche Bernard, 250 feet in length from stem to stern and carrying a crew of six hundred men. She was a two-decker but had about the same dimensions as the English ship.

Richelieu's death in 1642 was followed by a long period of naval inaction, and it was not until Colbert had become Minister of Marine that the position Richelieu had created was recovered. As Richelieu had done before him, Colbert ordered ships from the United Provinces; but it is interesting to see that from quite early on, the French were developing an individual type of warship that was slightly different from either the Dutch or the English man-of-war. Briefly, the difference was a shallower draft and a wider beam, with the lower deck 4 feet above the waterline, which made the ship a better gun platform and a better sailer than the English equivalent. The two-decked 70-gun French ship, which Pepys commented on as early as 1663, became the standard first-rate; and when the 74-gun *Superbe* visited Spithead in 1672, Anthony Deane was ordered to copy her measurements. The result was the 70-gun *Harwich*, which was such a success that nine similar ships were ordered; and after this, French prizes were studied carefully for new techniques and innovations in design.

Colbert's development of the navy as well as the French mercantile marine was part of his colonial policy, which need not concern us here. Shipping required a regular supply of timber, and his improved administration of the forests soon enabled France to be independent of supplies from the Baltic. He also subsidized shipbuilding, with the result that French tonnage increased greatly. By 1677, the French navy was comparable with the navies of the United Provinces and of England, for it consisted of 116 ships that year, a number which included 12 first-rates and 26 second-rates. The main difficulty was to find suitable officers, and especially those for the higher commands, with the result that two distinct types of officer could be seen: those promoted because of their service in the army or because of their high birth—for example, D'Estrées—and those actually trained at sea and promoted because of distinguished service on that element. At the end of the century, Duquesne and Tourville represented this latter class.

Probably the navy was Colbert's most lasting achievement, since the establishment of the great dockyards at Toulon and Brest, the arsenal at Rochefort, the naval hospitals, the school of naval gunnery, the trained reserve of about fifty thousand men, the establishment of regiments of marines, and the systematic study of hydrography, which led to more efficient charts, all contributed to the foundation of an accepted profession.

It has been suggested that the shallower-drafted French ships, some of which, to judge from sketches in the *Atlas de Colbert*, had no raised forecastle at all and therefore seem much lower in the water, were designed for galley warfare in the Mediterranean, especially as some of them were strongly armed fore and aft. A word should be said about the French galley fleet at this point. In the 1630's, it numbered twelve galleys and about the same number of auxiliary vessels. The galley commander's flagship was traditionally called *La Réale* from the early part of the sixteenth century onward. Landström illustrates one of them belonging to the year 1680 and tells us that these flagships could be propelled by a total of 462 oarsmen, though the normal number was about half of this.[10] In the Musée de la Marine in Paris the stern carving of one of these *Réales* can still be seen; she was the work of the sculptor Pierre Puget, whose style in ship decoration gave French ornamentation its particular character, often turning the stern into a kind of architectural fantasy, complete with open galleries, engaged pillars, window frames, and balustrades.

Later in the century, however, these decorations became simpler and less flamboyant. As men-of-war became heavier and more powerful, the galley became less and less useful. In any case, she could not hope to get the better of a sailing ship in a fresh wind, and because of her length, she was slow in turning. Thus she could only take the offensive in calm weather, when she could turn from the broadsides and choose her own battle position. But even then her comparatively light armament made her no match against any armed man-of-war. Louis XIV was often advised to dispense with the Mediterranean galley fleet, and there were many engagements that could be quoted to support this, such as the occasion when the ship *Le Bon* defeated thirty-five galleys single-handed in 1684. However, as we have seen, the galleys survived into the eighteenth century, and the last engagement in which they took a prominent part was in 1717 off Cape Matapan. The last *Réale* flagship was built in 1720.

A new weapon mounted in a new type of vessel appeared in 1682. This was the bomb ketch introduced by Abraham Duquesne that wrought such havoc on Algiers in that year. This ketch-rigged vessel was broad in the beam and had no foremast so as to make room for the two heavy mortars sited before the mainmast. She was stoutly constructed and strengthened from below so as to distribute the shock when the mortars were fired. The bombs apparently weighed about 200 pounds, a weight that should be compared with the 48-pound shot fired from the largest guns then in use. These *galiotes à bombes* were invented by Bernard Renau d'Eliçagaray, known familiarly as le petit Renau because of his diminutive size, and in them he seems to have invented an infernal machine that had a particularly devastating effect on the Barbary coasts of Africa during the 1680's.

Before we leave the seventeenth century and the magnificent ships that were being built in northwestern European waters, it is well to remind ourselves of some of the hardships that those who sailed in them endured. There was indifferent food, especially at the end of a long voyage away from land, but there were also broken nights and cramped quarters.

Edward Barlow, whom we have already met and who went to sea first in Montague's flagship, the *Naseby*, in 1659, described his cabin as "a thing much like to some gentleman's dog kennel." Also, there was the ever-present fear of fire caused by "some careless man in smoking a pipe of tobacco" or by an indolent cook. Once it started, "it is a hundred to one if that you put it out," Barlow has noted in his *Journal*,[11] "everything being so pitchy and tarry that the least fire setteth it all in a flame." Also, "there is great danger of the powder," he added, "for the least spark with a hammer or anything else in the room where it is, or the snuff of a candle causeth all to be turned into a blast, and in a moment no hopes of any persons' lives being saved from death in the twinkling of an eye."

Again, when he was serving in the *Monmouth* frigate, Barlow describes another routine emergency, the splitting of the sails in foul weather; and as we read we can feel ourselves transported back into the sailing ship era, so forcible is the impact of his words even on the reader of today:

> So having a fair wind, we directed our course again westerly for Genoa; but the day following we had a cross wind, blowing very hard and splitting our sails in pieces; and we being forced, poor men, to go up into the tops in the dark nights to put to our yards other sails, when it blowed and rained, with thunder and lightning as though Heaven and earth would come together, and then when we seemed to hang by our eyelids up in the air, when the ship rolled and tumbled so that we had much ado to hold ourselves fast from falling overboard, above us seeing nothing and underneath us the raging of the sea, each wave ready to swallow the ship and all up, then did I wish that I had taken my friends' counsel to have taken any calling rather than endure such miseries.[12]

NOTES

[1]See R. D. Merriman (ed.), *Queen Anne's Navy*, Navy Records Society, London, 1961, vol. cii, p. 81.

[2]*Additional Manuscripts 19889, The Jewell of Artes*, 1604, f. 135, quoted in Oppenheim, *The Administration of the Royal Navy*, p. 186.

[3]See W. G. Perrin (ed.), *The Autobiography of Phineas Pett*, Navy Records Society, London, 1917, vol. li, p. 51.

[4]*State Papers (Domestic)*, vol. 276, 64.

[5]See Oppenheim, *The Administration of the Royal Navy*, p. 260.

[6]*Ibid.*, pp. 330–337.

[7]M. A. Lewis, *The Navy of Britain*, p. 459.

[8]R. C. Anderson (ed.), *Journals and Narratives of the Third Dutch War*, Navy Records Society, London, 1946, vol. lxxvi, p. 302.

[9]Basil Lubbock (ed.), *Edward Barlow's Journal 1659–1703*, vol. i, pp. 123–125.

[10]See Björn Landström, *The Ship*, pp. 137–141.

[11]Lubbock, *op. cit.*, vol. i, p. 61.

[12]Lubbock, *op. cit.*, vol. i, pp. 164–165.

The 56-gun *Prince Royal*, launched by King James I in 1610 and built by Phineas Pett. She was renamed the *Resolution* under the Commonwealth but again was named *Prince* in 1660. She surrendered to the Dutch in 1666. Note her three complete gun decks, her three galleries, and the plume of the Prince of Wales, after whom she was named. This oil painting by Hendrik Cornelisz Vroom (1566–1640) is in Haarlem. *Science Museum, London*

The 100-gun *Sovereign of the Seas*, built by Peter Pett under the supervision of his father, Phineas, in 1637. She was the largest warship in the ship-money fleet of Charles I and the first three-masted three-decker line-of-

battle ship. She was renamed *Royal Sovereign* by Charles II and was accidentally destroyed by fire in 1696. Colored engraving by John Payne in the
National Maritime Museum, Greenwich. *Science Museum, London*

Bow view of the Swedish 64-gun *Vasa* seen in dry dock at Beckholmen near Stockholm after she had been raised to the surface in 1961. She had capsized during her maiden voyage on August 10, 1628. *Boktryckeriet P. A. Norstedt and Söner, Stockholm*

Contemporary model of the *Prince*, as on page 121, showing quarterdeck. *Science Museum, London*

Rigged contemporary model of the first-rate line-of-battle ship *Prince*, built in 1670, from Samuel Pepys' *Collection of Vessels Naval*, details of stern and quarter galleries. She was renamed *Royal William* in 1692 and was broken up in 1813. *Science Museum, London*

Model of the 96-gun *Loyal London*, built in 1666, stern view. She was set on fire by the Dutch in the Medway in 1667, but her remains were incorporated into the second *London*, built in 1670 and broken up in 1747. *Science Museum, London*

Dutch shipping in the Ij, near Amsterdam, oil painting by Willem Van de Velde the Younger (1633–1707). *Photo by permission of Fotocommissie, Rijksmuseum, Amsterdam*

Midship section of a first-rate warship (*c.* 1680), engraving by Edmund Dummer, shipwright, later Surveyor of the Navy. His *Draughts of the Body of an English Man of War*, which includes this engraving, is in Pepys' *Collections of Vessels Naval. Science Museum, London*

(Left) "The Cannon Shot," oil painting by Willem Van de Velde the Younger *Fotocommissie, Rijsmuseum, Amsterdam*

De Passebon's bomb ketch (*c.* 1690). Note the absence of a foremast so as to accommodate the heavy mortars. *Science Museum, London*

The 100-gun *Britannia*, built by Sir Phineas Pett in 1682. She was Edward Russell's flagship at Barfleur and the battle off Cape La Hogue in 1689. Line engraving by J. Sturt, after the painting by Willem Van de Velde the Elder (1611–1693). *National Maritime Museum, Greenwich*

The 130-gun Spanish *Santissima Trinidad,* from a line engraving by J. Hägg, 1913. Though she was in her day the largest ship in the world, she was not strictly a four-decker. She was built as an ordinary three-decker, and when she was twenty-six years old, she was equipped with a complete row of guns along her gangways, so that from outside she appeared to have four gun decks. She escaped capture at the Battle of Cape St. Vincent but succumbed at Trafalgar. *National Maritime Museum, Greenwich*

VI

The British Navy in the Eighteenth Century

THE series of wars that broke out between France and England in 1689 and ended in 1815 can be seen, from a naval point of view, as a series of episodes in a single, long-drawn-out struggle for sea power. The naval engagements themselves were not so evenly contested or, perhaps, so bloodily fought out as in the Dutch Wars, nor, of course, was the fighting continuous; but the five wars, culminating in the great struggle against Napoleon, led gradually to the realization by the French that they were a land and not a sea power, that "the far distant, storm-beaten ships upon which the Grand Army never looked," in Mahan's classic phrase, really did stand between them and the dominion of the world. The establishment of English supremacy at sea was a fact as early as the first decade of the eighteenth century, and it was never really in doubt during the hundred years that separate the capture of Gibraltar from the Battle of Trafalgar.

In view of all this, it is perhaps surprising to learn that at the beginning of King William's War in 1689, the English fleet was little better than the Dutch and was actually inferior to the French in numbers. The comparative figures were as follows: France had 93 "ships of the line of battle"—a phrase we shall examine presently—out of a total of 221; England, 100 out of a total of 173; and the United Provinces, 69 out of 102. From the English point of view, a new factor presented itself: France was a Mediterranean power. This meant that England had to face the possibility of fighting in unfamiliar waters, and she came to realize the necessity of a base in the Mediterranean from which to maintain any blockade of the southern French ports.

The great increase in the size of the English navy during the 1690's, from 173 ships of all kinds in 1689 to 323 in 1697, was the result; but the outcome of William's War was by no means a foregone conclusion. Indeed, victories such as Barfleur and Cape La Hogue followed the failure to intercept the French expeditionary force on its way to Ireland and the defeat suffered by Torrington off Beachy Head. It was a war of dramatic reversals of fortune, and its monuments are dramatic as well as durable. They were, as one historian of the period has written, "the naval dockyard at Devonport which guaranteed the Channel approaches and the hospital buildings at Greenwich which commemorate the defeat of an attempted invasion."[1]

Let us now consider the ships themselves in the last decade of the seventeenth century. Ehrman (see footnote 1 and Bibliography) makes the interesting point that even in England the ship was not yet automatically a general symbol of national strength, and the idea of protective wooden walls had neither achieved the comforting familiarity it was later to have nor become a threadbare and overused figure of speech. Men in their late seventies might actually still remember the controversy that raged over the building of the ship-money fleet of Charles I and wonder whether such monsters, following the lead of the *Sovereign of the Seas*, could justify the money lavished on them. Yet as the fact of naval supremacy became more familiar, so the warship was more readily absorbed into the language of simile, and the image, as we say today, of strength was built up.

Edward Ward's *The Wooden World Dissected* was first published in Queen Anne's reign, but it shows the process getting under way. The ship of war is likened to a "floating castle"; she is "an airy fortress . . . governed by the motions of the wind"; she "flies so far that no Bird of Nature, but a Woodcock, can hold way with her." Again, she is "the mighty Guardian of our Island, defending us all around from foreign Dangers as watchfully as a Mastiff does an Orchard." Not all the imagery, however, is so flattering; for the warship is also the "great Bridge of the Ocean, conveying over to all habitable Places Death, Pox and Drunkenness," and she is "Belzebub's grand Arsenal, where you meet so much Tumult, Thunder, Fire and Smoak, sometimes, that Old

Nick himself cannot know which way to turn himself." She is, in fact, "Noah's Ark improved to the best Advantage, with all the tame Beasts garbled out, that hate the Smell of Gun-powder."

One result of the Dutch Wars had been the realization that certain ships were suitable for fighting in the line of battle and others were not and that the two should not be mixed. This led to a change in classification; the rough-and-ready rating of ships according to the number of men they carried, which dated back to Blake and the first Dutch War, was superseded by classification by number of guns, which involved also a certain combination of size, strength, and stability. The more guns a ship carried, the heavier that ship had to be, so that maneuverability, which was England's strong suit in the wars against Spain, was gradually lost.

In consequence, there was a tendency to concentrate on building third- and fourth-rates, that is, ships with between 42 and 74 guns. For instance, the thirty new ships ordered to be laid down in 1677 consisted of one first-rate only, nine seconds, and twenty thirds; and during William's War, three second-rates, twenty thirds, thirty-five fourths but no firsts were built. Another point was that the first and second-rates were really too expensive: they cost much more per ton and they were harder to build. The fourth-rate warship, in fact, became gradually larger, as the rating system was not yet firm except insofar as the upper and lower limits had been fixed. Here the French had set the pace. With fewer guns and sharper lines, their ships had outsailed the Dutch and the English until attempts were made, at first rather unscientific ones, to modify the ships and increase their stability by such methods as "girdling," which was the fixing of additional strakes to the sides at the waterline.

The term "ship of the line" gradually became the accepted designation for those ships "fit to lie in the line of battle" during William's War. It was displacing the earlier phrase "capital ship," originally a Dutch term, used by Pepys as early as 1677, probably to describe the first four rates, but excluding the fifth.[2] Since these terms are a little confusing, it is worthwhile examining them as fully as possible at this stage. "Line-of-battle ship" was being used as well as "ship of the line of battle" by the early years of the eighteenth century, and these two expressions remain in common usage till the middle of the nineteenth century. The word "battleship," which emerges in the second half of Queen Victoria's reign derives directly from the former. "Capital" as an adjective to describe the higher-rated ships did not disappear completely, though by the middle of the eighteenth century it seems to have become entirely synonymous with "ships of the line," including two-deckers. Admiral Vernon used it as an alternative to "great," though in the 1740's it still seemed to specify the largest ship in the squadron, the flagship, thus retaining the meaning it had at the beginning of the century when admirals of the older generation used it to designate first- and second-rates only. Rooke, for example, used it when commenting on the suggestion that he should leave his one first-rate and five second-rates at Lisbon for the winter of 1702.[3]

In general, the actual ships in the French and English navies were very similar to each other to look at, especially at a distance. Indeed, from the middle of the seventeenth century onward, sailing under false colors was a regular *ruse de guerre,* and we learn that French colors were a fairly normal issue to ships in William's War.[4] This similarity was inevitable because of the limitations in the size of suitable lengths of timber for shipbuilding and because the requirements of the best guns available, as well as the nature of the guns themselves, remained static for a century or more.

The similarity in design between English, French, and Dutch men-of-war did not, however, mean that the fleets were similarly constituted, because each country specialized in a particular class of ship. As we saw in the last chapter, the Dutch found the lighter, shallower-drafted ship more suitable for their purposes, though they were compelled to rebuild most of their fleet in the 1670's and 1680's so that the ships should be more of a match for those of the most likely enemy, France.

France seems to have approached the whole question of warship development more scientifically than the English as the Conference of 1681 suggests. On this occasion, by the orders of Louis XIV himself, a great number of naval architects and scientists met in Paris to discuss the application of new theories of resistance and movement in water. It led to modifications to the *Ordonnances du roi* in 1689 and was typical of the great interest shown in such matters, which can also be seen in the variety of treatises printed in both France and the United Provinces in the seventeenth century, very few of which seem to have been translated into English. Always excepting the activities of the Royal Society in the 1660's and onward, English research lagged far behind, and there was little difference between the sea dictionaries and manuals such as Captain John Smith's *Accidence for Young Seamen* of 1626 and similar publications a century later.

Ehrman gives a masterly survey of the nature of the late seventeenth century man-of-war, including the limitations,[5] and we cannot do better than note some of the points he makes. The ships were clumsy, under-canvased for their size and overgunned, he says. Their sail plan was that of the square-rigged ship, with few modifications, and in spite of the introduction of the bowline and the reintroduction of the reef point, which enabled the sails to be more quickly adapted to the weather, they were difficult to trim accurately. Again, until the introduction of the steering wheel in the early eighteenth century,[6] the whipstaff was the universal method of steering, though it was not designed for the heavy ships of the higher rates and, indeed, had frequently to be abandoned in bad weather.

The guns in King William's ships were still those which were used in Elizabeth's reign: the cannon, with its short barrel and short range but heavy shot; the culverin, with its long barrel and medium range; and the minor pieces such as sakers and minions, which were short-range weapons designed to destroy the rigging and superstructures of ships. The English gun enjoyed a wide reputation throughout Europe, but it had progressed as far as was then possible, and it was to develop very little until the middle of the nineteenth century. By the 1690's it had a range of 400 yards, and though it could throw heavier shot than it could a century earlier, its accuracy was no more certain, and the greater recoil meant that the gun, and therefore ultimately the ship itself, became heavier and clumsier. Yet even so, they provided an unsteady platform for firing, and in the interests of gravity, the gun had to be sited as near to the waterline as possible—too near, Pepys thought, and Dryden may have been writing more accurately than he knew when he wrote of the "low-laid mouths" of the guns laved by "each mounting billow."[7]

Even successful shots did comparatively little damage, since a competent shipwright could easily plug the 8-inch-diameter hole the shot made, and sometimes, as in the *Sovereign*, the midships timbers near the waterline were more than 2 feet thick, with stout oak "knees" buttressing the strakes every 20 feet or so along the side of the gun deck. Also, it was difficult to control a broadside, especially as the rate of firing was painfully slow, and this may have been the reason for the victory of the formalist school of thought, the beginning of which we noted in the last chapter and the development of which we must consider a little later on. The cumulative effect of the continual firing of broadsides alone seemed likely to justify the "line" tactics, though in the process, it might be difficult to seize and exploit any unexpected opportunity.

A few general points must be cleared up about the War of the Spanish Succession, 1701–1714, which was known at the time as Queen Anne's War. The exploits on land of the first Duke of Marlborough have tended to overshadow the British achievements on sea, so that, to appreciate the part played by the navy, we must recall that by the terms of the Treaty of Utrecht, Britain retained Gibraltar and Minorca, those first Mediterranean bases that were to be so important during the rest of the century, gained further territory in the West Indies, and, further north, won from the French Nova Scotia, Newfoundland, and trading rights in the Hudson Bay area, all of which made the conquest and retention of Canada possible later on in the century. Great Britain, a title which itself belongs to this period, for the Act of Union between England and Scotland took place in 1707, had moved up to displace France as the leading maritime nation. The "exorbitant power" of France had been reduced, for the time being at any rate.

During the first decade of the eighteenth century, there was considerable shipbuilding activity, though there had been a concentration on the smaller rates. The third-rates of 70 and 80 guns proved to be the most useful, the ships Admiral Rooke called "light sailing frigates," yet even these were hardly maneuverable enough for operations in narrow waters;[8] so the fourth-rates, especially the 54-gun ship, proved the really effective fighting unit during this war. These again were sometimes rather loosely referred to as "frigates," but they were certainly "in the line." The lowest rates were often unsatisfactory: the *Hare*, for instance, is described as "such a wretched tool of a ship," and in 1708, only one of Byng's nine fifth-rates was fast enough to catch up with the French in the chase off Scotland. The first two rates were becoming less popular—for the reasons we saw obtaining in King William's War—and in any case, bad weather often meant that their lower gunports could not be opened, thus depriving them of a high percentage of their gunpower. Often, too, in consequence, these rates were laid up in harbor for six months of the year.

By 1714, however, 120 of the 200 rated ships in the queen's fleet had been built or rebuilt in her reign, and 160 of them were in good condition.

The design of ships was still going through a transitional stage, though in a sense this has always been so, and the Admiralty does not seem to have been satisfied during the early years of the war that the French lead was being diminished. French prizes were ordered to be studied carefully, since it was generally believed that all French ships were "very well contrived";[9] it is fair to add, however, that the French were viewing British ships in much the same way.

In general, the height at the stern and the steep downward "sheer" from the stern to the bow were being reduced and the tendency to overgun ships in relation to their tonnage was being checked. Also, in the 60-gun ships and below, the spritsail topmast, stepped on the bowsprit, disappeared, and a great advance was made in the introduction of the steering wheel, which had entirely superseded the whipstaff by 1710.

Committees were set up to consider new standard designs and to study the problem of achieving uniformity of performance—and, indeed, of exact tonnage—within a class of ships and the perennial question of ship stability. Highly elaborate decoration was ordered to be cut to the minimum: carved work was to be reduced "only to a lion and trailboard for the head with mouldings instead of brackets between the lights of the stern galleries and bulkheads to have moulding fixed against the timbers," we are told,[10] and "the joiner's work of the great cabin, coach, wardroom and roundhouse of each ship" was "to be fixed only with slit deals, glued and planed without any sort of moulding or cornice."

It is pleasant, though, to find the Earl of Peterborough, joint Admiral of the Fleet with Sir Clowdisley Shovell, asking permission for certain luxuries in the cabin of the *Britannia*, his flagship, in spite of these austerities. He wished to have a little rail and bannister across his cabin and on both sides of his bed. These items were to be "very small, about three feet high, and well turned." They were to be gilded to match his bed and chairs, and there were also to be "at proper distances little pedestals with a carved ornament on it, [such] as a casket with fruit and flowers."[11]

Two other contemporary difficulties are worth noting. The first was the universal tendency for captains to adapt the official sail plans and arrangements of rigging to meet their own sailing experience. This often caused friction between the sea officer and the administrator on shore, but it remained a regular, and natural, practice. More than a century later, Captain Boteler told a committee of inquiry in 1829 that he did not honestly think that a single ship in the fleet was rigged in accordance with her rigging warrant.[12]

The other difficulty was how best to clean the underwater parts of ships efficiently and quickly. We have seen earlier something of the development of sheathing and the final acceptance of copper as the best material for doing this, but it is interesting to learn that the Cruisers and Convoys Act of 1708 laid down officially that a ship should be cleaned "at least three times a year or oftener." Earlier, various remedies had been tried out, including a Mr. Ardsoif's special "composition," which does not seem to have been a success, to judge from the letter written by Sir Thomas Hardy, captain of the *Kent* to the Navy Board on March 8, 1706.[13]

This letter is interesting on its own account, as it gives a description of the process known as "hogging." This was a method of partially clearing weeds from the bottoms of ships while they were still afloat by means of a wooden "hog," or scrubber, which was hauled horizontally by ropes backward and forward and could be lowered under the keel from one side of the ship to the other: "We heeled and scrubbed several times," Hardy writes, "and hogged likewise, and found that the grass and foulness grew as fast on Mr. Ardsoif's composition as upon black, ordinary graving [stuff]. We brought up in the hog great quantity of barnacles. And upon heeling and hogging in Barcelona, where the water is very clear, we poked the barnacles off the rudder, and where the hog would not reach, with the iron of a shovel upon the end of a long spar. And all my officers and people that used the scrubbing were of opinion that the brass and barnacles stuck faster than usual.

"I stayed upon deck and in the dock all the time that the ship was breaming [that is, when the marine growths were being burned off by reed torches], and made the following observations, viz: that there was very little stuff remaining upon the ship's bottom, and the fire, which was greater than ordinary, would only hold at here and there a spot. Where there was no stuff left, there was a green film, such as usually grows on timber that lies wet and dry [that is, exposed to the weather]. From whence I concluded that the fish in the harbour had ate up the long grass, as is often observed.

"From five strakes under the lower wale, where we could not reach with our scrubbers in the term of the voyage, it was, down to the keel, like a perfect rock, being full of a small barnacle of about the bigness of a small nut. There was mixed with it some few large barnacles, which were three inches long, the stem and shell measured together.

"The ship's bottom is very much worm-eaten, as well where there was stuff left as where there was none. The caulkers run straws three inches right in, five inches lengthway of the plank. The builder ordered spiles [that is, wooden plugs] to be made to spile up the worm holes . . . . The caulkers say they had not seen a ship in the dock so full of barnacles in a great while; but for your better information I pray you'll order the officers of the yard to give you their report, and that they may call my officers for their observations during the voyage. It is the builder's opinion that he will not be able to dispatch the work under two springs [that is, spring tides]."

It is this last point which reveals a particular aspect of the whole problem—the time factor and the availability of ships. There must have been many occasions when offensive action was delayed, not because of any dilatoriness on the part of the naval commander but because sufficient ships were simply not available.

The eighteenth century is the classical century of the wooden sailing ship of the line, and so, apart from considering the ships, we should also attempt a general survey of the way in which these ships were used in battle. A convenient method of doing this seems to be to consider first the period in which all tactics were governed by written fighting instructions—the period from 1691 till 1783, though during the last half of this long stretch of time there were beginning to be changes—and then to study the kind of use the great captains made of their ships once they were freed from the enslaving influence of the instructions. This last and shorter period is, of course, dominated by such men as Nelson.

It is easy to ridicule the fighting instructions as being unimaginative, doctrinaire, and, in the long run, disastrous. Even the great Mahan called them "a caricature of systematized tactics,"[14] but it is worth remembering that Père Hoste's *L'Art des armées navales ou Traité des évolutions navales,* published in 1697 on the orders of the Comte de Tourville himself, shows many points of similarity. Seen in their context, they were sensibly drawn up and represented the result of discussions based on experience gained in war. They were, in fact, originally entirely empirical and were devised for specific occasions: only gradually did they become permanent.

We saw how the formalist school came to dominate tactical doctrine in the last stages of the Anglo-Dutch Wars, and we saw, too, that the reason for this was really the need for the commander in chief to keep continual control of his fleet. This had always been the weakness in the higher command, and it was felt that it was better to be in complete control than to allow too much latitude to subordinates, even though individual enterprise often proved dazzlingly successful.

The result of the action off Beachy Head in June, 1690, was not, perhaps, inevitable. The Earl of Torrington had inferior forces to those of that great sailor, de Tourville, but once Torrington began to avoid action and attempt to "keep his fleet in being," to use his own phrase, he was bound to lose public support. A "fleet-in-being" strategy—which has been relied on to advantage by both French and German navies later on in history—has the merit of pinning down at least a part of the superior force of an enemy, but it is essentially defensive, and it was for this reason that Torrington lost public support. Whether he was the victim of political intrigue or not is irrelevant today, for at least he was acquitted in the subsequent court-martial, but when we look more closely at the details of the action, we discover that two important things happened: first, he broke his line; and secondly, his van, the Dutch squadron, misunderstood his orders and engaged the enemy, thus allowing a dangerous melee to occur.

Most historians now agree that the Fighting Instructions issued in 1691, the year after this defeat but also after Torrington had been acquitted, were either drawn up by Torrington or at least based on his experiences, though they bear Russell's name. They are of great importance in the history of naval tactics and are framed in the stereotyped form that was to remain in force till the end of the American War in 1783. They existed "for the better ordering of the fleet in sailing by day and night, and in fighting," and there were also an indexed set of signals for both day and night and instructions for the pilots and the skippers of smaller vessels accompanying a fleet.[15] They confirmed the formalist viewpoint, which was the preservation of the line at all costs, though this clearly did not mean that the line was not at times flexible, as long as its control was in the hands of the commander in chief.

Article 20 might seem to suggest that individual initiative was curbed: "none of the ships in the fleet," it reads, "shall pursue any small number of the enemy's ships till the main body be disabled or run"; yet Article 25 does reveal a loophole, for "if the enemy be put to the run, and the admiral thinks it convenient the whole fleet shall follow them, he will make all the sail he can himself after the enemy, and fire two guns out of his fore-chase; then every ship in the fleet is to use his best endeavour to come up with the enemy, and lay them on board."

Only four of Rooke's thirty-two instructions, issued in 1703, differ from Russell's, so that this set can be treated as a confirmation of the earlier doctrine; and a study of the eighteenth century shows that, in fact, they became permanent. Though no instructions dated later than 1707 actually still exist, the evidence of their permanence is found scattered through the proceedings of courts-martial, in dispatches, and in signal books; for in these sources, individual instructions are often quoted in full, and their numbering tallies exactly with those of 1703.[16]

It is known, too, that "additional instructions" were issued from time to time, but only one complete set still exists. This is signed by Admiral Boscawen in April, 1759, but he was probably not the author; it is more likely that they were collected by Anson at the British Admiralty. They seem to be the ones the unfortunate Byng used, and they may well have been based on some of the "expeditional" orders issued by Vernon when he commanded the force that sailed to the Spanish Main in 1739. We know that Vernon did issue such instructions, for in a pamphlet inspired by Lestock and entitled *A Narrative of the Proceedings of His Majesty's Fleet in the Mediterranean 1740–44,* there is reference to them, and the author actually states that "men in the highest stations at sea will not deny but what our sailing and fighting instructions might be amended, and many added to them, which by every day's experience are found to be absolutely necessary." He continues by telling his readers that "that provident, great Admiral [Vernon] never suffered any useful precaution to escape him" and therefore "concerted some signals" for the line of battle, engaging, chasing, and leaving off the chase, "wisely foreseeing their use and necessity, giving them to the captains of the squadron under his command" and thereby showing "his judgement, abilities and zeal."[17]

Thus what to many may seem to be the dead hand of formalized Fighting Instructions came into being in the eighteenth century, and came to stay for eighty years, though there were opportunities as we have seen, for the imaginative commander to introduce amendments and, what is more, get away with them.

Let us now briefly turn to the way in which the ships were handled during the period of the Fighting Instructions.[18] In their first decade of existence, there were two victories that seemed to justify the logic of the instructions. These were Barfleur in 1692—which, together with its follow-up off Cape La Hogue, was a decisive reversal of Beachy Head two years earlier, an engagement which it resembled in a number of ways—and Rooke's action off Malaga in 1704, which, though a defensive action, resulted in the retention of Gibraltar, only recently won.

It was perhaps unfortunate that there was a long period of inactivity at sea after Queen Anne's War had ended, since it must have been during these thirty years that naval doctrine crystallized with, on the whole, such stultifying results. Officers who had served under Russell or Rooke in their youth may have felt, as they reached commands of their own, that what was good enough for such great men in the past was good enough for the present. The war broke out in the late 1730's, continued throughout most of the 1740's, and flared up again in the mid-1750's; these were times when the unimaginative tended to look back at past glories and not forward at possible ways in which the future might be made more glorious still.

Professor Lewis divides the naval commanders of the eighteenth century into four groups or schools. The first he calls the "Docile" school, that is, those commanders who did not rebel against the system but attempted, with varying success, to make it work as best they could.

He takes as an example the competent but not outstanding Sir Edward Hughes, whose career showed that even the combination of a good fleet and an able commander was not enough to make the line other than indecisive and unproductive. In his five engagements with the brilliant French admiral, Bailli de Suffren, no ship was lost by either side nor did any change hands even as late as 1782–1783.

The second group is that of the "Unfortunates." Two men stand out as victims of the system, and both were unlucky enough to be caught up too in the web of politics. The first, Admiral Thomas Mathews, was Commander in Chief, Mediterranean, in 1744 and found himself forced to break the line off Toulon because he saw the necessity of engaging the French and Spanish fleet as quickly as possible and as near the south coast of France as he could so that he could continue his original task of preventing a Spanish convoy from reaching northern Italy. Mathews was let down by his vice admiral, Richard Lestock, who had been temporarily holding the Mediterranean command before Mathews' arrival and so may have felt slighted at not having his appointment confirmed. By prompt action, Lestock could have formed a *corps de réserve,* when he saw what Mathews was doing, so that he could support any part of the British fleet that became too heavily involved.

Perhaps Mathews expected this to happen, but instead Lestock did nothing—whether deliberately or not need not concern us here—and Mathews' action petered out into an indecisive half battle, not least because even when some French and Spanish ships were attacked and withdrew from the line, no British captain dared follow them. Mathews was cashiered after being found guilty of bearing down upon the enemy without waiting to form line of battle, but he was not convicted for breaking the Fighting Instructions. Nevertheless, this was the general impression gained, and the significance of the whole incident was, therefore, the effect it had on the naval profession during the next forty years, not least upon such men as John Byng in 1756.

Byng's misfortunes are more interesting than those of Mathews. The epitaph on his monument records that "Bravery and Loyalty were Insufficient Securities for the Life and Honour of a Naval Officer," an example of the lapidary style at its best, but perhaps not words really in keeping with Byng's character. Though he was not a coward— indeed, he was acquitted on this charge and was condemned for negligence only—he was essentially a defeatist and was never more than a very average commander. He might easily have escaped the death sentence, but his tame withdrawal from Minorca to Gibraltar turned public opinion against him, and the government of the day, needing a victim to whom to transfer the blame for their own ineptitude, did not recommend him to the king for mercy.

What went wrong at Minorca was that when Byng arrived there with an inadequate force, he failed to establish contact with the besieged, and, more relevant to our purpose here, he adopted unfamiliar tactics, the method known as "lasking," or approaching aslant, neither in line ahead nor in line abreast, so as to protect his ships from being "raked" by enemy fire before they could retaliate. This was in itself a sensible maneuver, and it had been used in the seventeenth century, but there was no signal for correcting the mistakes that could easily happen and did happen on this occasion. Byng was bold enough at the start, but, remembering "the misfortunes of Mr. Mathews," as he said to his chief of staff, he did not risk the chance of breaking his line.

Thirdly, there were those who are described as "Experimenters within the Line." These men felt that there could be no question of dispensing with the fundamental principle of the line but that it needed to be made more elastic; and their number includes some of the best-known names in naval history. We have already seen how Vernon was in the habit of introducing special instructions for use in his own squadron, but he was not himself senior enough for his ideas to have had any wider application, had it not been for official support for the whole idea of additional instructions when Anson became First Lord of the Admiralty. Rodney, essentially a conservative leader and one who was in his late sixties when he fought his great battles, belongs to this school also. In his action off the island of Martinique in April, 1780, he introduced the old principle of "massing" by reducing the gaps between his own ships so that they were less than those between his opponents' ships. Two years later at the Battle of The Saints, fought off some islets between Guadeloupe and Dominica, Rodney quite deliberately led through the French line and thus out of his own. He was supported by Captain Gardner in the *Duke*, ahead of him, and by Commodore Affleck and all the ships of the rear astern of him. Tactically, this makes the Battle of The Saints "the most epoch-making fight since Barfleur,"[19]

as it rings down the curtain on the long ascendancy of the permanent
Fighting Instructions.

The fourth school is described by Professor Lewis as comprising
those who "experimented without the Line" even in the years before
1783. They were men of enterprise and ingenuity and were no doubt
glad to have found in Article 25, quoted previously, a loophole in the
formal system. It sanctioned, as they read it, the pursuit of a defeated
enemy; but above all, it contained the rudiments of independent action
in the phrase "if . . . the Admiral thinks it convenient." As early as 1718,
Sir George Byng used the chase as the main tactical intention in battle.
This was, admittedly, when he found he was opposed by an inferior
Spanish squadron off Cape Passaro, but the innovation was that he
ordered the chase immediately.

In the two battles off Finisterre in 1747, first Anson and then Hawke
discarded the normal line tactics and adopted the general chase. In the
former engagement, Anson captured every single French ship, a justification, if ever there was need of one, for the new plan; and Hawke's
success in the second battle stood him in good stead twelve years later
in Quiberon Bay. By that time, however, new chase tactics had been
evolved and definite instructions, composed perhaps by Hawke himself,
though no doubt adapted from those of John Norris much earlier, had
been introduced, as well as further refinements combining the strong
points of both line and chase.

Rodney can claim membership of this school too. At the attractively,
though misleadingly, styled "Moonlight" battle fought in January 1780
off the southwestern coast of Spain, he ordered his ships to engage "as
they came up by rotation and to take the lee gage in order to prevent the
enemy's retreat into their own ports," a further development of the
chase.

Before we leave the Fighting Instructions, we must remember that
their success depended on their clarity and particularly that of the signals
which announced the admiral's intentions. Intercommunication has
always been one of the great problems in warfare on both land and sea.
It requires both knowledge on the part of those who send signals and
those who receive them and a system of ready reference so that immediate action can be taken on the receipt of any signal, however
unfamiliar. In the eighteenth century, signal books were comparatively

rare and, anyway, were the product of local rather than official enter-prise—Howe issued the first of them for use in his own squadron in 1776. This meant that a new instruction entailed the introduction also of a signal for it, which might be difficult to file. In 1782, Rodney had forty-three different signaling flags, and as they could be hoisted in eight different places, it was possible to transmit well over three hundred messages. This meant many complications, such as lack of visibility and of clear-cut definition and, of course, the possibility that a hoisting position might be destroyed in action. Because of these things, we can appreciate the unwillingness felt by the average eighteenth century commander to attempt innovations; yet, while we can sympathize with them, we must admire all the more the initiative of leaders of the caliber of Vernon and Hawke.

We have seen how the action of Rodney at the Battle of The Saints in 1782 can be taken as a turning point in the history of naval tactics, though the failure of the tired and aged admiral to follow up his "most complete victory," to use his own phrase, caused considerable dismay at the time. Indeed, many years afterward, Nelson described the battle as "the greatest victory, if it had been followed up, that our Country ever saw." Nevertheless, it did herald a completely new approach to the conduct of war at sea, and it is in this, as well as in the tremendous boost to morale that it gave the British at a time when their fleet was experiencing considerable adversity, that its significance lies.

The new approach was, as we have seen, based on the repudiation of the permanent Fighting Instructions. As things turned out, there was to be only one more round in the long-drawn-out struggle with France, and by the time it came to an end, the end of the sailing ship her-self as a man-of-war was in sight owing to the new inventions springing from steam propulsion. Thus the comparatively short period of the final Anglo-French War, 1793 to 1815, forms the last chapter in a long story, or it can perhaps be likened to the cartouche that adorns the last page of a long book. And what a strikingly brilliant finish it is! Into this short period of time come crowding in some of the greatest names in naval history. The British leaders who stand out, men such as Nelson, Howe, Duncan, and Jervis, were great tacticians, not merely because they were free for the first time from the rigid authority of the instructions but because they were courageous enough to take the initiative and try out new ideas, however unconventional, when the occasion arose.

In the final analysis, it will always be found that great leaders will dictate their own terms over the materials at their disposal. But before we examine the particular contributions made to naval warfare by the leaders of the day, including those mentioned above, there are three important subjects to be considered. These are the carronade, the first new gun to be introduced since the days of Henry VIII; secondly, the frigate; and thirdly, perhaps the most important of the three, the introduction of a systematic method of signaling.

The carronade, deriving its name from the town near Falkirk in Scotland where the proximity of coal to the iron-ore deposits had attracted the iron foundries away from the Sussex weald, was a new version of the old perrier. It was a stumpy gun with a relatively wide bore, and it fired a hollow or cored shot, which required a lighter charge of powder than a solid projectile would. Because the carronades were thin-barreled and did not require a particularly heavy truck carriage and were light for their caliber, even 32-pounders of this type could be mounted in those parts of ships, such as the poop, quarterdeck, and forecastle, not normally built for guns. They were short-range weapons, since their most effective range was up to 100 yards only, but the Battle of The Saints, fought at very close range, proved the smashing power these weapons possessed—indeed, they were called "smashers" by contemporaries.

They were first tested in 1779, and very soon afterward they were adopted for almost every class of ship, acquitting themselves admirably at other close-fought actions, such as the Glorious First of June, 1794, and Camperdown, 1797, not to mention Nelson's battles later on. Some of the British ships were armed with it exclusively—for instance, the *Glatton,* called after the Huntingdonshire village where the builder of the ship lived. This fourth-rate was a converted East Indiaman, and she routed six French frigates off Goree in 1795, the first year of her career as a warship, a dramatic start that ended rather tamely when she was turned into a breakwater thirty-five years later. It was a risk, however, to rely so completely on a short-range weapon, because its success depended on the ability to keep within range. Incidents in the Anglo-American War of 1812 show the failure of such a reliance on both sides:

the United States frigate *Essex,* experimentally armed with carronades only, was captured in the neutral harbor of Valparaiso by the 36-gun *Phoebe,* whose captain could choose his range, since his armament was composed of long guns; and later on in the same war, we hear that the British commodore in one of the battles on the Great Lakes fought for many hours without being able to maneuver his ships into carronade range of the enemy.

Other innovations in British warships are associated with the name of Sir Charles Douglas. This officer was the enthusiastic and even brilliant gunnery expert whom Rodney appointed to be his first captain, or chief of staff, in 1782. Douglas was not suited to be a staff officer, and his reputation has suffered in consequence. Indeed, Hood, Rodney's second-in-command, wrote that Douglas "is no more fit for the station he fills that I am to be an Archbishop"; but it should also be remembered that Hood could offer pungent criticism of the commander in chief himself: "Sir George Rodney requires a monitor constantly at his elbow as much as a froward child."

Even if Douglas was unable to play the part of Rodney's monitor adequately, his other talents should not be forgotten. Before his unfortunate appointment, he had tried out a number of innovations in his ship, the three-decker *Duke,* and he was able to convince Rodney that these should be tried out in the *Formidable,* Rodney's flagship, too. Briefly, these improvements were limiting the violent and dangerous recoil of the guns by the insertion of strong springs into the breeching to take the first shock and mooring the guns more effectively by arranging for inclined planes to be placed behind the back wheels. He also introduced the use of wetted wads to eliminate the sparks that could cause such danger when the guns were firing to windward. Again, he improved the rate of fire, if such a modern expression can be used without conveying a false impression of speed, first by encasing the cartridges in flannel instead of the silk hitherto used that clogged up the barrel and necessitated "worming" to remove the carbon deposit; secondly, by simplifying the priming of the guns by means of goose quills filled with fine powder soaked in spirits of wine that could very simply be inserted into the gun's venthole; thirdly, by adapting a flintlock worked by the pull of a lanyard instead of by the old method of the lighted match at the end of a stick. These innovations show us very clearly some of the hazards that the sailor of those days had to put up with, quite apart from any damage inflicted by the enemy, and they also show a simplicity based on experience that comes near to genius.

But we have not yet seen what was perhaps Sir Charles Douglas' greatest contribution, which concerned the tactical use of the gun. This was the introduction of traversing, so that the guns could fire 45 degrees before or abaft the beam, a great improvement on the old method whereby the broadside could only be effective at a single moment, that is, when the target was exactly opposite the gun. This was, in fact, "oblique fire" for the first time, and Douglas actually used the expression himself. In a letter to Middleton, he described the purpose of de Grasse's officers in the captured French flagship *Ville de Paris* when she was fired on by a British ship lying 45 degrees on her bows. Being "ignorant as to the apparatus within," he wrote, "they attributed its effect to the superior width of our ports."[20]

We must now pass on to the second subject we set ourselves, and this is the frigate. In general, it is easy to be sure what the innovation in the second half of the eighteenth century was: it was the gradual realization by commanders that they needed a speedy and seaworthy small warship as a reconnaissance vessel, and it was the want of such ships, "the eyes of the fleet," that Nelson, in 1798, said would be found stamped on his heart if he were to die at that moment. The first of these frigates, sixth-rates with 28 to 30 guns on their upper decks but no guns on their lower decks at all, appeared in 1756, and there were thirty-five of them afloat by 1760. By 1798, there were a hundred, a number that was increased by nearly half as many again in the next ten years, but there still never seem to have been enough of them. Many of the British frigates in the last Anglo-French War were, in fact, French prizes and were welcome additions to the British fleet, as the French built excellent ships of this class. The *Pomone*, for example, with an armament of 44 guns, 26 of which were 24-pounders, was captured in 1794 in a frigate action off the Channel Islands, and she was used as a model for the *Endymion*, a worthy copy of a ship acknowledged by all to be an "incomparable sailer."

This seems a good opportunity to look at the history of the frigate more fully, since, through the centuries, the term, like "galley," as we saw earlier, has been used in a number of senses. There have been, in fact, at least six distinct types,[21] though at all stages the vessels concerned can be seen to have certain functions in common: they were small in relation to other warships; they were swift-moving, relatively speaking, and easily maneuvered; and they were used out of the line of battle for such tasks as reconnaissance and convoying.

The first type is the Mediterranean *fregata*, which was oared and was probably no more than the tender to the galley, which it closely resembled. Secondly, there was the English frigate of the second half of the sixteenth century, possibly imported, as it were, by Drake. It did not have oars, but it was a smaller version of the galleon. Thirdly, in the seventeenth century, the word is used rather loosely to describe a variety of English ships and not always the small two-decker, for the largest Commonwealth ship of all, the famous *Naseby*, is so called. It may be that there was some special detail in the construction not known today that differentiated these frigates from other warships. Traditionally, Peter Pett's *Constant Warwick*, built in 1645 and purchased from the Earl of Warwick in 1649, is the first English frigate, but it is possible that there has been confusion about her identity. She differs considerably from later frigate designs, so she may have been confused with the 22-gun *Old Warwick* frigate bought from Dunkirk in 1643. Fourthly, there is what we may call the Nelsonic frigate for the sake of convenience, the essentials of which we have already noted. Fifthly, anticipating a later chapter, there is the experimental steamship, perhaps built of iron, of the mid-nineteenth century. There seems to have been a reluctance in Britain to scrap the line ships even as late as the 1850's, so the new techniques were tried out on smaller vessels. Yet in the other European navies the word frigate was applied to ships that were distinctly large: the French *La Gloire* of 5,000 tons is described as a frigate, and so is the Austrian *Ferdinand Max,* Tegetthoff's flagship at Lissa. Lastly, the term "frigate" emerges again, as we shall see, in the twentieth century to describe the ship that was designed for convoy work in the Second World War and was not as fast as the destroyer but had very nearly the same firepower.

In passing, it should be noted that two other warships can be singled out in the eighteenth century—the French corvette and the British sloop. Once again, it is difficult to be sure of their exact nature, but it seems safe to say that by the last quarter of the century, they had become standardized as two-masted single-decked vessels with about 18 guns. Historically, the sloop descended from the oared pinnace of early Tudor times, which later took to sail and was called a shallop. The corvette seems to have been slightly smaller than her English equivalent.

We must now consider the third great development in the last quarter of the eighteenth century, one which it is no exaggeration to say revolutionized naval warfare. It is the introduction of an efficient system of signaling. We have noted already that intercommunication had always been a major problem and that lack of it had been one of the main justifications for the rigidity of the Fighting Instructions. We saw, too, that by the 1770's, Howe had seen the wisdom of issuing a book of signals for use in his squadron during the American War. We must now consider these innovations a little more closely.

Though no details have survived, the first code of flags for sea signaling in Britain was worked out in 1647, and six years later the Generals at Sea issued a set of signals to accompany their Fighting Instructions. These signals were given by five flags that could be hoisted in five prominent positions, notably the three mastheads, the ensign staff, and the mizzen peak. Gradually, more and more flags were introduced and new positions for them were agreed on, but there was as yet no attempt at systematization, so that after a century the accumulation of such signals led to almost prodigious exercises in memory and classification. There were, of course, a number of private signal books— Jonathan Greenwood's of 1714 seems to have been the first actually printed—and the earlier ones were based on combinations of sixteen and twenty-eight flags. The trouble was that the signals still represented specified instructions only, so that commanders in chief did not yet have "freedom of speech." Howe's book, issued in 1776, was the first official one, though its authority only covered the ships under his command. It was, however, a prelude to an extension of the idea, for the book he issued in 1790 was adopted for the navy as a whole. This book, the *Signal Book for the Ships of War*, enabled commanders to say a great deal; in fact, by a system of three- or four-flag hoists, combined with certain flags denoting numerals and other flags denoting often-needed information, such as "enemy in sight," up to 9,999 different things could be said. This was a great improvement, but it was still not possible for an admiral to send a message composed on the spur of the moment containing words and orders not already worked out into flag signals.

Richard Kempenfelt, the talented seaman who had also the attributes of a scholar and scientist, was an even greater pioneer than Howe in the development of signals; indeed, to go back a little, his tabular system was adopted by Howe in 1778 and was really the first numerary scheme, since it was based on a system of sixteen vertical and sixteen horizontal squares, the former representing pages in the signal book and the latter articles on those pages. Thus two flags were used in any signal, which meant that 256 messages could be sent. As we have seen, there was to be a further refinement of this that became universal in 1790, but it had already been accepted in principle by Howe as early as 1782, just before Kempenfelt so tragically lost his life in the *Royal George*. In Britain, the final stage in the development of signals was the vocabulary signal book devised by Sir Home Popham in 1800. This enabled words to be spelled out in full, but it also included "dictionaries" of useful words that could be sent out in three-flag hoists.

It is interesting to note that the French led the field in the development of signals. They had an official signal book as early as 1693, and Bourdé de Villehuet, in his *Le Manoeuvrier*, seems to have been one of the first to invent a numerary system of signaling; indeed, we know that Kempenfelt studied this man's works and those of his predecessor La Bourdonnais and based his own systems on them.

It must have been clear to the more enterprising naval commanders long before the Battle of The Saints that rigidly observed line tactics did not win battles, just as they must have become increasingly aware that the combination of line and chase, very often bringing about the melee, was both desirable and very effective. Yet above all, the real change must have been something more intangible, something in the attitude of the naval commanders themselves that enabled them to feel able to flout the conventions of naval fighting because they could see beyond such things to a fuller appreciation of the situation at hand.

A classic example of this is Nelson's action at the Battle of Cape St. Vincent in 1797. Jervis had seen a gap in the Spanish force and, attacking from the north, intended to keep the ships of the enemy fleet separated. He easily effected the break in the enemy line and then decided to order his ships to tack in succession, that is, to head about and sail back due north in order to prevent the enemy ships from joining up again. Possibly Jervis delayed too long in giving the signal for his head-about, but whether this was so or not, Nelson in the *Captain*, the last ship but two, saw that the leading vessels would, after carrying out Jervis's order, arrive too late to prevent the enemy ships from reforming their line. He therefore ordered the *Captain* to leave the line, heading her at first away from the enemy and then making for the gap, where he engaged seven Spanish ships, including the four-decked *Santissima Trinidad* and three other first-rates. Nelson was soon joined by Troubridge, Collingwood, and Frederick; and in the melee which ensued, four prizes were taken, though the *Santissima Trinidad* escaped.

The success of the action should not conceal the professional risk Nelson took in leaving the line without orders, nor should it blind us to the fact that this "splendid fault," to use Southey's phrase, was in a sense an example of a senior naval officer's "first disobedience" and thus itself a bold action. Nelson, it is true, realized that his decisive act might well land him in a "confounded scrape," so it was with some trepidation that he went on board the *Victory*, Jervis's flagship, that evening. However, Jervis received him on the quarterdeck and, Nelson wrote afterwards, "said he could not sufficiently thank me, and used every kind expression which could not fail to make me happy."

This incident has been dwelt on at some length because it shows two significant changes in outlook: first, the decision on the part of a responsible and experienced subordinate to break the rules because he was in a better position than his superior to appreciate the situation; and secondly, the magnanimity shown by even such a stern disciplinarian as Jervis in face of such disobedience, which a generation earlier could have meant a court-martial even though the subordinate's action was obviously the right one.

Nelson was well aware that he owed much of his success to his friend Captain Cuthbert Collingwood whose prompt supporting action made the result possible. " 'A friend in need is a friend indeed' was never more truly verified than by your most noble and gallant conduct," he wrote to Collingwood the day after the Battle of Cape St. Vincent. But Collingwood, with characteristic modesty, saw himself as only an accessory, though in a letter of congratulation to Nelson, written also on the day after the battle, he mentioned the satisfaction he felt "in thumping the Spaniards" and how it was heightened by the feeling that he was aiding his "dear Commodore." The tone of Collingwood's letter shows his complete acceptance of Nelson's unconventional and highly personal approach to the naval profession and shows him to have been very different from the critical Hood, for instance, who seems to have disapproved of Rodney highly.

Yet Collingwood was renowned as a disciplinarian, though chiefly because his discipline was tempered with imagination. He saw that such a punishment as flogging, for example, nearly always failed, because it made its victim an object of sympathy; instead, he found the type of punishment that exposed those punished to the ridicule of their messmates, such as menial fatigues, much more effective. A remarkable tribute to his popularity as an officer, one that might have been paid to Nelson himself, is that of a young sailor, Robert Hay, who was serving in the *Culloden* when this ship became Collingwood's flagship for a few months in the early part of 1804. "A better seaman, a better friend to seamen, a greater lover and more zealous defender of his country's rights and honour, never trod a quarterdeck," Hay wrote in 1828, years after he had left the service, adding that Collingwood and his dog Bounce were well known to every member of the crew. "How attentive he was to the health and happiness of his crew," Hay wrote also; "a man who could not be happy under him could have been happy nowhere."[22]

These, then, are two of the qualities that the great leaders show in what has been called the heyday of sailing-ship fighting, and they are different from each other. The ability to rise above the letter of the law and take bold action when the opportunity comes is a question of tactics; while the second, the importance of gaining the confidence of subordinates, is largely a personal matter, though it too would have its tactical effect, since it would engender prompt and unquestioning obedience. There are, of course, others; and though it is not our intention to examine here all or, indeed, any of the great battles in detail, there are a few further points that will help us to understand how the sailing warship was handled in those stirring times at very nearly the end of her career.

Howe on the Glorious First of June, 1794, and Duncan at Camperdown, 1797, fought very different battles; but there were striking similarities, for both actions were a vindication of the instantaneous melee, and both were based on the same maneuver—breaking the enemy line in as many places as possible from to windward. Howe's victory came as the culminating point in a long career at sea, for he had started off with Anson on his famous voyage fifty-four years earlier, but it was not a strategic success, since it did not prevent the American corn ships from reaching France. Nevertheless, it involved a new maneuver, the deliberately planned decision to "divide the enemy at all points from to windward," which was a difficult operation in itself and one which only partly succeeded. Briefly, Howe's intention was to gain the wind, then, at a moment of his own choosing, to order a controlled approach, with the object of pushing as many of his ships as possible through the enemy line at a number of points, and then, by taking up their position on the leeward side of the French, to prevent them from retreating. In the melee, which Howe anticipated, the fighting was violent and at very close range, which suited the carronades in the British ships, and six prizes were taken.

Duncan's plan at Camperdown three years later was perhaps less premeditated, for his decision to advance on the Dutch in two parallel line-ahead columns of eight ships each and break through the enemy line at two points was arrived at because the Dutch ships, far lighter than the British, were very near the coast and Duncan feared de Winter would avoid action by seeking the shallows. Speed therefore was essential. The plan worked, and the two columns passed through the enemy line and gained the leeward position, thus making escape impossible for the Dutch. There was considerable risk in the approach, as the Dutch were quite likely to "rake" the approaching columns, but once battle was joined, Duncan was certain that his ships would show their superiority. This they did, and eleven Dutch ships were captured; but the victory was a costly one, as most of the prizes were too badly damaged to be repaired and almost as many British were killed and wounded as Dutch.

No account of the handling of warships at the end of the eighteenth century can be complete without a study of Nelson's professional career, but it is sometimes difficult to get behind the personality to the experienced seaman. Perhaps elasticity of mind is the keynote, for it seems certain that Nelson understood more clearly than most of his contemporaries that the conduct of a sea battle must depend on the unexpected and that plans should be adaptable rather than immutable. The toleration shown by Jervis after his "disobedience" at the Battle of Cape St. Vincent must have impressed Nelson ever afterward, for he concentrated more on building up a team which could have an almost telepathic awareness of what the admiral was thinking—this is the real significance of the idea of the band of brothers, surely—than one which relied on a constant relaying of signals.

Nelson, in fact, relied very little on signals. At the Battle of the Nile, for example, he sent out "Engage the enemy more closely" ten minutes after fire had been opened, but no other signals followed. Much the same happened at Trafalgar. This was all the more remarkable because only eight of Nelson's twenty-seven captains at Trafalgar had served with him before, and only five of these had commanded line ships in action.[23] It was, in fact, an example of the combined effect of an outstanding personality able to instill into his subordinates his every wish and painstaking attention to briefing before battle was ever joined. When Duff of the *Mars* said that Nelson was "so good and pleasant that we all wish to do what he likes, without any kind of orders," he was paying tribute to Nelson both as a man and as a professional sailor.

In spite of the comment made by Henry Blackwood, Nelson's senior frigate captain, in a letter written to his wife the day after the battle, that "no history can record such a brilliant victory," Trafalgar has probably been written about more than any other battle in history. Here it is enough to note that it was the final and most dazzling repudiation of the line tactics we have been examining, though this is undoubtedly obscured by the "great chasm," to use another of Blackwood's expressions, caused by Nelson's death. First, the British fleet was separated into two divisions, and the general aim was to contain the French and Spanish van and center with one, Nelson's, while the other, Collingwood's, destroyed the rear. Secondly, Nelson deliberately brought on the melee in order to attack Villeneuve's flagship, *Bucentaure*; and so close was the fighting that some of the *Victory*'s guns could not be run out their proper length, if we can believe Midshipman Roberts, a member of the ship's company.[24]

The Battle of the Nile, to go back to 1798, offers a good example of an apparently carefully selected position turning out to be disastrous because the circumstances were not, after all, similar to those when it

had been tried successfully before. The French admiral, Brueys, drew
up his fleet in a V-formation with the arms pointing west-southwest, the
left one almost on the inner shoal that cuts across Abukir Bay. The
precedents for such a position were in the American War twenty years
earlier, when numerically inferior forces had, nevertheless, managed
to defeat the enemy. But Brueys did not have his V-angle bisected by the
wind as Hood had done in Frigate Bay when he defeated de Grasse,
which on that occasion made it impossible for de Grasse to break the
British line at any point, since he could not bring his ships within six
points of the wind—the angle of the V was 135 degrees, that is, twelve
compass points. In any case, it was dangerous to assume in the Mediterranean that the winds would have the constancy of the trade wind in
the Caribbean. Brueys made two other errors: his ships were too far
apart, and they were anchored only by the bows and so were able to
swing at their moorings, two factors which were serious weaknesses in a
plan which was based on waiting for the enemy to attack, if he could,
and even then remaining in the moorings to fight it out. Nelson was
quick enough to see these weaknesses in Brueys's position before darkness fell, and he exploited them brilliantly. Foley in *Goliath*, followed
by four other ships, was able to sail between the first French ship and the
shoal, since this vessel had swung around considerably; and in the
growing darkness, the French were surprised to find themselves attacked
from to landward, while Nelson himself in *Vanguard* and the two ships
following him attacked simultaneously from to seaward.

NOTES

[1]John Ehrman, *The Navy in the War of William III*, p. xx.

[2]See J. R. Tanner (ed.), *A Descriptive Catalogue of the Naval Manuscript in the Pepysian Library*, Navy Records Society, London, 1903, vol. i, p. 52.

[3]See L. G. Carr Laughton, "Capital Ships," *The Mariner's Mirror*, 1926, vol. xii, pp. 396–405.

[4]Ehrman, *op. cit.*, p. 14.

[5]Ehrman, *op. cit.*, pp. 3–37.

[6]See H. S. Vaughan, article in *The Mariner's Mirror*, 1913, vol. iii, pp. 230–237.

[7]See Dryden, *Annus Mirabilis*, canto 153.

[8]See J. H. Owen, *War at Sea Under Queen Anne*, p. 27.

[9]R. D. Merriman (ed.), *Queen Anne's Navy*, Navy Records Society, London, 1961, vol. ciii, p. 68, letter from Navy Board to Lord High Admiral, Dec. 30, 1702.

[10]*Ibid.*, vol. ciii, p. 71, letter from Lord High Admiral's Council to Navy Board, Jan. 16, 1704.

[11]*Ibid.*, vol. ciii, p. 71, letter to Commissioner of Portsmouth Dockyard, Apr. 21, 1705.

[12]D. Bonner-Smith (ed.), *Boteler's Recollections*, Navy Records Society, London, 1942, vol. lxxxii, p. 231.

[13]Merriman (ed.), *op. cit.*, vol. ciii, pp. 77–78.

[14]A. T. Mahan, *Types of Naval Officer*, Little, Brown and Company, Boston, 1901, p. 15.

[15]See J. S. Corbett (ed.), *Fighting Instructions 1530–1816*, Navy Records Society, London, 1905, vol. xxix, p. 175.

[16]See B. McL. Ranft (ed.), *The Vernon Papers*, Navy Records Society, London, 1958, vol. xcix, pp. 285–303.

[17]Corbett (ed.), *op. cit.*, vol. xxix, pp. 206–207.

[18]In what follows, I am greatly indebted to Professor Michael Lewis for his analysis of the evolution of naval tactics in *The Navy of Britain*, pp. 482–533.

[19]Lewis, *op. cit.*, p. 513.

[20]J. K. Laughton (ed.), *Letters and Papers of Charles Lord Barham*, Navy Records Society, London, 1897, vol. xxxii, pp. 282–286.

[21]Lewis, *op. cit.*, pp. 101–102.

[22]M. D. Hay (ed.), *Landsman Hay*, p. 66.

[23]See Oliver Warner, *A Portrait of Lord Nelson*, p. 336.

[24]See E. Hallam Moorhouse, *Letters of the English Seamen*, p. 293.

Oil painting of an English brigantine by John Cleveley the Elder (died
1792?). Brigantines were used mainly as dispatch vessels and were usually
small two-masted vessels with square sails on both masts. *Science Museum,
London*

The Battle of the Saintes, April, 1782, in which George Rodney defeated the French under De Grasse after a determined pursuit. Years later, Horatio Nelson said that this was "the greatest victory, if it had been followed up, that our country ever saw." Oil painting by Richard Paton (1717–1791), in the Greenwich Hospital Collection. *National Maritime Museum, Greenwich*

The Battle of the Nile, August, 1798, oil painting by Nicholas Pocock (1741–1821). Nelson's squadron had been detached in May by St. Vincent with orders to find the French fleet. The picture shows the beginning of the action in Aboukir Bay, near Alexandria, in the evening, when the 74-gun *Goliath* rounded the bows of the *Guerrier*, the leading ship in the anchored French line. Only the two rearmost French ships and two frigates escaped capture, and the Mediterranean became a British lake once more. *National Maritime Museum, Greenwich*

(*Above*) The Battle of Copenhagen, March, 1801, oil painting by Nicholas Pocock. Nelson's nine ships successfully defeated a Danish fleet twice as strong, though they were mere hulks being used as floating batteries. It was at this battle that the famous "blind eye" incident took place. *National Maritime Museum, Greenwich*

(*Left*) HMS *Victory*, 100-gun first-rate launched in 1765. Frequently used as a flagship because of her good sailing qualities, she is seen here at Portsmouth. *Imperial War Museum, London*

The Battle of Trafalgar, October, 1805, line and aquatint by T. Hellyer.
The bows of the *Victory* are shown second in the line on the right. *National
Maritime Museum, Greenwich*

(Below) Model of HMS *Victory* showing forecastle and waist and as she was rigged in 1805. *Science Museum, London*

The 44-gun United States frigate *Constitution*, "Old Ironsides," built by Edward, Joseph, and Edmund Hartt at Boston and launched October, 1797. She is seen here in Boston Harbor in 1931. *The Bettmann Archive, Inc., New York*

VII

The American Navy in the Days of Sail

IT IS NOT our purpose to give a complete account of the sailing navy of the United States, but it is important to study some of the circumstances that led to the choice of certain kinds of ship rather than others and to examine the type of sea warfare that took place during the early days after the struggle for independence had been fought and won.

Officially, the United States Navy began with the decision made on December 13, 1775, by the Continental Congress on the advice of its Naval Committee to build thirteen ships to be completed by the following April, though we must not forget the craft chartered by Washington and manned with soldiers from the New England regiments. Yet perhaps the appointment of Silas Deane, John Adams, and John Langdon in October, 1775, as a committee with authority to fit out two ships, one of ten guns, the other of fourteen, was the real starting point. These ships were intended to cruise "eastwards" to intercept and capture British transports carrying arms and ammunition to Quebec.

A fortnight later, it was decided to equip two additional ships with more guns, and three men were added to the original members of the committee—Stephen Hopkins, Joseph Hewes, and Richard Henry Lee. This committee of six, later enlarged further, was thenceforward responsible for all naval matters, though the Continental Congress reserved final decisions to itself. At this early stage, a permanent separation from Britain was not generally thought to be inevitable, so there was some hesitation before acts of open rebellion were allowed.

But gradually the only possible outcome became more and more obvious, and by the end of November, 1775, the capture of any armed vessel employed against the colonies or any vessel carrying arms was authorized.

These details are, however, only the official beginnings. Behind them throughout the whole of the colonial period were the attitudes of mind of seafaring people. Almost all the settlers had come from the maritime countries of Europe and had, therefore, something of the long traditions of seafaring and shipbuilding in their bones. Also, in an underdeveloped country with a long coastline heavily indented with creeks, lagoons, and river estuaries, transport by boat was far more natural than transport by land. As early as 1639, fishermen in New England were exempted from military service during the fishing season and shipwrights were granted such exemption all the year round. Ship-building was, in fact, greatly encouraged, and we find that the Dutch settlers in New Amsterdam were already building ships for the Indian trade in the first quarter of the seventeenth century. In 1614, Adriaen Block built the first decked vessel that was launched in the Hudson River; it had an overall length of 44½ feet and a beam of 11 feet. By the end of the century, Massachusetts alone had built more than seven hundred vessels, and in 1690 the first ship of the line, the *Falkland*, was launched in the Piscataqua, the year when Massachusetts took the town of Port Royal in Nova Scotia. In 1714, the first American schooner was built by Henry Robinson of Cape Ann.

Two factors made the European colonists on the eastern seaboard of North America aware of the importance of being able to use their merchantmen offensively. The French spheres of influence in the St. Lawrence Basin and at the delta of the Mississippi, the Spanish settlements in Florida, the Dutch, Swedish, and British colonies inter-mingled, as chance had directed settlers to suitable harbors, meant that trade was always a risky affair, especially as the home countries, whether at war with each other or not, encouraged their colonists to harass their neighbors. The second factor was the problem of piracy, symbolized perhaps by the exploits of Captain William Kidd, though Samuel Bellamy and his 130 men in the twenty-three-gun *Whiddah* was, for a short time, an equal menace. It was against this kind of threat that the tiny 30-ton *Blessing of the Bay* was built by the colony of Plymouth as early as 1631, a defensive precaution that recommended itself to other colonies.

All this is not just of antiquarian interest to the student of American naval history, for it helps to explain the remarkable successes which the republican navy achieved in its early years, successes which would have been quite impossible had there not been a solid maritime tradition on which to build. Nelson was greatly impressed by the way in which the Americans handled their ships in the Mediterranean: "There is in the handling of those transatlantic ships," he said with remarkable vision, "a nucleus of trouble for the Navy of Great Britain." This must have been at least seven years before the War of 1812 broke out, proving with its fierce engagements the correctness of his prophecy. At about the same time, Napoleon accurately forecast the future too: when he sold Louisiana and the French Mississippi regions to President Jefferson in 1803, he said that he had given to England "a maritime rival that will sooner or later humble her pride."

As in the European navies, the naval architects and shipwrights in America were up against the old problem of speed versus stability: if the ends of ships were too sharp, for instance, hogging and strain generally would develop; while full ends made a ship slow in the water, a tactical deficiency that could only be met by the provision of a great spread of sail. Their early warships, therefore, tended to be built as a compromise, trying to incorporate as many of the known virtues as possible, yet abandoning fore-and-aft in favor of square rigging, since it enabled ships to stop dead in their course and even to be backed, though it was the less weatherly of the two types of rigs.

The thirteen ships mentioned above were the first American men-of-war, since there was no organized navy at the outbreak of war, though, as we have seen, Washington chartered a number of fishing boats, and some merchantmen provided by individual colonies were hastily fitted out as cruisers. In general, however, there were no ships large or fast enough for naval purposes or even for privateering. The thirteen were built at widely separated places such as Providence, Rhode Island, Poughkeepsie, New York, North Point, Maryland, and elsewhere. Five had 32 guns: *Washington, Raleigh, Hancock, Randolph,* and *Warren;* five had 28: *Virginia, Trumbull, Effingham, Congress,* and *Providence;* and three had 24: *Boston, Delaware,* and *Montgomery.* Later in the year, three other vessels were laid down, the 32-gun *Confederacy,* the 32-gun *Alliance,* and the 28- or 32-gun *Bourbon.*

These ships were the nucleus of the new Continental Navy, which

totaled about sixty or seventy vessels, since it included armed merchantmen, galleys, and other craft borrowed from the states, ships purchased
from the French, and a number of prizes. The ships named above were
known as frigates, and this class of warship, carrying guns on a single
flush deck and on the forecastle and quarterdeck, proved to be the most
acceptable. Later, the forecastle and quarterdeck were connected along
the side by gangways that gave the impression of a continuous upper
deck. Later on still, the Americans placed guns on these gangways,
and the most popular of these "double-backed" frigates, as they were
called, were those that had between 28 and 44 guns.

There were no ships of the line, if we mean by this term ships with
between 70 and 140 guns, in the Revolutionary War; indeed, they did
not come in until after the War of 1812 and then only in small numbers.

Of these early frigates, only two will be mentioned further. The
first is the 32-gun *Hancock*, traditionally considered the fastest frigate
in the world, built by Jonathan Greenleaf, a member of the state
legislature, and Stephen and Ralph Cross at Newburyport, Massachusetts, and launched in 1776. Commanded by Captain John Manley,
she sailed with the 24-gun *Boston* in June, 1777, and they captured the
British 28-gun frigate *Fox* after a two hours' struggle. Ten days later,
the tables were turned and *Hancock* fell to Sir George Collins' 44-gun
Rainbow after a magnificent chase lasting thirty-six hours. As the *Iris*,
she captured many privateers and other vessels, including the *Trumbull*,
one of the original thirteen frigates; but in 1781, she was herself captured
by the French and became a powder hulk at Toulon. She was destroyed
by the British in 1793 when Toulon was captured. After her original
capture, *Hancock* was repaired, thoroughly overhauled, and coppered
at Plymouth, England, and at this time, it seems that the drafts of her
lines were taken, which still exist.

The 32-gun *Alliance*, built at Salisbury Point on the Merrimack by
William Hackett, the best-known ship designer of his day, had the
distinction of being the only American-built frigate still in service at
the end of the Revolution; but her career was not yet over, for, instead
of being scrapped when the navy was completely disbanded in 1784,
she was sold to the East India Company.

Other war vessels included sloops, that is, ship-rigged vessels with
less than 24 guns, all mounted on one deck; brigs, two-masted vessels
with the two masts of equal height and both square-rigged, but carrying on the mainmast a lower fore and aft sail with a gaff and a boom;

schooners, which seem to have been an American invention—the first one was said to have been built at Gloucester, Massachusetts, in 1713; and galleys varying in size and carrying up to 12 guns and fitted for rowing, though also rigged as one- or two-masted lateeners, cutters, or sloops. There were also gondolas, which were flat-bottomed and double-ended vessels with deep bulwarks and gunports designed for use on lakes; *radeaux,* a general term for square-ended punts used for harbor defense; flat-bottomed *bateaux* for inshore or lake use; and fire ships and bomb ketches were occasionally used.

The decision to disband both the navy and the army in 1784 was natural in a society that feared military autocracy above all else. William Maclay, one of the two original senators from Pennsylvania, saw the maintenance of regular forces as "the entering of a new monarchy" and gravely suspected the motives of both those who urged that the Indian threat justified a standing army and those who claimed that the enslavement of the crews of the *Maria* and the *Dauphin* in 1785 by Algerian corsairs was a "pretext for fitting out a fleet." Even the Secretary of the Naval Board, Charles W. Goldsborough, felt that "the finances of the nation did not justify expensive fleets," that the friendship of Algiers could be bought, as other nations had done, and that "we might subsidize some of the European naval powers to protect our trade."

Nevertheless, public opinion had changed by 1794, and legislation was passed by Congress to build frigates once more. Three were ordered to carry 44 guns: the *United States,* built by Joshua Humphreys, one of the great names in shipbuilding, and launched at Philadelphia in May, 1797; the *Constitution,* known as "Old Ironsides," built by Edward, Joseph, and Edmund Hartt at Boston and launched in October, 1797; and the *President,* built under the supervision of Foreman Cheeseman, similar to the other two but lighter and not launched until 1800. The *President* was a fast ship and became a flagship in the Mediterranean on several occasions, wearing the flag of such men as Commodore John Rodgers and Commodore Stephen Decatur. A second trio was originally ordered to have 36 guns, but this number was raised to 38. They were the *Constellation,* launched at Baltimore in September, 1797, and still afloat though rebuilt many times; the *Congress,* built at Portsmouth, New Hampshire, and completed in 1799, and the famous *Chesapeake,* launched in June, 1799.

As in the days when they were colonies, the states built ships of all types and presented them to the nation. Thus we find, in 1799, the citizens of Charleston presenting the 28-gun *John Adams,* and the citizens of Salem, the 32-gun *Essex.* By the end of the century, a reasonable navy existed, but many of the ships were sold in 1801, though we need not blame Jefferson alone for the decision, since both Congress and senior naval officers favored the building up of a fleet of gunboats. These vessels enjoyed a great vogue for a time and usually had an armament of a 32- or 24-pounder medium gun and a small carronade. The crews were small too. *No. 5,* which was built at Baltimore and operated off Tunis in 1805, for instance, had only two officers and twenty-one men.

An interesting aspect of the war of the Revolution was the realization that a special type of craft was needed for naval purposes on inland waters. The battle of Lake Champlain in October, 1776, proved this early on, since this long but narrow lake and the Hudson River Valley south of it were the best line of inland communication for the British between Canada and their rebel colonies. General Benedict Arnold's force was a mixed collection of vessels, fifteen in all, ranging from the 12-gun schooner *Royal Savage* and the 10-gun sloop *Enterprise* to 8-gun galleys and 3-gun gondolas.

On the eve of battle, Arnold was despondent about his chances of success: his ships were undermanned, and what men there were he described as "a miserable set . . . not equal to half their number of good men." Many of them were soldiers, unwillingly drafted into the navy. "The Marines," Arnold wrote, "are the refuse of every regiment, and the seamen, few of them were ever wet with salt water."

Captain Pringle's British squadron was in better shape. His 18-gun, 14-gun, and 12-gun schooners, *Inflexible, Maria,* and *Carleton,* had been built in England, but they had been taken to pieces on arrival in the St. Lawrence and reassembled and adapted for lake service at St. John's. The action was a tactical victory for the British, but it had little effect on the strategic issues. Rather, its real significance was that it showed the British that the Americans could, and did, fight well: the personal heroism of Arnold and the bold escape of the American force at night through the enemy line are examples of this. It also showed that in a narrow lake with the prevailing wind blowing along its length, the oared galley was often the most maneuverable form of vessel. The Americans learned too that it was an advantage to have a uniform caliber throughout the armament of a ship. A shortage of guns in general had made mixed armaments unavoidable, but the confusion in General Waterbury's *Washington*, which mounted one 18-pounder and one 12-pounder, as well as 9-pounders and 4-pounders, seriously affected her efficiency as a fighting ship.

In the early years of the nineteenth century, the naval authorities realized that there was a need for some vessel between the frigate and the gunboat. The result was the building of 18-gun brigs such as the *Hornet* and *Wasp* in 1803, which were later converted to ship-sloops, and the smaller 12-gun *Argus*. The *Vixen*, which was built at this time also, started as a schooner but became a brig and served in the Mediterranean until she was captured in 1812. In 1813, more 44-gun frigates were ordered—such as the *Columbia* and *Java*, which were very like the *President* of 1797 mentioned above—as well as ship sloops armed with twenty carronades, usually 32-pounders, and two long cannon. The *Peacock* was a distinguished member of this last class. She had an interesting war career under the command of Lewis Warrington; and her excellent design, which made her both speedy and easy to handle, made the class popular during the remaining years of the sailing navy.

The experiences of the War of 1812 convinced Congress that the navy should be permanently enlarged, so four ships of the line were built—*Franklin, Washington, Columbus,* and *Independence*—though they do not seem to have been very successful and in any case were not used except as guardships. More frigates were laid down in the early 1820's to meet the growing menace of West Indian piracy, and William Doughty and Henry Eckford designed seven new 74-gun ships. In general, in this last stage before the introduction of steam-propulsion shipbuilding was less haphazard, and under the influence of Samuel Humphreys, who was appointed Chief Constructor in 1826, designers and architects met officially to pool their ideas and discuss their projects jointly.

The 120-gun *Pennsylvania*, with her four complete and armed decks, was launched in 1837, having been fifteen years in building. She was probably not as poor a sailer as many thought her to be, since her officers, being unaccustomed to ships of her size, tended to handle her like a frigate. We know too that Samuel Humphreys studied the lines of the British 100-gun *Royal Sovereign* and the Spanish *Santissima Trinidad*, ships that took part in the Battle of Trafalgar, and introduced details from them into this great ship. Historians have often argued about the extent to which American ships incorporated French designs. There is no space to enter this controversy here, but it is significant that Humphreys certainly makes no mention of French plans in relation to the *Pennsylvania*.

The schooners of the 1830's were interesting craft. They were lightly built, carrying eight 24-pounder carronades and two long 9-pounder cannon, and were fast enough to keep up with slavers and pirate vessels. Many of them were soon converted into brigs. Several brigantines were also built and seem to have been broader in the beam and deeper.

In the 1840's, various types of ship-sloops were designed, their variety revealing the idiosyncrasies of particular naval architects. Among them was Francis Grice's *Albany*, launched at Norfolk in 1846, which was a ship-rigged bark, but clipper-built and very attractive to look at. Josiah Barker's *Portsmouth* was another of these ship-sloops, but was longer than the *Albany*, though slightly narrower and shallower. She was built at Portsmouth, New Hampshire, launched in 1843, and remained on the navy list till 1915. These two ships and five others built at about the same time marked another stage in American naval history, the transition from the "frigate idea" to the "sloop idea," as it has been expressed. With the growing popularity of the ship-sloop, many frigates were cut down or rearmed as sloops.

The last naval brigs of the age of sail were all based on the Baltimore Clipper model.[1] It is difficult to know when the first clipper was built, and, indeed, as we have seen with other types of ships, it probably evolved gradually until the time came when the particular name was applied to a particular type. It seems true, however, to say that the sharp-bowed, very swift, cutter-rigged vessels mentioned in southern newspapers as early as 1746 are the first clippers and that they did originate in Baltimore. It is known, too, that these vessels were already schooner-rigged in pre-Revolutionary times, since such rig could be handled by a smaller crew, thus making the vessel lighter, and could be used in longer and narrower vessels. The brigs of the 1840's were appreciably smaller than the sloops, but they resembled them in many ways, and, like them, they were designed for speed. Sometimes they seem to have been overrigged—one of them capsized—but their pleasing lines made them very popular. The last of them, the *Lawrence*, designed by Lawrence B. Culley at Baltimore and launched in 1843, drew more water than the other four and therefore may have been less useful. She has, however, been described as "the most extreme example of the Baltimore clipper model in the navy" and was a very handsome ship.

A historian of the American sailing ship has remarked that the particular accomplishments of the naval constructors in the early days of the United States included the introduction of faster and larger frigates, the design of flush-decked sloops, the use of the Baltimore clipper as a model for the smaller classes of warships, and a design for ships that enabled them to be fast-moving even when carrying heavy guns. We need not go into the vexed question of the extent to which the above items can be said to have been actually invented by Americans, but we can be sure that the use and development of them were the contribution made to the sailing warship by the United States.

No survey of the early American navy would be complete without an account of at least one action associated with John Paul Jones. This brilliant man, whom John Adams described in 1779 as "the most ambitious and intriguing officer in the American navy," took part in the very first expedition of the Revolutionary War. He was commissioned as first lieutenant on December 7, 1775, the earliest naval lieutenant's commission the Congress granted; but before that, he seems to have been employed by the Marine Committee in fitting out the merchant-man *Black Prince* as a warship.

As the *Alfred*, this 350-ton ship was typical of those that made up the first rather haphazard Continental Navy. Pending the arrival of Dudley Saltonstall of Connecticut as captain, Jones had the unenviable task of building up the morale of the crew of this new warship without being really sure that she would ever see the enemy, and a cold winter that blocked the Delaware River with ice for many weeks did little to improve the situation.

Wisely, he decided to "exercise the guns," to use his own phrase. The cast-iron muzzle-loading smooth-bore guns were classed, as elsewhere, by the weight of their shot, and those mounted on the broadside were the important ones. They could fire grape and chain shot as well as cannon balls and were mounted on wooden-wheeled gun carriages. The *Alfred* had twenty 9-pounders and ten 6-pounders and also smaller swivel guns and mortars, so it was imperative that her gun crews and the "powder monkeys," the ship's boys who replenished the cartridge boxes, should have practice in dealing with these different weapons.

The *Alfred* became the flagship of Commodore Esek Hopkins of Rhode Island, a middle-aged merchant skipper and something of an "antique character," to quote a contemporary opinion. His fleet was "to proceed directly for Chesapeak Bay in Virginia . . . to gain intelligence of the Enemie's Situation and Strength" and, if it proved "not greatly superiour," to attack and destroy any enemy force. Congress was anxious that the British warships in Chesapeake Bay should be dislodged, so that the hold on Maryland and Virginia might be strengthened. There was, however, a saving clause in the instructions, and Hopkins took advantage of this and made instead for New Providence in the Bahamas in order to capture guns and gunpowder for the army.

The force was made up of the *Alfred*, with her yellow topsides and figurehead of a knight brandishing a sword, the only slightly smaller 28-gun *Columbus*, the 16-gun *Andrew Doria*, the 14-gun brig *Cabot*, the sloops *Providence* and *Hornet*, and the schooners *Wasp* and *Fly*. The smaller vessels had black topsides, which seems to have been the normal color for ships of their size. The first success was the capture of two enemy sloops off the island of Great Abaco. The two hundred marines shipped aboard the American vessels effected an unopposed landing, after an initial setback, on New Providence itself, and the island fell into American hands. In early April, on the return journey north, Commodore Hopkins' force fell in with the British 20-gun *Glasgow*, commanded by Captain Tryingham Howe, off Block Island; and in the ensuing battle, *Alfred* lost her wheel block by a lucky shot from *Glasgow* and suffered considerably before she became manageable again. An hour and a half after the engagement had begun, *Glasgow* withdrew. But in spite of the heavy structural damage she had suffered, Hopkins' ships did not catch her; and it was this that disgusted many of those taking part in the action, though Hopkins himself received many congratulations from those on shore on accomplishing his self-appointed mission with his fleet still intact.

Thus ended the first serious action in which the Continental Navy was involved. Professor Samuel Eliot Morison makes the interesting point that this first battle was fought only a few miles from where the last battle fought between the United States Navy and Germany took place in the Second World War. This was when *Atherton* and *Moberly* sank *U.853* on May 5–6, 1944.[2]

On May 10, 1776, John Paul Jones was given command of the sloop *Providence*, and in August he received orders at last "to proceed immediately on a Cruize against our Enemies & we think in & about the Lattitude of Bermuda may prove the most favourable ground for your purpose."[3] This sloop, with a crew of over seventy packed on board, had been the flagship of the Rhode Island navy and was a fast ship. Though no pictures or plans of her exist, experts imagine that she would have been about 70 feet in length overall, though this would exclude her 39-foot bowsprit, and 20 feet in the beam and would have carried an 84-foot mast with a gaff-headed fore-and-aft mainsail, three headsails, a large square topsail, and a smaller square topgallant. Her armament, we know, comprised twelve 4-pounder guns, eight mounted on the open gun deck and four on the quarterdeck. There would also have been a number of swivel guns mounted on the bulwarks. Within a week of leaving the Delaware capes, this nimble vessel had captured the brigantine *Britannia* and, by bold seamanship, herself escaped capture by the 28-gun frigate *Solebay* soon after. Two days after that, another brigantine, the fast *Sea Nymph*, bound for London from Barbados with a cargo of sugar, rum, ginger, and "twelve pipes best particular London market Madeira wine," was captured—"a pretty good prize," Jones wrote.

These exploits were the beginnings of a naval career that, along with the person of John Paul Jones himself, has passed into legend; and though later on the ships *Ranger* and *Bonhomme Richard* contributed more dramatically to its growth, there is evidence that Jones looked back on his days in the *Providence* with both pleasure and affection.

NOTES

[1]See Howard I. Chapelle, *The History of American Sailing Ships*, p. 126.
[2]See Samuel Eliot Morison, *John Paul Jones*, p. 48.
[3]See Orders from Marine Committee of the Continental Congress, dated Philadelphia, Aug. 6, 1776.

The 44-gun United States frigate *Alliance*, laid down in 1775, seen here in 1781. She was built at Salisbury Point by William Hackett and was the only American-built frigate still in service at the end of the War of Independence. She was sold to the East India Company when the United States Navy was disbanded in 1784. *The Mariners Museum, Newport News, Virginia*

United States frigate *Constitution*. *Brown Brothers,
New York*

(Above) The crew of HMS *Shannon* are seen boarding the United States frigate *Chesapeake* off Boston on June 1, 1813, from an engraving after the drawing made by G. Webster under the direction of an eyewitness. *The Mariners Museum, Newport News, Virginia*

(Top, left) The action on Lake Champlain, October 11–13, 1776, from a painting. *The Mariners Museum, Newport News, Virginia*

(Left) The action on Lake Champlain, October 11–13, 1776, from a contemporary line engraving by R. Sayer. The picture shows Captain Pringle's British squadron, including *Inflexible,* the schooners *Carleton* and *Maria,* and the galleys *Congress* and *Washington. National Maritime Museum, Greenwich*

The United States steam frigate *Mississippi* on her passage from Japan to the Sandwich Islands in a typhoon, October 7, 1854, from a colored lithograph by Currier and Ives, New York, after the drawing by E. Brown, Jr. *The Mariners Museum, Newport News, Virginia*

VIII

The Nineteenth Century Revolution: Paddle Wheel and Screw Propeller

THERE ARE comparatively few naval engagements between Trafalgar and Jutland, and those that there are seem in retrospect tactically disappointing as well as inconclusive in their results. However, this period of rapid development in the fighting ship is absorbingly interesting and even dramatic. Professor Michael Lewis has said that there was far more basic difference between the *Sanspareil*, the last ship to be laid down as a sailing ship in 1851, and the *Dreadnought* of 1905 than there was between Henry VII's *Regent*, with her 225 little guns, and the *Sanspareil*.[1] "Revolution" therefore seems the right word to describe this development, and its main features are the awareness that steam instead of sail should be the propellant force; the change from wood to iron as the basic material for shipbuilding; the introduction of armored protection, caused by the efficacy of the shell-firing gun; the tremendous strides forward made in gunnery, which included the introduction of breech-loading mechanism and the rifled barrel, of the revolving turret and the armor-piercing shell; and lastly, the introduction of new devices such as the submarine, the torpedo, and the mine. All these features must now be examined.

Let us first consider steam propulsion. It is hard to be sure of the earliest reference to the paddle wheel. The Romans certainly knew of it, though they probably did not invent it. We know that much later on, in 1543, Blasco de Garoy showed Emperor Charles V a ship with hand-operated paddles. Ramelli's *canot automobile*, mentioned in his book of 1588, is another early reference; and Torelli, the Governor of Malta, is known to have passed through the Straits of Messina against the tide in a ship fitted with paddles in 1619.

Among the many talented amateurs, Sir Samuel Morland and the Marquis of Worcester can be cited as typical of those with a general interest in "philosophy," and both seem to have come somewhere near the realization that steam might become the prime factor in the propulsion of ships. The Frenchman Denis Papin, who settled in England and suggested the application of steam to propulsion in 1690, is an important figure, especially as later on in Germany he may have actually propelled a boat with his engine. Thomas Savery, in England, did produce a successful engine, but he did not appear very sanguine about its application to navigation. He was, nevertheless, a believer in propulsion by hand-operated paddle wheels. His book, published in 1698 with the fascinating title *Navigation Improv'd; Or the Art of Rowing Ships of All Rates, in Calms, with a More Easy, Swift and Steady Motion Than Oars Can*, described a paddle-wheel mechanism made of oars fitted to drumheads radially and mounted on the end of an iron bar as the axis of a capstan. The device was successfully tried out on the Thames, but the Navy Board turned it down, occasioning an angry Savery to describe the whole business in his book, showing how "an improvement as great to shipping as turning to windward is automatically turned down and damned."

Next came Newcomen, who, sixty years before Watt took out his patent, constructed an engine operated by steam that seems to have been used on a fairly large scale. Jonathan Hulls, the clockmaker, took out a patent in 1736 that certainly seems to be the first detailed scheme for applying steam power to ships; and, indeed, he stated that "he hath with much labour and study and at great expense invented and formed a machine for carrying ships and vessels out of or into any harbour which . . . may be of great service to our Royal Navy."[2] However, as was to happen so often, the inventor's ideas, which were only paper projects, were ridiculed and then dropped through lack of support. The Marquis de Jouffroi ran a steamboat for more than a year on the Saône near Lyons in 1783; and at about the same time in the United States, James Rumsey of Maryland and the luckless John Fitch built boats driven by steam engines. Back in England, the third Earl Stanhope built a small steamer, the *Kent*, for the Admiralty that was to be driven by vibrators sited below the waterline, but it proved to be a failure. In 1794, however, Stanhope predicted that the time would come when Britain's supremacy at sea would be lost unless she were prepared to build a steam fleet.

Two further stages are both associated with Scotland. In 1787, William Symington installed one of his own 1-horsepower engines in a small paddle boat designed by one Patrick Miller. This was successfully tried out on the lake at Dalswinton, Miller's property in Dumfriesshire, and Robert Burns, the poet and a tenant on the estate, is said to have been a witness. "The vessel moved delightfully," said another spectator, "and notwithstanding the smallness of the cylinder, four inches in diameter, at the rate of 5 miles per hour. After amusing ourselves a few days, the engine was removed and carried into the house where it remained as a piece of ornamental furniture for a number of years."[3]

Two years later a larger engine on the same principle of a piston rod guided by rollers connected to a crank, itself attached to a paddle-wheel shaft, was tried out on the Forth-Clyde Canal and achieved a speed of 7 miles per hour. Though Miller and Symington parted company over a difference of opinion on their next experiment, Symington found a more influential patron and had some success with his *Charlotte Dundas*, launched in 1801. This sturdy vessel, 56 feet long and 18 feet broad, was able to tow two 70-ton barges against the wind at an average speed of more than 3 miles per hour.

Robert Fulton, the best-known name in the early history of steam navigation, had been on board the *Charlotte Dundas*, but he found Britain unsympathetic to his inventive genius, so he went to live in the United States and there, in 1807, produced the first pleasure steamer, the *Clermont*, which incorporated an engine bought in Soho, London, and a boiler from Smithfield. "Fulton's Folly," as she was called, was 166 feet long and only 18 feet in beam, but her success was dramatic: she seemed "a monster moving on the waters, defying the winds and tide and breathing flames and smoke." Fulton's real claim to a place in our story is that he designed what can certainly be called the first steam warship. This vessel, the *Demologos*, later renamed the *Fulton*, was launched in October, 1814, and was intended for the defense of New York against the British. She did well in her trials, but the war was over before she was ready for use. Her most remarkable feature was her double hull system—one housing the engines, the other her boiler—between which came the paddle. She had a battery of thirty 32-pounder guns for firing red-hot shot behind wooden walls nearly 5 feet thick. She also had some submarine guns able to fire 100-pound projectiles below the waterline. She was destroyed in an accidental explosion at Brooklyn Navy Yard in 1829.

The next stage was when Henry Bell, a hotelkeeper at Helensburgh, saw the steamship as an exciting new factor in the tourist trade. Later, when he started pestering the British Admiralty about the desirability of applying steam to warships, he succeeded in interesting no less a man than Nelson, who said, "My Lords and Gentlemen, if you do not adopt Mr. Bell's scheme, other nations will, and, in the end, vex every vein of Empire." It is interesting to speculate in passing on what difference Nelson might have made had he survived to lend his support to the campaign for steam navigation. Bell's 30-ton *Comet* of 1812 was intended to ply between Glasgow and Greenock. This she did successfully and in so doing was the first passenger steamer to operate in European waters.

These early experiments are interesting reading today, but when we consider their isolation from each other for the most part, we can see that progress was slow. The real improvements that made the steam engine adaptable to marine use were contained in Watt's discovery of the principle of "double impulse" and Pickard's invention of the crank and connecting rod. These two made the steam engine "capable of imparting to a shaft a continuous rotary motion without the medium of noisy, brittle or inefficient gearing. As soon as engines having this power were placed on the public market, attempts were made to mount them in boats and larger vessels."[4]

In 1812, the steamship *Thames* sailed from Greenock to London, and in 1819, the 300-ton *Savannah*, built at New York, crossed the Atlantic in twenty-five days; and it might be said that thereafter the early stages of the development from sail to steam were over. In 1824, the *Falcon*, though little more than a yacht, completed the journey from London to India. It should, however, be stressed that all these vessels were sailing ships and that their engines were subsidiary to the sails, which were still thought of as the normal means of propulsion.

In Britain, where the Industrial Revolution began, the response of the Admiralty to the potentialities of the steam age and all it implied was cautious in the extreme but not entirely hostile as is usually thought. On the one hand, there is the familiar picture of British trust in improvisation, which can be seen in the reluctance to approach the whole matter of shipbuilding in a scientific manner, and in the reliance on practical experience instead. It was not till the Barham Commissioners had reported unfavorably in 1806 on the general state of affairs that the government of the day thought fit to organize a school of naval architecture, and even then it was not till the mid-century that its graduates were in a position to submit an original design for a warship.[5]

Yet on the other hand, Melville, the First Lord, no doubt impressed after all by Henry Bell's *Comet*, did direct the Navy Board to try out a sloop with a steam engine in 1815, though this came to nothing, and in the following year encouraged Marc Isambard Brunel to press on with his scheme for steam tugs. The official attitude is admirably presented in Melville's own words on this occasion: ". . . the Board deem it unnecessary to enter at present into the consideration of the question as to how far the power of the steam engine may be made applicable to the purposes of navigation: but . . . it would be attended with material advantages to his Majesty's service, if it could be used for the purpose of towing ships of war out of harbour . . . when they would be prevented from sailing by contrary winds . . ."[6] The Admiralty's caution, however, proved too strong, and it was not till the 1830's that the subsidizing of steam navigation was officially taken on. Brunel, indeed, had to carry out his experiments at his own expense. There was some justification, in fact, for the exasperation Whitbread expressed in a speech in Parliament in 1815 that "the improvements which to a wonderful extent had been made in all the private concerns of the country were so slow in finding their way into the public establishments and especially the dockyards."[7]

In view of all this, the purchase of the 212-ton *Monkey*, built at

Rotherhithe with an 80-horsepower engine in 1821, and the launching of the Admiralty's first paddle-wheel steamship, the *Comet*, at Deptford in 1822 are something of a milestone. The *Comet* displaced 238 tons, with an engine also of 80 horsepower, and was fitted with four 9-pounder guns. She had a boiler that could raise steam to a pressure of about 3 ½ pounds, a long bell-mouthed chimney, and a single-cylinder reciprocating engine pointing upward and turning a pair of unboxed paddle wheels. The whole was handmade of hammered iron, and she could maintain a speed of from 4 to 5 knots.

There were further developments in the 1820's and 1830's, perhaps too many for the wishes of the Admiralty, torn, as always, between its desire to be up with the times and an official scepticism strongly laced with frugality. In 1835, Minto, the First Lord in Grey's Whig government, and by no means an unimaginative administrator, complained that it was "not easy to satisfy or get rid of" the many speculative inventors "especially when they happen to be naval officers of high rank." Sir Charles Napier, a naval officer later to have the Baltic command in the Crimean War, assured an Admiralty official that "in another war steam will become to the Navy what the cavalry is to the army. It will be the post of honour."

The acceptance of steam came late for another reason, one which it is easy to appreciate at its full value. In 1825, Joseph Hume made the point in the House of Commons, and not for the last time, that the discovery of steam navigation had altered the nature of maritime warfare completely. "Come war when it might," he said, "the mode of warfare in the narrow seas would be very different," and he foresaw that it was dangerous to suppose that the traditional fleet might not be just so much lumber in the next war. The point was that though the wooden walls had stood Britain in good stead in the past, they were dangerously old-fashioned now. It might well be true, as Palmerston himself had once admitted, that "the French, Spanish and American ships are all better sailers than ours"[8] and that, until recently, the British had been the most unscientific shipbuilders in the world. Yet there was an understandable feeling in Britain that the French and others had less to lose by experimenting than the British had, so they could afford to try things out. Again, quite apart from the problems of coaling, it was felt that only a certainty should be backed and that the steam paddle-wheel ship was not yet in this category. Though indispensable as a tug, she did not seem likely to become an efficient seagoing warship. Her paddles were vulnerable, and they restricted the arc of fire. As Professor Graham has pointed out, it was not till 1829 that a method of feathering the paddles as they entered, passed through, and left the water was invented. Till then the paddle wheel became too deeply immersed and much of its power was wasted in churning up the water.

Before we turn to the next development, the replacement of the paddle wheel by the screw propeller, we must note the actions in which steam paddle ships received their baptism of fire. The United States ship *Seagull* took part in the hunt for the last pirates in the West Indies, where piracy had become so general that the United States government had to take measures to suppress it. It had arisen in the period after the end of the Napoleonic War when the Spanish colonies were tempted to revolt and outlaws and adventurers from many countries joined in, attracted by the chance of gain. The republics of Buenos Aires and Venezuela commissioned several swift-sailing privateers to prey on Spanish merchantmen in the Caribbean, and these soon began to plunder neutral vessels as well.

Early in 1822, Captain James Biddle was sent to take control of a rapidly worsening situation. He and his successors in the next few years succeeded in doing this, though a squadron was kept in West Indian waters till 1828. The work of clearing up these nests of pirates was slow and laborious; much of it had to be done in open boats and under a burning sun, while the cruisers ran the continual risk of grounding. Soon it became clear that smaller vessels would be more useful, so in 1823 Captain David Porter took command with his "mosquito fleet" of five 20-oared barges, eight small armed schooners, and the New York steam ferryboat *Seagull*, which thus became the first American steamer to see any sort of action. In March, 1825, we know that Lieutenant McKeever in the *Seagull* commanded a hastily collected force that included the boats of the British frigate *Dartmouth* and seems to have had an exciting time overpowering pirates on land and sea.

In the Mexican War, which began in May, 1846, several steamships were involved. There was the 10-gun paddle-wheeler *Mississippi*, commanded by the famous Matthew Calbraith Perry, who had from 1838–1840 commanded the *Fulton II*, the first American steam warship.

The steamers *Vixen, McLane, Petrita, Spitfire,* and *Scourge* and the screw-driven *Princeton* also saw action in the Gulf of Mexico at this time. They were largely used for towing sailing vessels into position or bombarding forts from inshore positions.[9]

Again, in the first Burma War of 1824–1825, the East India Company paddle-wheeler *Diana* played a by no means insignificant part, largely on the initiative of Captain Frederick Marryat, the novelist. Indeed, to quote Oliver Warner, "she was the one unqualified and spectacular success of the invasion." She was the first steamer to be used by the British navy in actual warfare, and for this reason she deserves our attention.

Diana had been launched at Kidderpore in 1823 and had an engine of 60 horsepower and a distinctive funnel almost as tall as her masts, to judge from contemporary illustrations. She had been designed for service on the Hoogli River and according to the Calcutta *John Bull*, she was considered to be a "great ornament" and was hailed, in the rather fulsome language of that periodical, "as the harbinger of her kind who will waft us to our native shore with speed and pleasure." Marryat, on whom the control of the naval side of the war had fallen owing to the sickness of Commodore Grant, could see the use of steam in its right perspective. He realized that *Diana,* drawing only 5 feet of water, could travel upriver where sailing ships might either run aground or be becalmed. He used her to precede the force of sixty-three ships and nine thousand troops upriver after the capture of Rangoon, and as Professor Lloyd says, "the very sight of her created more consternation than a herd of armed elephants."

An interesting episode that deserves to be rescued from oblivion is that at one point *Diana* was run down by a transport and her engines damaged. Marryat has recorded that he releveled her engine, as the only engineer had been injured, and "worked her himself," though this probably only means that he took command and saw that this useful little vessel was restored to operational order. It is a rare example of a naval officer brought up in the sailing age looking forward rather than back. Marryat, indeed, was fascinated by engines, and ten years later in Brussels he wrote of a locomotive in some memorable words: "it is impossible to contemplate any steam engine without feeling wonder and admiration at the ingenuity of man; but this feeling is raised to a

degree of awe when you look at a locomotive engine—there is such
enormous power compassed into so small a space; I can never divest
myself of the idea that it is possessed of vitality—that it is a living as
well as a moving being."

The *Perseverance* showed the shape of things to come in the Greek
War of Independence. This ship was the only practical outcome of
the memorandum submitted by Lord Cochrane to the London Committee in November, 1825, in which he had asked for "six steam vessels
having each two guns in the bow and perhaps two in the stern not less
than 68-pounder long guns." If the complete flotilla had been built, the
revolution from sail to steam might well have been more rapid, since in
Cochrane's hands it would certainly have been successful. Indeed, when
he heard of the plan, Lord Exmouth said, "It's not only the Turkish
fleet but all the navies of the world that you will be able to conquer with
such craft as these."[10] The chance, however, was not to come in this
way; even the *Perseverance* did not arrive in Greek waters till spring,
1827, as her engineer, Galloway, that "impudent liar," was working on
a contract for Ibrahim Pasha at the same time.

As the only steamship to take part in the war, the *Perseverance* is
worthy of note. She had an 84-horsepower engine and was armed with
45-pound mortars and 68-pounder guns. Her captain was Abney
Hastings, a Trafalgar veteran of considerable ability, who had seen
early on that the Greek cause would fail without maritime superiority.
Cochrane himself never actually fought the steamship, but *Perseverance*,
by this time named *Karteria*, acquitted herself well, firing red-hot shot
from her 68-pounders and destroying enemy shipping.

Professor Lewis wisely says that it is impossible to attribute the
invention of the screw to any one person, any more than it is possible to
be sure who was the inventor of the paddle wheel. Nevertheless, it is
worthwhile to recall some of the great names associated with its early
days. In 1836, the Swedish army officer John Ericsson, who was later
to startle the world with his armored gun turret in the *Monitor*, was
attempting to interest the Admiralty in his patented screw propeller.
After leaving the army, Ericsson had come to England and set himself
up as a civil engineer. He had invented a locomotive, which he had
entered for the competition in 1829 won by George Stephenson with
his *Rocket*. Steam power for ships, his next interest, had already begun

to be developed commercially, but in fighting ships the paddle wheel, with its vulnerability and space-occupying disadvantage, seemed to have little to recommend it. However, the screw propeller did not appeal to the Admiralty either, and though the power of a helical blade in water had been known to Archimedes of Syracuse centuries back, it was not till 1752 that the Frenchman Bernoulli demonstrated, though rather clumsily, that a screw propeller could be worked by horses or men on board a ship. In 1785, Joseph Bramah patented a screw for driving vessels through water, a device that Bushnell and Fulton in the United States proved to be workable.

With this background knowledge, then, Ericsson built a 40-foot steam launch, the *Francis B. Ogden*, with twin propellers, and successfully towed Admiralty officials in a barge down the Thames from Somerset House to the Limehouse Reach at 10 knots. Though the voyage itself could hardly have been more satisfactory, the Admiralty disapproved of the steering, being convinced that a ship could never be accurately steered when its driving force was at the stern, surely one of the most surprisingly wrong decisions ever made. So the idea was turned down. Ericsson then gained the support of two Americans who had witnessed the trial—Ogden, himself an engineer who had been United States Consul at Liverpool, and Captain Stockton, a naval officer. The latter, especially, saw the possibilities of the screw in naval vessels and encouraged Ericsson to go to the United States, saying, ". . . we'll make your name ring on the Delaware." Consequently, the Ericsson propeller was fitted to a small iron steamer built by Laird's of Birkenhead, and this vessel, completed in 1840, crossed the Atlantic to serve as a tug on the big rivers.

In 1843, the *Princeton* was launched at Philadelphia. She was a large 10-gun sloop and had a six-bladed Ericsson screw and with her 400-horsepower engine could travel at 13 knots. Yet here, as before, Ericsson was unlucky. Stockton and he had each designed a 12-inch wrought-iron gun, and when these were tried out on the quarterdeck of the new *Princeton*, Stockton's burst, killing the Secretary of State, the Secretary of the Navy, and some others. Ericsson had warned Stockton that his design was faulty, but there was a quarrel, and Ericsson decided to offer his next "device for aquatic attack"—in fact, the first revolving gun turret—to the French. Here again he met with little interest, so the "device" was shelved for some years and will be considered in its proper place later on.

In France, the frigate *Pomone* had been fitted with screws in 1845, but the *Napoléon* was the first ship in which the sails were really subordinate to steam.

Francis Pettit Smith in Britain took out a patent for a screw propeller in 1836. Its particular feature was its position in an open space formed in the deadwood, and this was generally thought to be the right position for it to work in. A 6-ton vessel was equipped with Pettit Smith's screw, and trials were carried out first on the City and Paddington Canal in London and then between Blackwall and Folkestone. Though heavy weather was experienced off the Kent coast, it proved the success of the screw, especially as the sailing qualities of the vessel were seen to be unimpaired. Later, a company was formed, and in spite of much shrill opposition, the *Archimedes* was built, with a 3-foot stroke engine working at 27 strokes a minute. She was tested against the *Widgeon*, the fastest paddle steamer of the Dover mail packets, but with inconclusive results, though later a voyage from Plymouth to Oporto was achieved, creating a new record for a steam passage.

Yet in spite of this proof that the screw had great possibilities, its acceptance was only slowly won, and as has been rather wistfully recorded, even the new edition of the *Encyclopaedia Britannica* appearing at the time did not include any reference to screw propulsion in its article on steam navigation.[11] However, in December, 1840, it was decided, no doubt as a result of the performance of the *Archimedes*, to change over the Atlantic liner *Great Britain*, then under construction, to screw propulsion. Another success for Pettit Smith was in the tug-of-war in 1845 between two sloops, screw-driven *Rattler* and paddle-driven *Alecto*, which will be mentioned presently. *Rattler*'s screw was Pettit Smith's short two-bladed version, selected after many trials had been made of other patterns.

Though, as we have seen, the acceptance of the screw propeller came about slowly, its attractions were more obvious than those of the paddle wheel. Its adoption would restore the warship's complete broadside armament and, more important, the vital machinery could be safely placed below water level. More attractive still, perhaps, was the proposition that above decks, all would be clear again for the traditional working of the vessel as a sailing ship. It was still naval doctrine that full sail power was the normal method of progress and steam propulsion should be used as the last resort only. Even into the 1850's this was to remain the accepted view, and not till 1861 was the "lifting" screw abolished in all ironclads under construction. Before that, it had been possible, though not very easy, to lift the screw right out of the water so as not to impede the ship's progress under sail.

Arguments were being put forward in advanced circles that the steaming ability of a ship ought to be superior to her sailing qualities, but this was exceptional; and naval architects, playing for safety, were content to build "marine hermaphrodites," to use Professor Graham's phrase, that still had the lines of the traditional sailing ship. The Admiralty too, in spite of growing French rivalry, simply could not afford to throw over the sailing ship until they were really convinced that the screw propeller was always going to be efficient, even in rough weather. Isambard Brunel's *Great Britain* achieved her trial trip from Bristol to London in 1844, the first time the screw had been applied to a vessel of large burden, and this success must have convinced many waverers of the efficacy of the screw.

Next followed the famous duel between the sloop *Rattler*, fitted with Pettit's screw, as mentioned above, and the paddle ship *Alecto* in 1845. After three ordinary races on different-length courses off the Isle of Wight, which *Rattler* won comparatively easily, a tug-of-war was tried. This, too, *Rattler* won, being able to tow *Alecto* at the steady rate of 2½ knots. The "pretty toy," as the screw had been slightingly described ten years earlier when Berthon sent his model to the Admiralty, had proved itself. Captain Chappell, who had been in charge of the trials, summed up the achievement in his report in these words:

In vessels of war the screw propeller admits of the whole machinery being kept below the water-line; of the ship being ordinarily used with sails only, but of being converted into a steamer in a few minutes; or as the action of the screw is equal whatever may be the inclination of the ship, the screw will allow of using both sails and steam when required. The propelling apparatus is placed wholly out of reach of injury from shot, the falling of masts or collision with vessels; the whole broadside battery is left unmolested, and should every mast be shot away the propeller might still enable a ship to maintain an efficient fighting position, to follow an enemy if required, or to convey the vessel into port however crippled.[12]

The Admiralty reaction to the *Rattler*'s vindication of the screw over the paddle wheel was to have the frigate *Amphion* converted on the stocks to screw propulsion. She had been ordered as far back as 1828, but work on her had been delayed. All her fittings, except the engines, boilers, and screw, were the same as those in an ordinary sailing frigate; and it was remarked at her launching that "she was the first war steamer built in this country which had the whole of her machinery and boilers below water and therefore secure from the enemy's shot." Her screw was probably the Ericsson type, and we know that in 1853, when Captain Cooper Key took command, she was capable of making only a little over 5 knots. She was at last launched in 1846, the year the *Rifleman*, the first screw ship to be built in dry dock at Portsmouth, was brought to the Thames to have her engines fitted.

In 1852, the 91-gun *Agamemnon* was launched, the first "line" ship to be fitted with screw machinery from the very beginning, though in every other way she was a traditional sailing ship. Before she was taken out to the Mediterranean by Captain (later Admiral Sir William) Mends in the autumn of 1853 to be Sir Edward Lyons' flagship, she had a trial run around the Eddystone lighthouse to test a new propeller. When she was going at full speed, the blades suddenly broke off, but as Mends later recorded, ". . . the engines being by Penn of Greenwich and therefore as perfect as possible both in workmanship and material," only very little damage was done.

At the bombardment of Sevastopol on October 17, 1854, that rather inefficiently conducted episode, she acquitted herself with dignity and even distinction, opening fire at far shorter range than the cumbersome sailing ships, which had to be maneuvered into action stations by the steam tugs. Lyons placed his "superb Agamemnon" so close to land that, according to Kinglake, she only had 2½ feet of water under her keel and her jib guys were in contact with those of the *Rodney*, which was actually aground.[13] Captain Mends was apparently able to test her in really bad weather conditions, too, and found that he could "trust much to good anchor and cable, good screw and steam to help her through very much bad weather." He was even able to say off Sevastopol that "the dear old screw is slowly working away to ease our cable and affords us much comfort."

Captain Mends's experience was not, however, general, because most screw-propelled ships were, in fact, conversions, with their hulls—

and especially their sterns, with their overhanging upper sections—
entirely unsuitable for screw propulsion. A main weakness was that the
submerged part of the afterhull was not designed for effective propeller
thrust and the avoidance of slip. Also, it took time to perfect the screw
itself in shape and pitch, and, indeed, it was not till 1867 that the whole
question of water resistance was scientifically studied by William
Froude. Again, greater speed had to be given to the engines when the
screw replaced the paddle wheel, which meant new problems of vibra-
tion and friction. Eventually, a vertical engine was found to be the most
effective, straddling the shaft and working fast with a direct drive,
though this did not solve the problem of wear and tear. The use of
lignum vitae for certain bearings was a partial answer, but in the long
run we can see now that the iron hull was the only real solution. As
Scott Russell said to an assembly of naval architects in 1864, ". . . bits of
wood kept together with bits of metal cannot stand the continuous day-
after-day wear and tear of the wriggle of a 1,000 horse-power screw in the
tail of a ship."

Before we leave the early days of the British screw steamship,
mention must be made of the *Dauntless*. She was laid down in 1844 and
seems to have been the first ship in the Royal Navy designed to fight
under full steam, for her sister ship, the *Arrogant*, had only auxiliary
engines. Yet her performance was disappointing, as she was slower than
many paddle steamers, achieving only 10 knots, in spite of her screw
and 580-horsepower engine. This was owing to a point that we have
already noted about most ships of this period: their actual shape was not
suited to the new means of propulsion—sterns were too bluff to allow
an adequate flow of water for the screw to grip properly.

The middle 1850's forms a suitable point at which to end this part of
our account of the first of the chief effects of the Industrial Revolution
on warship construction. The changeover to steam had been slow and
perhaps reluctant, but although it was still by no means universal, it had
been accepted in principle, and no longer was a First Lord likely to
reiterate Melville's classic words when he flatly told the British Colonial
Office that "Their Lordships felt it their bounden duty to discourage to
the utmost of their ability the employment of steam vessels, as they considered that the introduction of steam was calculated to strike a fatal
blow at the Naval Supremacy of the Empire."

This was in 1828, and Hay, the representative of the Colonial Office, had merely suggested that a steamer might be used to carry mails from Malta to Corfu.

NOTES

[1]See Michael Lewis, *The Navy of Britain*, p. 112.

[2]See Geoffrey Penn, *Up Funnel, Down Screw!*, p. 3.

[3]See F. L. Robertson, *The Evolution of Naval Armament*, p. 218, evidence of Taylor, tutor to Miller's sons, before Select Committee 1824.

[4]*Ibid*, p. 217.

[5]See G. S. Graham, "The Transition from Paddle-Wheel to Screw-Propeller," *The Mariner's Mirror*, 1958, vol. xliv, p. 36.

[6]Sir John Barrow, *An Autobiographical Memoir of Sir John Barrow*, London, 1847, pp. 388–389.

[7]See *Parliamentary Debates*, vol. xxx, p. 809.

[8]See *Broadlands Papers*, letter to Lord Durham, dated Apr. 8, 1832.

[9]See E. S. Maclay, *The History of the United States Navy*, vol. ii, pp. 103–126.

[10]C. C. Lloyd, *Lord Cochrane*, p. 176.

[11]Robertson, *op. cit.*, p. 238.

[12]Penn, *op. cit.*, p. 59.

[13]See A. W. Kinglake, *The Invasion of the Crimea*, Blackwood & Sons, Edinburgh, 1901, vol. iv, p. 416.

(Right) The third-rate HMS *Hastings,* with Queen Adelaide on board, being towed into Malta Harbor by the sloop *Rhadamanthus* on November 30, 1838. Lithograph by C. von Brocktorff. *Science Museum, London*

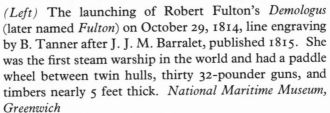

(Left) The launching of Robert Fulton's *Demologus* (later named *Fulton*) on October 29, 1814, line engraving by B. Tanner after J. J. M. Barralet, published 1815. She was the first steam warship in the world and had a paddle wheel between twin hulls, thirty 32-pounder guns, and timbers nearly 5 feet thick. *National Maritime Museum, Greenwich*

The 91-gun HMS *Agamemnon*, launched in 1852, from a colored lithograph by T. G. Dutton, after O. W. Brierley, published 1853. She was the first "line" ship to be built with screw machinery, though she was still a traditional sailing ship. Later she became Sir Edward Lyons' flagship in the Crimean War. *National Maritime Museum, Greenwich*

The "tug-of-war" between HM steam sloops *Rattler* and *Alecto* "in a perfect calm" on April 3, 1845, to test the comparative merits of the paddle wheel and screw propeller. *Rattler*, screw-driven, was victorious and towed *Alecto* stern foremost at a rate of nearly three miles per hour, "both vessels exerting their full power in opposite directions." *Science Museum, London*

The explosion on board the 10-gun United States sloop *Princeton* on February 28, 1844, colored lithograph by N. Currier. *Princeton* was equipped with the six-bladed Ericsson screw and a 400-horsepower engine. Captain Stockton's experimental 12-inch wrought-iron gun killed the Secretary of State and the Secretary of the Navy on this occasion. *National Maritime Museum, Greenwich*

HMS *Devastation*, photograph taken off Southend showing her dressed for the review on June 28, 1897, to mark Queen Victoria's Diamond Jubilee. *National Maritime Museum, Greenwich*

IX

The Nineteenth Century Revolution: The Ironclad Vessel and the Naval Gun

IT IS BEST not to separate the development of the ironclad vessel from the improvements in the naval gun and especially the introduction of the shell. In the following pages, therefore, these two important aspects of the naval revolution of the nineteenth century will frequently overlap.

At two distinct points, the French took the initiative in this revolution. The first was when they introduced the shell, which made the second, the introduction of the ironclad warship, inevitable. The early stages of shell firing are instructive to us today, but it is doubtful whether many learned the lessons at the time. Sir Samuel Bentham, an ex-shipwright from Deptford but then working for the Russian government, equipped a force of long boats with brass guns mounted on his own nonrecoil system and furnished them with shells as well as solid shot. These inferior vessels scored a great success against a far larger Turkish force, the shells tearing holes in the sides of the Turkish ships and starting fires that spread rapidly. This was in 1788 in the Sea of Azov, more than sixty years before a similar occurrence on the eve of the Crimean War opened the eyes of the world to the efficacy of such ammunition against wooden ships.

A year earlier, Lieutenant Shrapnel of the Royal Artillery demonstrated his invention of a shell containing case shot exploded by a small bursting charge, and this and other earlier trials of firing shells horizontally might have been the beginnings of the adoption of the shell into the Royal Navy. This, however, did not happen, and it may well have been discouraged deliberately in case foreign powers took up the challenge with similar devices and rendered the existing British superiority in material useless. The French, with nothing to lose, did explore the possibilities of shellfire in fighting ships and, after successful trials at Meudon in which 24- and 36-pounders were fired at mock-up ships at ranges from 400 to 600 yards, succeeded in 1798 in convincing Napoleon himself that shellfire was worthy of serious consideration.

Henri-Joseph Paixhans, at one time a general of French artillery, developed the particular ship's armament that was eventually to be adopted by the French navy. His *Nouvelle force maritime et artillerie* of 1822 and *Expériences faites sur une arme nouvelle* of 1825 did not claim anything new, and, indeed, he quoted a French inventor, Deschiens, who had in 1690 devised a means of firing bombs from long guns horizontally instead of parabolically as from mortars and had moreover had successes against two Dutch ships. Paixhans hoped to see solid shot superseded by shell—*boulets creux*—throughout the French fleet, and if this were done, he felt that the balance between the French and British fleets would at last be adjusted more favorably. Also, he thought the small but fast and well-armed steam vessel was the warship of the future: she would be less vulnerable than the old three-decker, and she would be quicker to build and easier to man—a lack of trained seamen had always been one of France's main handicaps.

Paixhans saw the advantage, too, of a standardized caliber for guns, though the actual guns themselves could be of different weights and would take different charges, thus giving different muzzle velocities. His schemes had two other main features: he decided to do away with a tier of guns and so reduce the height of a ship above the waterline and to have the sides of all ships encased in iron plates. At the time, this was rejected, probably because it would give the advantage back to the solid-shot gun, but his principle of unity of caliber was applied almost at once. The Paixhans gun, a chambered howitzer, was designed to project a shell weighing 62½ pounds when filled with powder; it was tested successfully at Brest in the early 1820's. In 1824, the range and accuracy when firing at the moored frigate *Pacificateur* were remarkable and so were the incendiary effects of the shells. It was not, however, till 1837 when public opinion had been sufficiently won over on the grounds of safety that the principle of shellfire was accepted by the French government.

The British were forced to follow suit, and by 1839 tentative proposals of fifteen years earlier were adopted; but the shell-firing gun was still thought of as an auxiliary to the solid-shot gun, and so the two types, with their differing calibers, were mounted side by side, each with its different function to perform. The drawbacks to shell-firing guns were seen at first to be several: their range was seriously reduced because a limit had to be put on the powder charge that could be safely used; it was also thought at first that the shells themselves were too dangerous to warrant their carriage on board a wooden ship; the flight of shells, for a variety of reasons, was not nearly so certain as that of solid shot; and lastly, the feeling that battles between steam warships might be fought at greater range seemed to justify the retention of solid-shot guns.

More advanced thinking, however, such as that of Captain Simmons in his *Effects of Heavy Ordnance,* published in 1837, began to fore-shadow later developments in which it would be generally accepted that a large number of small guns might be replaced by a few of the largest caliber—in fact, the supersession of the broadside by the pivot gun. Simmons wrote: "Instead of determining the armament of a ship from the length of her decks and crowding as many together as possible . . . it might be safer to place on board a few of the most powerful guns which [the ship's] construction would admit . . . making the *number* and not the *nature* of the guns depend on what is inevitably fixed: the capacity of the vessel."

It was not till after the Crimean War that the rifled cannon materialized and the cylindrical shell superseded the spherical. These factors increased range, striking velocity, and volume, and they must be considered briefly.

The invention of rifling itself went back to the sixteenth century. Straight grooving came first and has been attributed to the Viennese gunsmith Gaspard Zoellner. Helical grooving followed soon after, and the name of Augustin Kutter of Nuremberg, who died in 1630, is associated with it. It was, however, a long time before the accuracy of rifles superseded the almost unbelievable inefficiency of the ¾-inch smooth-bore "Brown Bess" musket, which was still being carried by some soldiers in the Crimea in the mid-1850's. The Enfield rifle, however, which "smote the enemy like a destroying angel," according to William Howard Russell, *The Times'* war correspondent in the field, was beginning to replace it. Thus rifling began to be used in the hand gun, and its extended use in artillery was only a matter of time. France took the initiative yet again, and Napoleon III, himself a considerable expert on guns, deserves to be remembered in this connection. His field guns made history on the battlefields of Magenta and Solferino in 1859. Once again, Britain was compelled to follow; and the names of Joseph Whitworth and William Armstrong come into the story, both playing a prominent part in the development of rifled ordnance. Whitworth concentrated on precision and thereby modernized the whole science of gun-making. Armstrong, on the other hand, was a greater inventor, and the gun bearing his name was a real advance. It had a breech-loading apparatus and polygroove rifling; elongated cylindrical projectiles were used to overcome air resistance; and, for strength, the gun was built up of several parts welded together and not merely cast from a single piece of metal.

Not all of Armstrong's ideas were accepted outright, for a controversy arose about the best method of loading—muzzle or breech. The British and the Prussians alone persisted in retaining the removable breech at this time, though fully aware of its potential dangers, long after the French, the Americans, and the Italians had abandoned it. But in 1864, after there had been accidents, Britain too reverted to muzzle-loaders for use in ships, which she maintained stoutly till 1880, even though by this time improvements in breech-loading equipment had altered the whole picture. The short muzzle-loading gun had become out of date because its power could not be increased to keep up with improved armor plating and warship design. It came to be seen that a longer gun and a larger slow-burning charge of powder needed larger chambers; in fact, a new shape of gun altogether was needed, with powder chambers larger in diameter than the bore, and these new guns, for technical reasons that need not be gone into here, could not be made muzzle-loading, quite apart from the difficulty of actually inserting the projectile into a gun of more than a certain length.

The Whitworth guns adopted by the British Admiralty in the early 1860's included several of the Armstrong features. They were strong, solid, and simply constructed and could be loaded easily and rapidly. They were also commendably accurate, especially after a new "gas check" had been fitted to the projectile to reduce the "windage." Another impressive feature was the considerably increased range: one of them hurled its shot five and a half miles.

The next development in gunnery is concerned with the actual position of the guns in a ship and can be summed up in the change from the traditional broadside first to the central battery, often of a "citadel" type, and then to the revolving turret. The desire was to increase the angle of fire and, above all, to employ "fire-ahead" tactics. The retention of masts and rigging in the British fleet was a considerable handicap; indeed, the *Devastation*, completed in 1873, is really the first modern battleship, because as well as being steam-propelled, built of iron, and armored, she had completely abandoned the appurtenances of sail and had her guns mounted in turrets and not sited along the length of the ship. This is, however, to anticipate, for it is intended first to consider the introduction of protective armor plating and the completely iron warship.

The intensive study of protective armor which led to the ironclad was the result of the improvements in the naval gun just discussed. Yet the idea of ship protection went back a good deal further. Toward the end of the sixteenth century, the Korean admiral Yi-Sun-Sin attacked the Japanese with his "tortoise boat," which has a claim to being the first armored warship. She had a domed deck armored with plates of iron and studded with spikes. At more or less the same date in Europe, the Spaniards and the English adopted forms of protection but chiefly to protect the men on board and not the ships themselves. These were not, of course, made of iron, but mention must be made of the Genoese admiral Andreas Doria, who had a ship completely encased in lead. In the eighteenth century, the French superimposed on the sides of some of their floating batteries a layer of unseasoned wood, an inner one of cork, and a padding of sand between the two that could be kept moist; but in spite of these precautions, the ships were burned out by the enemy at the siege of Gibraltar in 1782.

Nevertheless, in general it was thought that a wooden ship was not likely to suffer very severely from gunfire—until the introduction of the shell described above. Paixhans' books had appeared in the early 1820's, and French tests had confirmed his theories, but it was not until 1838 and onward that the British conducted trials at Portsmouth and saw for themselves that no defensive measure existed against shellfire. Iron was not, however, entirely untried. Aaron Manby, in partnership with Admiral Sir Charles Napier who put up the money, built the first British iron steamer. Napier navigated this vessel across the Channel and up the Seine to Paris in 1822. In 1838, I. K. Brunel's *Great Britain*, the first really large iron ship for transatlantic work, had proved the durability of iron in an unexpected way. On her fourth trip, she grounded off Ireland and had to remain for nearly a year before she could be recovered, but it was found that she was very little damaged.

In 1839, Laird's had made two iron gunboats for the East India Company, *Phlegethon* and *Nemesis*, which played an important part in the first China War. *Nemesis* proved the strength of iron, rather as *Great Britain* had done, when she ran aground on rocks off Scilly but survived the ordeal, though this may have been due to another innovation, her watertight bulkheads. In the early 1840's, the British Admiralty went so far as to order a small iron packet steamer, the *Dover*, and a flotilla of iron frigates that included the *Birkenhead*, later to be lost off South Africa with all hands in 1852. Nevertheless, the opposition to iron was still considerable both in the service and out of it, even though its efficacy as a building material was at last becoming appreciated by a wider circle of people.

No British iron ships took part in the Crimean War, but two incidents in it are of great importance, not least because the theories of shellfire were at last being put to the test of war. In November, 1853, a Russian squadron destroyed a squadron of Turkish frigates off Sinope, confirming thereby Paixhans' theory that the concentration of force in smaller vessels would overpower the radiating fire of the much larger three-deckers. The lesson to be learned was obscured, as also happened in the second incident, the French bombardment of the Kinburn forts two years later; for in both cases, the inferior force was defeated, and this numerical inferiority was thought to be the cause of the defeats.

The French, however, had seen what had happened off Sinope, and they succeeded at the Kinburn forts because in the period separating the two events, they had built a special flotilla of floating batteries with a light draft that would carry heavy shell guns close inshore and were armored sufficiently to resist solid shot and the effects of explosive shells. The bombardment of the Kinburn forts in October, 1855, by the armored, flat-bottomed, steam-propelled floating batteries *Dévastation*, *Tonnante*, and *Lave*, firing their shells at less than 1,000 yards, yet impervious to enemy retaliation, has come to be seen by naval historians as a tremendously important stage in the history of the warship. Thereafter, almost every expert was converted to the view that the wooden walls had had their day, and public opinion, hitherto so hesitant, at last came to see that the ironclad was the only possible warship of the future. The French ships were protected by 4½-inch iron plates with a wooden backing 17 inches thick, and this seemed to be the pattern for the future.

Britain hurriedly replied by constructing four armored steamers, *Trusty*, *Thunder*, *Glatton*, and *Meteor*, which were direct copies of the French Kinburn flotilla; but in 1856, improvements were introduced and the first iron-hulled, armored, steam-driven warships in the world were completed—*Thunderbolt*, *Terror*, *Aetna*, and *Erebus*. Though for years Britain's "comfortable faith in her wooden fleet," as one historian has put it, had persisted, her commercial interests had led her to build iron ships for foreign countries, notably light-draft gunboats for Russia, as early as 1850, for use in shallow water only and certainly not envisaged as offensive warships for use on the open sea. When the Baltic part of the Russian War proved inconclusive in its early stages, with the failure to reduce Cronstadt, it seemed clear that there was little to be gained by sending the old ships of the line on such missions, and it was decided to build a number of small gunboats. By the autumn of 1855, sixteen of these were ready to join the French fleet in the bombardment of Sveaborg in Finland, and it is worth noting the tremendous capacity of the shipbuilding industry in Britain at this stage of the industrial revolution: for example, Messrs. Penn of Greenwich contracted to build eighty sets of main engines in three months and succeeded in doing so through distributing duplicate patterns and contracting the work out among firms up and down the country.

But we must return to the French navy, because it was in France that the lessons of Sinope and Kinburn were really learned. After 1855, not one wooden ship of the line was laid down, and the French Admiralty was inundated with new ideas and projects, many of which were tried out and accepted. The emperor himself took a personal interest, especially in questions relating to gunnery in ships; but Dupuy de Lôme, who became Directeur du Matériel, the key position in the Ministry of Marine, in 1857 is the outstanding figure. As far back as 1845, he had advocated a 28-gun ironclad with a 600-horsepower engine; but in the late 1840's, the time was not ripe for it, as there was still the feeling that persisted so long in England that iron was not sufficiently durable and would anyway be too susceptible to fouling. Also, the political crises associated with the overthrow of the Orléanist monarchy and the short-lived Second Republic brought with them a need for economy.

After the Crimean War, however, things were different. Napoleon III was firmly established, and France became the first country to own anything approaching an ironclad fleet. *Gloire*, completed in November, 1859, is the symbol of this advance. But it is worth noting that Dupuy de Lôme argued that it would be unwise to concentrate on one type of ironclad only, so three "frigates," as they were rather misleadingly called, were laid down in all, *Gloire* and *Invincible* at Toulon and *Couronne*, an iron-hulled ship unlike the other two, at Lorient. A little later, four more ironclad frigates were laid down, the *Normandie* at Cherbourg and the others at Toulon and Brest.

Dupuy de Lôme maintained that *Gloire* was an entirely new ship. He says this specifically in the autobiographical sketch he submitted when applying to join the Académie des Sciences in 1866. This probably just means that she was not merely an adaptation of his *Napoléon* with one deck less, but that her wooden hull was intentionally redesigned to carry a 4¾-inch belt of armor around the waterline. She and her sister ships were armed with thirty-six 50-pound guns, and their engines were designed to give a speed of 12 knots. In the summer of 1860, she conveyed the emperor and empress to Algiers, making 11 knots and using only half her engine power and not resorting to her sails at all.

To outward appearances, she was a three-masted sailing ship still, though, in fact, her sailing equipment was not intended to be more than an auxiliary means of propulsion.

After the Crimean War, British relations with France, never very cordial, broke down under the strain of the peace treaty. There was the feeling at that time when wars had not yet become ideological that France and Russia might soon combine and provide Britain with a formidable adversary in the next war. Something very like panic had broken out by the early 1860's, though Cobden and Gladstone thought this French scare merely a more successful hoax than the Popish Plot. Yet Palmerston had some justification for suspecting Napoleon III for his annexation of Nice and Savoy as a reward for his aid to the House of Piedmont and for his uncomfortable way of referring to the Mediterranean as a European lake.

British naval policy included the axiom that Britain should never take the initiative in the development of warships but rather that she should counter the inventions of others with something better. This policy had allowed France to attain parity in fast screw-propelled ships of the line, but the launching of *Gloire* and her sister ships made more definite action necessary. A Parliamentary committee was set up to examine the relative strengths of the two navies, and it reported early in 1859, recommending that Britain should accelerate the conversion of her remaining sailing ships to steam and go into the whole question of ironclad vessels.

The result was the *Warrior*, laid down in June, 1859, the first large iron-hulled ironclad fighting ship. She was not, however, launched till December, 1860, because work was delayed owing to the generally held belief that iron would foul rapidly and that, in action, splintering and the difficulty of plugging up holes would prove serious handicaps to efficiency. Eventually, even such formidable opponents of the ironclad as General Sir Howard Douglas were won over, and this ship marks the beginning of a new phase in which the all-iron capital ship is the accepted large fighting unit, for *Warrior* can be seen as the first true ironclad battleship.

Superficially, she looked very like most contemporary clippers, but she was very long, 380 feet, and her 1,250-horsepower engine enabled her to make 14½ knots. Her 4½-inch armor plating backed with teak was confined to the waterline and amidships, but at bow and stern she was unprotected, and these extremities were divided into watertight compartments. Yet, although *Warrior* was the prototype of a new development in warships, there was, besides her masts and rigging, another link with the past: the broadside position of her armament. A sister ship, the *Black Prince,* originally *Invincible,* was built on the Clyde and was commissioned in June, 1862.

Though a number of other ironclads were launched in the early 1860's, there was a general feeling of frustration at the slowness of progress—"hobbling after the French," as the Prince Consort said—especially as the Russians were beginning to build ironclads too. Nevertheless, there was an understandable reluctance in certain quarters to order too many large ironclads until at least the *Warrior's* trials had taken place. Lord Charles Paget voiced the opinion of many when he said in Parliament[1] that the bottoms of vessels would become so fouled after any length of time in equatorial waters that they would resemble lawyers' wigs. Early in 1861, Robinson, the new Comptroller of the Navy, criticized the view that Britain should never take the lead, but Gladstone, then Chancellor of the Exchequer, with his eyes on the purse strings, was hesitant about demanding a supplementary £3,000,000 within a few weeks of the submission of the annual estimates. He advocated instead a return to the conversion of wooden-hulled ships into ironclads.

Yet very soon it was clear that France had forced Britain into taking further and more drastic action. *Caledonia, Ocean, Prince Consort,* and *Royal Alfred,* all wooden ships, were ordered to be prepared for iron plating in 1860. They mark the first stage and were soon to be followed by parliamentary acceptance of the construction of six new iron ships. Palmerston's fears that unprotected extremities would, when smashed, reduce ships to mere boxes "floating on the water . . . water-logged and . . . comparatively unmanageable" were allayed. *Minotaur, Agincourt, Northumberland,* the longest and largest single-screw fighting ships ever built, belong to this group. They were the only steamships to have five masts.

We must now turn to the United States, for the famous clash between the *Monitor* and the *Merrimack* at Hampton Roads on March 8–9, 1862, was to be another milestone in the history of the fighting ship. It is not true, however, to say that this exciting event converted Europeans to the necessity of the ironclad warship; it really only convinced the general public of a fact that experts had already come to accept. Nor is it true to imagine that the Union Navy Department had ignored ironclad ships before the Civil War. Lincoln had, in fact, been inundated with proposals, and three ironclads had already been begun and plans for a further twenty at the cost of $12,000,000 had passed through Congress by the time the Hampton Roads incident took place. These vessels were intended for the task of blockading the 3,500 miles of coastline.

Also, in July, 1861, a bill had been introduced ordering the Secretary of the Navy to appoint a board of three skillful naval officers to investigate plans for constructing steam batteries. This bill became law and resulted in the *Galena* and the *New Ironsides*, as well as *Monitor*, John Ericsson's vessel, capable of being built in ten weeks for "scouring the Southern rivers and inlets of all craft protected by the rebel batteries." Lincoln was distinctly interested, though Commander Charles H. Davis of the above-mentioned board had pungent things to say about the experiment. The story goes, according to Bushnell, that Ericsson was told he "might take the little thing home and worship it, as it would not be idolatry, because it was made in the image of nothing in the heaven above, or in the earth below, or in the waters under the earth."[2] It seems, then, that by early 1862 the Navy Department was beyond the stage of hesitating between wooden and armored ships and had even got as far as deciding between the English system of turreted ship, that of Cowper Coles, and Ericsson's independently arrived at scheme.

It is, however, true to say that no ironclad ship was completed before the Civil War broke out and that such early inventions as the Stevens' battery, accepted in principle as far back as 1842 by a special committee of Congress, failed to sell even after 1862. "The Slaughter Pen," General Abner Doubleday's name for Captain John Randolph Hamilton's crude floating battery of 1861, is a characteristic comment, in tune with the feelings of the time, but these details must not obscure the fact that new inventions were being made and accepted: how else could *Merrimack* and *Monitor* have appeared when they did?

The circumstances of the battle at Hampton Roads, the outlet of the long estuary of the Appomattox River in Virginia, can be quickly told, as we are not concerned here with more than the barest details. When the federal government abandoned the navy yard at Norfolk, Virginia, in April, 1861, stores and shipping that could not be moved were ordered to be destroyed. The frigate *Merrimack* was one of these ships. She was, however, salvaged and repaired by the Confederates and re-named the *Virginia*, though there is controversy about her actual designer. Porter, Williamson, and Brooke certainly worked closely together on her, but the idea of inclined armor on an ironclad, her most remarkable feature perhaps, was quite an old one.

At all events, a steam engine was refitted and a low penthouse of teak was built over the whole deck. This was covered with two separate layers of iron hammered into 2-inch plates, and each was riveted trans-versely, so that the whole became an armored shelter 4 inches thick. *Merrimack* had also a heavy ram fastened to her prow and a battery of ten 7-inch rifled guns firing through portholes in the side of the pent-house. Only two days after she was completed—and, indeed, before there had been time for any trials—*Merrimack* went into action on March 8, 1862. She engaged *Cumberland* and *Congress*, the two nearest federal ships that were blockading the York and James rivers. In spite of broadsides from these two ships and a concentration of fire from all the shore batteries, she rammed the *Cumberland* almost at right angles, causing her to heel over and sink; and at 200-yard range, she fired on the *Congress* so effectively that the latter soon capitulated.

A third federal ship, *Minnesota*, might have been attacked likewise, but the ebb tide saved her, and the next day the situation changed. Ericsson's much-talked-of *Monitor* came onto the scene and protected *Minnesota*. As Sir Winston Churchill has written, " . . . the *Merrimack* had made the naval revolution, but the *Monitor*, one day later, was a whole lap ahead of her."[3] This strange vessel, as we have noted above, was one of three of a kind. Her keel was laid down at Green Point, Brooklyn, by Thomas F. Rowlands in October, 1861, and she was ready for the sea in a hundred days. She had only two 11-inch Dahlgren guns, but they were mounted in a circular revolving iron turret, 9 inches thick, which served also as a conning tower. Her heavily protected deck was only a few inches above water, and she drew only 12 feet of water; and she was described with some justification, as "a cheesebox on a raft."

The *Merrimack* approached her, and for six hours these two new warships fought each other with hardly any advantage on either side. At the end of the day, both withdrew, never to meet again, and the war moved on into another phase. When later on the Confederates had to evacuate Norfolk, it proved impossible to take *Merrimack* up the James River, so Flag Officer Josiah Tattnall ordered her to be burned and sunk, "a sorry ending," as Professor Baxter (see footnote 2 and bibliography) has written, "for the first ship to prove in action the truth of Dupuy de Lôme's proud boast that a single ironclad in the midst of a hostile wooden fleet would resemble a lion amid a flock of sheep."

This was in May, 1862, but *Monitor* survived very little longer than her rival. She was lost at sea in the following December, showing her limitations the first time she met a gale. Of her sister ships, *Galena* was proved to be "a most miserable contrivance—entirely beneath naval criticism" and not even shotproof, but the *New Ironsides*, built at Philadelphia by Merrick and Sons and commissioned in August, 1862, was a success with her 18 heavy guns, and she took a greater part in action than any other ironclad. Moreover, she proved to be a good example of the "belt-and-battery" class of warship that we must now consider.

One of the several results of Hampton Roads was the realization by naval experts everywhere, if they were not already aware of it, that naval guns must be improved and their actual position in ships more seriously considered. Adoption of armor protection had met the particular menace of the shell-firing gun; it was now necessary for the gun, the offensive weapon, to counter the temporary advantage the defense had gained. Certainly also, "ahead fire" was needed more and more now that steam had given ships more free movement. Though it was never intended to abandon broadside firing, its weakness was that it was not feasible for technical reasons concerning seaworthiness to protect the complete length of a ship's side with sufficiently thick armor. The answer, therefore, was to have the guns concentrated amidships and to equip this armored "citadel" with more powerful guns to compensate for their smaller number.

Thus the invention of the revolving turret, *Monitor's* great practical contribution, can be seen as a natural development, and we shall return to the point that it was also being pioneered in Britain independently of Ericsson's successes in America. Also, there was the question of improving the arc of fire: the revolving turret presented the obvious solution and one that was, in fact, to be generally adopted; but until masts and rigging had been finally abandoned, there were formidable drawbacks to its introduction. Between 1860 and 1880, however, many suggestions were being tried out, such as indenting the sides of ships so guns placed forward could fire, though on a limited arc, in the direction the ship was moving. Other ideas were gun positions in transverse bulkheads for firing ahead, sponsons, that is, circular projecting platforms allowing a 180-degree field of fire, and, above all, the central battery. This last, especially later on when combined with the revolving turret, gave great scope for further refinements: it could be octagonal in shape, or, as the French tried, it could allow the guns to be mounted *en caponnière,* in overhung circular turntables at each corner of the central battery. The *Minotaur* class, begun in 1861, seems to have contained the germ of the central battery, but the development of the idea was accelerated by the French: the two wooden ships *Magenta* and *Solferino,* laid down in 1859, each had a two-decked central battery armored to protect her fifty-two 5-ton cannon, the remaining part of the ship's waterline being protected by only a very narrow belt.

In 1863, Edward Reed was appointed Chief Constructor of the British Navy. His first ships showed new developments, as can be seen in the *Bellerophon.* She was a fully rigged belt-and-battery ship, with ten 12-ton Armstrong guns for broadside fire but also two 6-ton guns for ahead fire in another armored battery in the bow. His next ship, the *Enterprise,* carried the innovation further by including bow fire from the central battery. In his next two, *Pallas* and *Penelope,* indentation of the sides gave the corner guns of the battery a greater arc of fire. *Hercules,* the next to follow, was very like *Bellerophon,* but she had indented sides and alternative ports for corner guns so that they could fire either on the beam or nearly in line with the keel. There were technical difficulties here, but in the later *Kaiser* class, which Reed designed for Germany, muzzle-pivoting guns and ports in facets placed at 45 degrees with the keel line largely surmounted them.

Reed's *Audacious* class, of which the best known are the *Iron Duke* and the *Vanguard,* was the result of the British Admiralty's decision in 1868 to invite shipbuilders to compete. In these ships, there were two central batteries of the same size, one superimposed on the other, and the arc of fire was improved greatly by such devices as the ports cut in armored facets and an adaptation of the sponson. *Alexandra*, laid down in 1872 and commissioned in 1877, was the last purely central battery ironclad; formidable as she was, with her ability to provide end-on fire as well as broadside, and though she was able to give as complete an all-round fire as was possible in a central battery, there were distinct disadvantages—especially as, with the abandonment of masts and rigging, the turret was beginning to be seen as a really practical proposition.

We have seen the outcome of John Ericsson's invention of the turret in America, so we must now look at the part played by Cowper Coles in Great Britain at about the same time. This naval officer had been flag lieutenant to Sir Edward Lyons in *Agamemnon* but had soon been promoted to his own command. He distinguished himself when, in the spring of 1855, he built a raft capable of bearing a 68-pounder gun on a centrally pivoted platform protected by a dish-cover-like shield that he called a cupola. This raft, the *Lady Nancy*, was designed for being towed and then anchored so as to attack shore positions from water too shallow for ordinary ships. She successfully destroyed Russian stores at Taganrog, and this led her inventor to turn his hand to designing other shallow-draft vessels, with protected artillery. From this, it was an easy stage to the turret, or cupola, especially as Brunel gave Coles technical assistance. In 1861 a two-turreted gunboat, the *Rolf Krake*, was built privately for Denmark, with two 68-pounder guns in each turret and Prussia, Russia, Holland, and even Brazil were ordering turreted ships.

There were two other ironclad turreted ships built in Britain, which were accidentally acquired by the British Navy in 1863. Originally, they had been built by Laird's at Birkenhead and were intended to follow the *Alabama* across the Atlantic to join the Confederates. They appeared, however, to be destined for the Pasha of Egypt, to judge from their names, *El Toussan* and *El Mounassir*. That they should hoist the Confederate flag on leaving British territorial waters was tantamount to an act of war, so the Admiralty acquired the ships instead. They had continuous armor belts and two turrets amidships, each containing a pair of 68-pounders. They were also bark-rigged and very seaworthy and had tripod masts, that is, wooden struts instead of shrouds, so that the turret guns would not be covered up. Their names were changed to *Scorpion* and *Wivern*.

Eventually, the British Admiralty decided to try out turret ships. The *Royal Sovereign*, the sixth ship of this name, converted from a three-decker and completed in 1864, was, in fact, the only wooden-hulled turreted warship in the British fleet. There were four center-line turrets, but neither she nor the iron-hulled, four-turreted *Prince Albert*, ready for service by 1866, was really an oceangoing ship—their bunkers carried coal for only about three days' steaming from a home base. *Monarch*, designed by Reed, was tested out against the *Bellerophon* and *Hercules* in 1869 and proved herself to be efficient, though Cowper Coles disapproved of her design, thinking that it missed the real point of a turret—easy all-round fire. He was, however, able to persuade the Admiralty to finance the construction by Laird's of a ship of his own design. This was to be the unlucky *Captain*, launched in 1869. Like *Scorpion* and *Wivern*, there were tripod masts, for *Captain* was still fully rigged; but owing to a constructional error, her 8-foot freeboard, suspected by many to be too little for her great height above the waterline, proved to be only 6 feet. Though she acquitted herself surprisingly well on her trials, she capsized off Cape Finisterre in a storm in September, 1870, with the loss of nearly five hundred men, including Coles himself.

The best memorial to the ingenuity and determination of this gallant naval officer is that in spite of this disaster, which affected public opinion very considerably, as might be expected, the idea of the turreted warship was not discarded. A committee of design reported in 1871 that sail in line-of-battle ships should be completely given up and that the *Devastation*, then in process of building, was the best type of fighting ship possible. The incorporation of the double-screw propeller had helped to build up this complete confidence in steam as the sole means of propulsion.

Devastation can be considered the first really modern battleship. She was steam-driven, she had an iron hull, she was armored, she had no mast and sails, and her guns were mounted in a turret and not broadside. Steam, in fact, had at last accommodated itself to the line-of-battle ship, "leaving her in all respects perfect as before," as was said by a contemporary, "her noble broadsides clear and unencumbered." She had four muzzle-loading 12-inch guns, each weighing 35 tons and sited in two turrets on the center line, one at each end of a central breastwork, 150 feet long, built around the funnels. The shells she fired weighed 700 pounds, and the details of this armament show that the increase in size since the 1860's was spectacular. It was due to the introduction of forging, instead of casting, iron—a fact that posed its own problems: concentration of weight and the consequent greater violence of recoil, the need for reducing the number of guns in any ship and therefore the allocation of extra work to the guns that could be carried.

Another problem was the necessity of making such ships really oceangoing; that is, quite apart from other considerations, they had to be able to take a much greater quantity of coal if they were going to be anything other than mere coastal-defense vessels, and they had to have improved berthing accommodation for the crews. *Devastation* had bunkerage for 1,800 tons of coal, which was more than double the capacity of any contemporary battleship—and any to come for fifteen years— except her own sister ship *Thunderer*. When her original engines were replaced with triple expansion machinery and cylindrical boilers that could supply steam at 60 pounds, she could cross the Atlantic and return without coaling.

This great armored ship, with her turrets protected with plating 12 to 14 inches thick throughout, was completed at the end of 1872. Her first captain, Hewett, one of the first recipients of the Victoria Cross in the Crimean War, found her a good seagoing vessel, though hard to drive against a head gale because she had too little freeboard in the bows. She was in the eastern Mediterranean during the Russo-Turkish War during the late 1870's but thereafter saw little service away from the British Isles. Indeed, between 1895 and 1902, she was port guard ship at Plymouth and then Gibraltar and was finally sold for breaking up in 1908.[4]

Her sister ships, *Thunderer* and *Dreadnought,* were laid down soon after with minor variations, but they need not detain us long here, as the main point to be established is that all these British warships of the early 1870's show a movement away from the *Monitor* type of warship, lying very low in the water, toward the modern design in which a high freeboard made the ship steadier and more easily propelled and at the same time more habitable. *Thunderer* and *Dreadnought* had externally loaded guns worked by the recently introduced Armstrong hydraulic system, and their turrets were steam-revolving. A misfire and the consequent overloading caused an explosion in *Thunderer* in 1879, a disastrous incident that led in the end to the reintroduction of breech-loading mechanism.

It will be remembered that British policy during the nineteenth century was not to take the initiative in introducing new measures in ship design but to improve on those introduced by others. Consequently, two ships laid down in 1872 and 1873, respectively, to the designs of Benedetto Brin were responsible for further British developments in the big-gun warship. These Italian ships *Duilio* and *Dandolo* had two diagonally placed turrets designed to carry two 60-ton Armstrong guns each, though these were later changed to 100-ton 17¾-inch guns after Britain had replied with the *Inflexible*. This ship, laid down in 1874 but not commissioned till 1881, had two turrets, weighing 750 tons each, on a central armored "citadel" plated with 24-inch compound armor but was virtually unarmored elsewhere, like the two Italian ships. She was perhaps the heaviest and most powerful warship ever built, and she was 320 feet long and, because of the height of her turrets, 75 feet broad at the waterline. After she had been built, improved methods of manufacturing steel plating enabled reductions to be made in weight, while protective capacity actually increased. She was brig-rigged at first, in spite of her forty-eight separate engines, but the masts were fitted in such a way that they could be abandoned easily. In fact, her sailing equipment was never needed either to steady her at sea or to remedy any breakdown, so it was felt that an error had been made on the side of caution and that *Inflexible*, in fact, vindicated the sole reliance on engines that had been the most important feature in *Devastation*.

The British Admiralty was very concerned with the inefficiency of heavy guns in the 1870's. There had been tests in Portland Harbor in 1872 during which, even in such calm waters, the *Hotspur* had had great difficulty in hitting the turret of the *Glatton* even at 200 yards. This merely proved that Captain Colomb's unflattering analysis of the gunpower of the *Monarch* off Vigo the year before was a truer picture of the situation than was comfortable. It can be seen that during the 1870's, experience was bringing about a gradual change in the general view of what a modern battleship should be like. The use and actual positioning of armor especially aroused controversy. Some thought that inadequate armor—and the rapid evolution of the naval gun made this increasingly likely—was worse than no armor at all and advocated saving weight for offensive action by abandoning the armored citadel as seen in *Inflexible*. Others, however, thought that this would encourage the enemy to increase the number of machine guns on board. The French persisted in retaining the complete waterline belt of armor protection, while the Italians, as can be seen in *Italia* and *Lepanto*, preferred protective decks and no waterline armor at all.

Meanwhile, other devices were beginning to affect the design and, indeed, function of warships. The torpedo, the mine, and the development of the submarine are the items which concern us most, and they will be considered in the next chapter. First, however, the battleship *Collingwood* must be mentioned, because this type of ship, emerging in the 1880's, remained in favor long enough to become the basis of many classes of warships in the future and so can be a convenient point at which to end this long account of the development of the ironclad.

Captain Cooper Key had set down his specifications for a first-class battleship as early as 1866. These included moderate speed, handiness, protection of vital parts with armor, a waterline protective belt, an upper-deck armament of four large guns in two unarmored barbettes, and a main-deck armament of medium broadside guns amidships. The French ship, *Caiman*, laid down in 1878, had something of this ideal vessel in her, and so by the time Cooper Key joined the Board of Admiralty, a similar ship, the *Collingwood*, had actually been laid down in Britain. She had Key's particular disposition of guns, two at bow and two at stern, on turntables, with broadside guns between them amidships. Key, who had flown his flag in the *Thunderer* in 1878, had experienced at firsthand her successful performance without sail, as well as the reliability of her guns. He was therefore already reconciled to the abandonment of sail propulsion even as an auxiliary.

Collingwood was a great advance on the citadel type of ship, such as *Inflexible*. Four more ships like her were laid down in 1882, and these five ships, the largest number of first-class ironclads to date to be on the stocks at the same time, formed the *Admiral* class. They were, in fact, the first example of a class of ships being laid down at about the same time and to the same specifications, which becomes such a familiar feature of all naval programs after this date. It was, however, only practicable to do this when some agreement had been reached about the permanency of certain designs. We are apt to forget that the technical advances in engineering, gun design, and naval architecture generally were so rapid in the period from the end of the Crimean War onward that the effect on the planners can have been little less than utterly bewildering. The atmosphere, as well as something of the exasperation a taxpayer might feel about it all, is admirably conveyed to us by Walter Bagehot:

> First the Admiralty took away some money [he writes, rather waspishly] with which it made wooden ships; and then it discovered its error, and acknowledged that wooden sailing ships were useless; so it asked for additional money and made wooden *steam*-ships with much *éclat*. And I for one was convinced it would be all right, and that England was now safe. But in less than a year the Admiralty discovered its error again, and pronounced all wooden ships, whether steam or sailing ships, to be useless; so it abstracted further money and constructed "iron-plated ships," the *Warrior* and that sort of thing, which cost almost fabulous sums apiece; and now "the Admiralty is discovering its error" again, or something like it, for it wants more money, and is making what I must call naval *nondescripts*—a sort of *Merrimacs* and *Monitors*—things more like an ugly insect than a ship.[5]

NOTES

[1]See *Hansard*, Mar. 11, 1861.
[2]James P. Baxter, *The Introduction of the Ironclad Warship*, p. 256.
[3]Winston S. Churchill, *History of the English-speaking Peoples*, Cassell, London, vol. iv, p. 159.
[4]See G. A. Ballard, article on the *Devastation* in *The Mariner's Mirror*, 1946, vol. xxxii, pp. 2–20.
[5]Walter Bagehot, *The Works of Walter Bagehot*, vol. iv, pp. 41–42.

HMS *Victoria*, launched in 1859, was the last wooden three-decker first-rate to serve at sea. She was flagship in the Mediterranean from 1864–1867 and was sold in 1893. This photograph was taken at Malta (*c.* 1865). *National Maritime Museum, Greenwich*

(Right) Britain's first armored battleship *Warrior* was built in 1860 to meet the challenge of *Gloire*. She was built entirely of iron (her sides were 4½ inches thick and backed by 18 inches of teak), and she had a speed under steam of 14 knots. Her original armament was twenty-six 68-pounder smooth-bore muzzle-loaders and ten 110-pounder and four 70-pounder smooth-bore breech-loaders, but in 1867 these were changed to twenty-eight 7-inch and four 8-inch rifled muzzle-loaders and four 20-pounder breech-loaders. This photograph, taken at Plymouth, can be dated to before 1864, as *Warrior* is not yet flying the white ensign universally adopted in the Royal Navy in that year. In the background on the right can be seen the wooden two-decker *Implacable*. *Warrior* not only was the first armored British battleship, but also can claim to be the last afloat, as she is now the oil-pipeline jetty at Pembroke. *National Maritime Museum, Greenwich*

(Left) The French ironclad battleship *Gloire,* built at Toulon in 1859, from a colored lithograph by Le Breton. She and her sister ships *Invincible* and *Couronne* were armed with thirty-six 50-pounder guns and had a 4¾-inch belt of armor at the waterline. Outwardly, she still appeared to be a traditional three-master, but her sailing equipment was planned to be subsidiary to her engines. *National Maritime Museum, Greenwich*

The battle between the 2-gun federal ship *Monitor* and the 10-gun Confederate ship *Merrimack* at Hampton Roads, near Norfolk, Virginia, on March 9, 1862, during the Civil War. Lithograph by Kurz and Allison. *Culver Pictures, Inc., New York*

A closer view of the first conflict between ironclad warships at the Battle of Hampton Roads, from a lithograph by Currier and Ives. The ability of the tiny *Monitor*, a mere "cheesebox on a raft," to stand up to the larger *Merrimack* for six hours did much to justify the adoption of Ericsson's revolving turret. *The Bettmann Archive, Inc., New York*

Oil painting by William Heysham Overend of a scene aboard Farragut's flagship *Hartford* during the Battle of Mobile Bay, August 5, 1864. The Confederate ship on the right of the picture is probably the *Tennessee*. *Brown Brothers, New York*

(Left) Painting of the United States steam sloop *Hartford*, Admiral David G. Farragut's flagship at the Battle of Mobile Bay, August 5, 1864. In spite of a federal blockade from 1861 onward, Confederate vessels continued to trade with the West Indies until Farragut entered the channel and captured the ironclad ram *Tennessee*. The city did not, however, fall until a year later. *Peabody Museum of Salem*

(Above) HMS *Minotaur* (1863), one of the three five-masters of the mid-nineteenth century Royal Navy, from a colored lithograph by T. C. Dutton, published 1867. With her sister ships *Agincourt* and *Northumberland*, she was the longest and largest single-screw fighting ship, but their great expanse of canvas and lack of steam-assisted steering gear made them poor sailers and very soon obsolete. *National Maritime Museum, Greenwich*

(Top left) Lithograph of the federal ship *New Ironsides* off Philadelphia by W. H. Rease. This ship was built in 1862 and, unlike her sister ship *Galena*, turned out to be a great success and was a good example of the "belt and battery" class of warship. *National Maritime Museum, Greenwich*

(Left) HMS *Majestic* keeping watch over the double-turret steam rams *El Toussan* and *El Mounassir*. These ships were built by Laird's at Birkenhead for the Confederates in 1863, though ostensibly they were destined for the Pasha of Egypt. They were later seized by the Admiralty and renamed *Scorpion* and *Wivern*. *Photograph by National Maritime Museum, Greenwich, from the* Illustrated London News, *1863*

(Left) HMS *Agincourt* (see previous plate), sister ship of the *Minotaur* and *Northumberland*, launched 1865. Chiefly used as a flagship, she was converted into a coal hulk in 1908 and was towed to the breakers on Trafalgar Day, 1961, the day the first British atomic submarine, *Dreadnought,* was launched. *Photograph, Imperial War Museum, London; National Maritime Museum, Greenwich*

The first French armored coastal-defense vessel, *Taureau* (1865). She was designed by Dupuy de Lôme. Colored lithograph by Morel-Fatio. *National Maritime Museum, Greenwich*

(Above) The United States ram ship *Dictator* (1863), from a contemporary lithograph. *Science Museum, London*

The Battle of Lissa, in the Adriatic, July 20, 1866, was the first engagement on the open sea in which modern ironclad warships took part. The sinking by the Austrians of the Italian ships *Re d'Italia* and *Re di Portogallo*, the latter by ramming, seemed to suggest that the ram would become a weapon of some importance in sea warfare. *From the drawing and lithograph by C. Leduc.*

The British turret-ship *Cyclops* (1871), intended for coastal defense. Lithograph by T. G. Dutton, published 1873. *National Maritime Museum, Greenwich*

HMS *Alexandra*, launched in 1875, the last "central battery" battleship to be built. She was one of the last to have a sailing rig. This photograph, taken at Malta after 1886, shows her painted white at the request of the commander in chief, HRH Prince Alfred, Duke of Edinburgh. She was mainly used as a flagship. *National Maritime Museum, Greenwich*

(Left) HMS *Devastation,* launched in 1871, lithograph by T. G. Dutton, published 1876. She was the first really modern British battleship, as she was steam-driven, had an iron hull, was armored (sides 12 inches, turrets 14 inches with 18-inch teak backing), and had four 12-inch rifled muzzle-loaders in her two turrets. Above all, she was the first "mastless" battleship to join the fleet, showing that complete confidence had at last been placed in her engines. *National Maritime Museum, Greenwich*

The Russian coastal-defense ship *Novgorod*, from an engraving in the *Illustrated London News* (1876). This circular ship, diameter 101 feet, was launched in 1873 and was one of the *popoffkas*, named after their designer, Admiral Popoff. She had six propellers and two 11-inch guns. *National Maritime Museum, Greenwich*

HMS *Inflexible,* launched in 1876, "perhaps the heaviest armored and most powerful warship ever built." Her four 16-inch guns were the biggest ever put into any ship. This photograph, taken at Malta, shows her with her original sailing rig, which was replaced with pole masts and fighting tops in 1885. *National Maritime Museum, Greenwich; Photographer, Captain T. D. Manning*

German turreted battleship *Friedrich der Grosse*, launched in 1874. Her armament included four 26-centimeter 18-ton Krupp guns. *Imperial War Museum, London*

HMS *Royal Sovereign*, launched in 1891, gave her name to a class of seven battleships. Her design, which included a return to the high freeboard, was so successful that it established a general pattern that lasted until *Dreadnought* was built in 1906. *Photograph Imperial War Museum and National Maritime Museum, Greenwich*

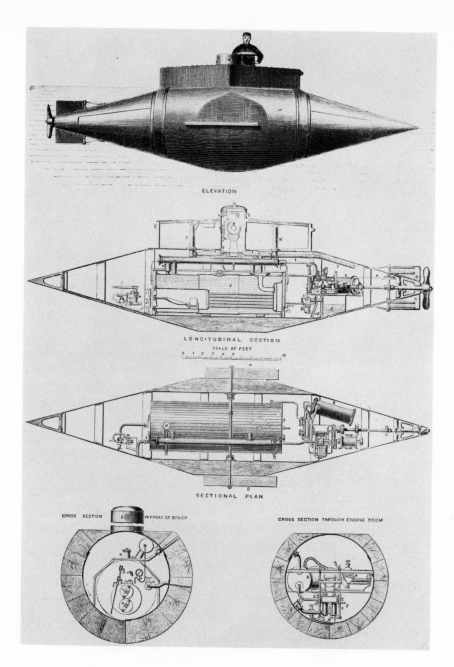

ELEVATION

LONGITUDINAL SECTION

SCALE OF FEET

SECTIONAL PLAN

CROSS SECTION IN FRONT OF BOILER

CROSS SECTION THROUGH ENGINE ROOM

Diagram of *Resurgam*. *Science Museum, London*

X

Early Submarines, Destroyers, and Cruisers

LET US NOW consider the mine and the torpedo and their effect on the warship, since the introduction and development of these devices led to considerable changes in the whole technique of sea warfare as well as to the introduction of entirely new classes of warships.

The mine and the torpedo are very closely connected—indeed, the first mines to block a sea-lane in war were actually called "torpedoes." This was in the Baltic in 1855, and these Russian mines were cone-shaped canisters made of zinc, 2 feet deep and 18 inches wide, containing charges of gunpowder and tubular glass detonators filled with acid that broke on being struck. Luckily for the British squadron, the mines were small, or they might have caused more serious damage than they did. The modern torpedo differs, of course, from the mine in that it is not stationary but travels to its destination. Yet in spite of this difference, it can be thought of as a moving mine, automatically propelled, though not from the muzzle of a gun, and like the mine, its intention is to detonate explosives against the underparts of ships.

The old "explosion vessel" may be the ancestor of the torpedo, but a very much closer relative is the device which was attached to Bushnell's submarine and which nearly destroyed *Eagle*, Howe's flagship, in 1776. A particular problem was how to enable it to reach its destination unseen and unsuspected. Among the various methods tried in the second half of the nineteenth century, there was the pole projecting from the bow of a ship carrying the explosive at its extremity. This was lowered on a wire after arrival and detonated by pulling a string, and it was by this means that Lieutenant Cushing sank the Confederate ironclad *Albemarle* in 1864. The British "Harvey" torpedo of 1869 was dragged by a small boat in such a way that it did not follow directly astern but diverged and so hit its mark. This method required the cover of darkness, which brought its own problems, such as the risk of fouling the towing cable on small boats lying alongside the victim. Again, the Australian "Brennan" device involved great lengths of very fine wire, which was difficult to handle on board, so it was used only from the shore and was thus the precursor of the wireless-controlled torpedo.

Captain Luppis of the Austrian navy deserves the credit for the invention of the locomotive torpedo, but Robert Whitehead, a Scottish engineer, collaborated with him. Crude though their 1866 torpedo was, it traveled submerged and was therefore comparatively invisible. It was propelled by compressed air and so, for the first time, could reach its target under its own power. Later, Whitehead refined his original model by introducing two screws that revolved in opposite directions so as to correct directional errors.

In 1877, the first Whitehead torpedo to be fired in action proved to be unspectacular. The British frigate *Shah* attacked the rebel Peruvian monitor *Huascar* ahead of her, but *Huascar* was easily able to change course. The lesson learned on this occasion was that, with the limited range of only 600 yards over which a torpedo could travel and with its lack of pace, avoiding action was comparatively easy.

The first success was in 1878 when the Russians sank a Turkish ship in Batum Harbor, scoring two direct hits at 80-yard range. But even as late as the Russo-Japanese War a quarter of a century later, the torpedo had not really proved itself. Apparently only about 4 per cent of those fired by the Japanese hit their targets.

The first torpedo boat with a revolving launching tube was the *Lightning* of 1877, carrying one Whitehead torpedo; though some years earlier, *Miranda*, a light river launch, can perhaps claim to be the pioneer in this class of vessel. Professor Lewis says that the real descendants of *Lightning* and *Miranda* were the motor launches and coastal motorboats of the First World War and the motor torpedo boats and motor gunboats of the Second,[1] but we must note that torpedo tubes could be fitted to any of the older types of ships. Since, however, the requirements were speed, elusiveness, and even invisibility, if possible, for surprise was of paramount importance in their tactical use, it was inevitable that a new type of ship would soon be evolved.

There was also an incentive to develop a ship to deal with the torpedo boat, so the next new type to appear was the torpedo-boat destroyer, a name soon shortened to "destroyer." *Havock*, completed in 1893 and the first of the *Daring* class, was also the first British destroyer and was capable of 26 knots. She had an armament of one 12-pounder and three 6-pounder guns and three torpedo tubes. These vessels were intended to be speedy, and *Viper*, completed in 1899, achieved 34 knots and was the first British warship to have steam turbines, a new development dramatically demonstrated first by Charles Parsons' Marine Steam Turbine Company's *Turbinia* at the naval review held in honor of Queen Victoria's Diamond Jubilee in 1897. Destroyers gradually became stronger, more seaworthy, and more habitable; and it was soon clear that a magnificent new warship had come into being, handy, ready for a variety of tasks, a modern version of those frigates described by Nelson as the eyes of the fleet.

By 1900, the principle of the submarine was generally accepted as a weapon of naval attack. Many inventors had been working on it, and among them stand out Lake of the United States and Goubet of France and especially John Philip Holland, also from the United States, though born in Ireland. As we have seen so often before, the basic idea was already several centuries old. As far back as 1578, William Bourne had outlined the principles of positive and negative buoyancy in *The Treasure for Travellers*, and he seems to have been the first man to understand how to make a boat dive. But if Bourne was the pioneer of the theory, we do not know whether any boat of his actually put it to the test. This honor must go to Cornelius van Drebbel, whose boat made a successful journey from Westminster to Greenwich and was watched by King James I. There were other experiments in the seventeenth and eighteenth century, but the Americans David Bushnell and Robert Fulton are the real fathers of the modern submarine. Bushnell realized that the pressure of water increased with depth and also that gunpowder exploded more effectively underwater than in the open air, two very important discoveries. One of his first boats might have sunk Howe's flagship, *Eagle*, in 1776, had she not been sufficiently protected by her copper sheathing, and a later model nearly succeeded against Hardy's *Ramillies* in 1812.

It is interesting to see what Bushnell's device was. Basically the idea was simple: a one-man submarine traveled submerged so as to enable a charge of explosive to be fastened to the enemy ship's bottom without detection. The "crew," his head encased in a small conning tower and seated on a strong wooden block inside an oval compartment that traveled with its length vertical, drove the submarine forward by turning a crank with either a hand or a foot, and this revolved a screw propeller. Descent was obtained by flooding the vessel's bilges and ascent by drying them out again. The charge was a wooden container with about 150 pounds of gunpowder in it, carried on the outside of the vessel and released by the withdrawal of a bolt that set off a time detonator. There was also a safety device that allowed the operator to withdraw some distance before the explosion was due.

The experiment failed, as neither Bushnell nor his brother, who had been carefully trained to deputize for him, could take part, and the operator, one Sergeant Lee, gave away his position by too frequent surfacing and was forced into releasing his charge—we can thus almost call it a form of torpedo—in order to escape his pursuers.

The *Nautilus* of 1797, product of the genius of that versatile Robert Fulton, whose name has already been mentioned, was almost too successful, as the exploits of a second model, built on Napoleon's orders, showed when she blew up an old schooner off Brest. The French hesitated to use such a terrible weapon, and much the same happened when Fulton tried to persuade the British to take up his idea soon after. Back in the United States, Fulton received aid for other projects, but his death in 1815 held up further developments, as he had not cared to entrust others with the detailed results of his research.

In the middle of the nineteenth century, Charles Brun invented a submarine driven mechanically by a compressed-air engine, and Wilhelm Bauer, a Bavarian soldier, pushed the frontiers of knowledge further back with his *Le Plongeur-Marin* and *Le Diable-Marin*. More important were the midget "Davids," very small boats that did, nevertheless, alter the nature of naval warfare during the American Civil War considerably. They were built by the Confederates in the South and were not really taken seriously until the sinking by one of them of the federal ship *Housatonic* in 1864, the first time a warship had been sunk by such means. In the 1890's, the French continued to take the lead in developing submarines as well as in other naval improvements. Of their early submarines, the performances of the *Gustave Zédé* in mock battles in the Mediterranean are the best known and had a great influence on public opinion about the efficacy of this new development in warship design, so much so that even the scepticism of the British Admiralty was overcome by the turn of the century.

The designs of John Philip Holland were finally perfected after many vicissitudes in 1898 and deserve further mention. His whole interest in submarine vessels arose from the fight between *Merrimack* and *Monitor* at Hampton Roads. His invention of horizontal rudders was important in that it contained the principle of the hydroplane, enabling a boat to achieve a controlled dive and not merely sink like a stone, and it also made the maintenance of a constant depth possible for the first time. Lake may have been the real pioneer in this direction, since he was able to prove that submarine vessels did not need to dive at an angle, and he seems to have experimented with hydroplanes too; but it it safe to say that, between them these two men made the submarine a possibility. Holland's patents for designs, which included the introduction of a petrol engine for surface use and electric storage batteries for use when submerged, were eventually acquired by Britain, though the inventor himself had wanted to invent a war vessel that would help to overcome Britain's supremacy on the sea. It was only after this that he built submarine vessels especially for the United States Navy.

It should not, however, be supposed that Britain took a leading part in accepting this new type of warship. Her attitude is well illustrated by a First Lord of the Admiralty who stated in the House of Commons at the end of the nineteenth century that the Admiralty was "not prepared to take any steps in regard to submarines because this vessel is only the weapon of the weaker nation." Nevertheless, this interesting point of view was modified by the hypothesis that if the submarine could "be rendered practical," the nation that possessed it would "cease to be weak." Last of the great navies, Britain bowed to public opinion and in 1901 ordered "five submarines of the type invented by Mr.

Holland." The contract was turned over to Vickers, Sons, and Maxim, and the first was built at Barrow-in-Furness and launched by the end of the year. In 1914, Britain had sixty-four submarines in commission, more than any other navy had; but by that time, the Holland type and its immediate successor, the A-boat, had been scrapped, giving way to the very successful E-boat, fifty-six of which were built when Fisher was First Sea Lord. Of the earlier classes, the D-boat of the 1907–1908 program is noteworthy: this vessel was much larger and could be used for patrolling and not merely for coastal defense, since it no longer relied on dangerously explosive petrol for its engines when surfaced but used instead Diesel's heavy oil.

As early as 1902, Fisher had seen that submarines could become offensive weapons, and two years later he was to write that it was *"perfectly astounding* how the very best amongst us absolutely fail to realise the vast impending revolution in naval warfare and naval strategy that the submarine will accomplish." Luckily, he was the man to remedy such a defect, or as Roger Keyes put it, ". . . his dynamic energy overrode all naval and departmental obstruction and gave it a good start in life,"[2] and the appointment of R. H. Bacon to the new post of inspecting captain of submarine boats in January, 1903, was a good choice, as this brilliant torpedo officer was given a very free hand to build up the new branch of the service.

One other new class of warship must be noted here—the cruiser. The name was first used in the American Civil War to describe the swift unarmored vessels that carried sixteen 10-inch or 11-inch smooth-bore guns. The *Inconstant*, laid down in 1866, was the first British vessel of this kind, and a later cruiser, the *Iris*, laid down in 1875, was the first British warship of any sort to be built of mild steel throughout, for the earlier *Inconstant*, though partly built of iron, had been sheathed with wood and coppered. The development toward the modern cruiser can be seen in three distinct classes. First came the armored cruiser in the 1870's and 1880's, such as *Warspite*, completed in 1884, and the French *Dupuy de Lôme* of 1890. Then there was the introduction, during the next twenty years, of a belt of side armor, such as is found in the *Orlando* and *Minotaur* classes. Simultaneously, however, protected cruisers, such as the *Leander*, laid down in 1880, were being built. They had no side armor, but they did have steel decks. Of these, the *Diadem* of 1896 was more than 450 feet long and had a speed of slightly more than 20 knots. Thirdly, when armored cruisers gave way to battle cruisers, a class of vessel that will be examined separately in the next chapter, light nonarmored cruisers were laid down that were capable, above all, of high speeds. One of these, the *Amethyst*, completed in 1904, was the first cruiser to be fitted with turbine machinery. Later on, cruisers tended to become larger in size and more heavily armed, though after the introduction of the battle cruiser, their real role became that of the frigate in the old days of the sailing ship of the line. Like the destroyer herself in one of her roles, they were intended in particular to be reconnaissance vessels, but in the First World War they were used to protect convoys and attack those of the enemy, to operate in groups so that they could tackle strong detachments of the enemy, and they were expected to be fast enough to escape the guns of battleships and destroyers yet still be able to locate and report on such vessels.

NOTES

[1] See Michael Lewis, *The Navy of Britain*, p. 147.
[2] Sir Roger Keyes, *Naval Memoirs*, Dutton, New York, 1934, vol. i, p. 28.

Drawing of David Bushnell's explosion vessel, *Turtle,* which nearly destroyed Howe's flagship, *Eagle,* in 1776. Quite possibly, this very efficient vessel was the first to be driven by a screw propeller. *Brown Brothers, New York, from the drawing by Cyril Field*

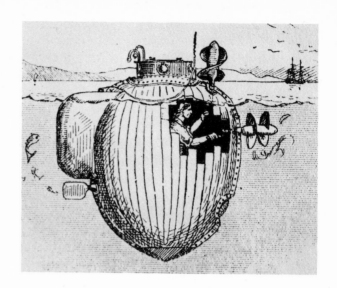

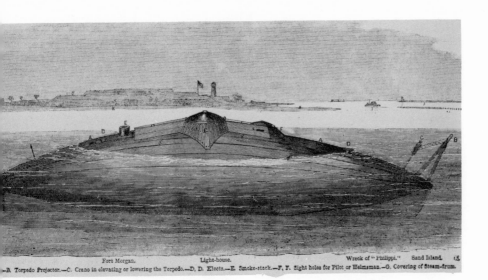

Fort Morgan.   Light-house.   Wreck of "Philippi."   Sand Island.   15
—B. Torpedo Projector.—C. Crane in elevating or lowering the Torpedo.—D, D. Eleets.—E. Smoke-stack.—F, F. Sight holes for Pilot or Helmsman.—G. Covering of Steam-drum.

(Above) Drawing of an early torpedo boat by R. Wier, United States Navy. *Collections of the Library of Congress, Washington*

Broadside view of the Reverend G. W. Garrett's second submarine boat, *Resurgam,* built in 1879. She was nearly 50 feet long and was sheathed with thick timber amidships and carried an enormous boiler to enable sufficient steam to be generated to carry her a dozen miles after the furnaces and chimney had been sealed up before diving. *Science Museum, London*

(Left) The 160-foot-long *Gustave Zédé*, completed in 1893, the prototype for most French submarines after that date. She displaced 270 tons and could travel forty-eight miles at 6 knots surfaced, while her usual endurance underwater was four to six hours at a maximum speed of 5 knots. She carried three 18-inch Whitehead torpedoes but had only one firing tube. *Imperial War Museum, London*

(Bottom left) British Holland-type submarine *A 1* (1904). The five vessels of this class were 200 feet in length, had two torpedo tubes, and could remain three hours underwater. A characteristic was the high conning tower with short periscope. It was this that led to the loss of *A 1* during maneuvers at Spithead, when she was run down by the liner *Berwick Castle*. *Imperial War Museum, London*

(Below) United States submarine *Octopus*, launched in 1906. She was 106 feet long, displaced 273 tons, and was an elementary Holland-type boat with high periscopes. *Submarine Library, General Dynamic Corporation, Groton, Connecticut*

United States Holland-type submarine *Cuttlefish,* one of the three boats in the *Viper* class of 1905. She displaced 170 tons and was 81 feet long. *Culver Pictures, Inc., New York*

(Right) United States C-class submarines in Gatun Locks, Panama Canal. These five Holland-type boats were completed in 1909 and displaced 250 tons each on average. They each had two torpedo tubes and a crew of ten men. *Submarine Library, General Dynamics Corporation, Groton, Connecticut*

The cruiser *Inconstant,* laid down in 1866, was the first British ship to be built on the lines of the American vessels of this name first used in the Civil War. They were unarmored at first and carried sixteen 10-inch or 11-inch smooth-bore guns. *Imperial War Museum, London*

(Right) HMS *Viper,* an early British destroyer, was completed in 1899. She was a speedy vessel, achieving 34 knots, and was the first British warship to have steam-turbine engines. She carried two single 18-inch torpedo tubes. *Science Museum, London*

HMS *Iris,* a cruiser launched in 1875, was the first British warship to be built of mild steel throughout. *Inconstant,* though partly built of iron, had been sheathed with wood and coppered. *Imperial War Museum, London*

United States ship *Connecticut,* laid down in 1903. *Brown Brothers, New York*

XI

The Twentieth Century Battleship

W̲E ARE NOW in a position to consider in some detail the next stage in the development of the warship, the introduction of the all-big-gun battleship. The British *Dreadnought* of 1905–1906 characterizes such a ship, but the general concept can be dated back some years and was by no means solely a British one. The United States Navy intended much the same thing, and the lesson of the Spanish-American War of 1898 had been that the heavy ship's most important asset was its armament;[1] indeed, Mahan had written that even the element of speed should be subordinated to gunpower. The Russian ships *Sinope* and *Catherine II*, built in the late 1880's, carried six 12-inch guns each and the German *Brandenburg* class of the early 1890's six 11-inch guns; and though these armaments were considered by other nations to be almost laughably exaggerated, their mere existence can be seen now as the writing on the wall.

Before the end of the century, it became the "settled fashion" in Britain to carry four big guns, two forward and two aft.[2] There was a tendency, too, toward a uniform big-gun armament, which can be seen in the two *Nelson* class ships, *Lord Nelson* and *Agamemnon*, the last pre-dreadnoughts. These ships kept the primary armament of their eight predecessors in the *King Edward* class, that is, four 12-inch guns, but the secondary armament was composed of ten 9.2-inch guns instead of a mixture of 9.2-inch and 6-inch. Fire control was difficult to establish and accurate spotting almost impossible when mixed batteries disgorged different-sized shells at differing rates of loading. Further confusion was caused by differences in flight time and fall of shot, so gradually naval opinion came around to the view that uniform armament was the only answer.

It is interesting to find that as early as 1903, Cuniberti, the Italian naval constructor, wrote an article in which he upheld the then still revolutionary view that the ideal warship for Britain should have twelve 12-inch guns and a speed superior to all battleships then afloat. One comment, in view of what was to happen so soon, is worth quoting here: a writer in *The Engineer* (February 4, 1904) thought that, though such a vessel was inevitable, the time for her arrival had not yet come, and he added that such a ship "would render obsolete too many other fine vessels for any nation to build her without very long and serious thought."

At the end of 1901, the United States General Board flatly turned down the suggestions of the Bureau of Construction advocating an all-big-gun battleship. Nevertheless, the *South Carolina* and *Michigan*, authorized in March, 1905, though not completed until 1909, may be taken as the forerunners of the *Delaware* and *North Dakota* of 1907, usually held to be the first American dreadnoughts. What is important is that Fisher knew in the early part of 1904 that the United States was about to build dreadnoughts and that this must therefore have influenced his own thinking.

Before we study the *Dreadnought*, so inextricably linked with the name of Admiral Sir John Fisher—though it should be recalled that he had the unanimous support of the design committee—this seems an appropriate place to turn back and look more closely at the position of the British navy at the opening of the twentieth century.

In the last decades of the nineteenth century, British confidence in a basically old-fashioned navy was undermined. The reward of having more ships than any other navy was of doubtful value if those ships were obsolete or could be seriously challenged by a single up-to-date man-of-war. The appearance of the shell gun, which upset the balance between offence and defense, episodes such as the Russian destruction of the Turks at Sinope, the French silencing of the Kinburn forts, the battle at Hampton Roads—all played a part in bringing about this realization. Guns were, in fact, growing bigger, but the French remained the pioneers, and as late as the 1880's, English guns were "short dumpy things like soda-water bottles," in the words of Admiral Penrose FitzGerald, "muzzle-loaders, rifled and with studded projectiles which frequently broke up in the gun, or else turned end over end and went in any direction except the right one."[3]

Nevertheless, there is plenty of evidence of progress. In 1859, the *Warrior*'s 8-inch 4¾-ton smooth-bore muzzle-loading guns were the most powerful in the fleet; yet in 1875, the guns of the seventh *Dreadnought* were 12.5-inch 38-ton muzzle-loaders, and ten years later the *Benbow*'s were 16½-inch 110½-ton breech-loaders. Later, there was a reduction in sheer size owing to improvements in the manufacture of powder and projectiles, so that, as we have already seen, the 12-inch gun had become the accepted big gun by the end of the pre-dreadnought era. Other improvements were the doubling of the piercing power of guns, which had its effect on armor plating, the introduction of quick-firing guns, such as the light Hotchkiss 6-pounder of 1883, designed to deal with swift-moving torpedo boats, and the application of electricity in the early 1870's, when Pile-type batteries and, later, Laclanché cells were used in the gun-firing equipment. The *Inflexible* was actually fitted with electric light throughout, supplied from a 800-volt generator; and by 1881, a dynamo had been installed to operate searchlights for the first time.

The natural development in armor plating was to increase its thickness—*Inflexible's* plating in 1876 was 10 inches thicker than that of the thickest in existence four years earlier—but there clearly would come a point beyond which a ship could not carry more than a certain weight and still be expected to float. The solution to this technical problem was the introduction of compound armor, that is, iron with steel plates affixed to it. But even the 18-inch thickness of this reinforced armor soon proved insufficient, so, thanks to the Bessemer method of making steel plates and then to the more reliable Siemens-Martin "open-hearth" process, all-steel armor came in. Reliable plates and angles were introduced into the cruisers *Iris* and *Mercury* in the 1870's and the battleships *Colossus* and *Edinburgh*. The hulls of these four ships were constructed throughout of mild steel joined together, at first, with iron rivets.

Further developments were the Harvey process for toughening the surface of the steel, used for the first time in the *Majestic* class of battleship in 1895, and, later still, the introduction of Krupp steel in the six ships in the *Canopus* class. The French had been pioneers here, too, for as early as 1873, they had completely substituted mild steel for iron in the construction of the *Redoubtable*.

In the more general field, the fundamental problems were connected with an ironclad ship's radius of action and her speed. As long as coal was the sole fuel, the former problem could be solved only by increasing the ship's carrying capacity, which meant also increasing the displacement. The latter problem can be seen in sharper relief when it is appreciated that the earliest ironclad's speed of 14 knots had been increased to only just over 18 knots by the end of the century.

All these new techniques in the construction and equipping of warships, as well as the uncertainty of what would really be required of ships in any foreseeable war, led to an understandable lack of common doctrine. Ship design was, according to Gladstone, as fickle as that of ladies' hats, and there was something to be said for a journalist's description of the age as an epoch of ironmongery, with all the undertones of disapproval that the phrase contains.[4] Since there were no naval actions to test the new British ironclads for so long, the lessons to be learned from the struggles of other nations became all the more important, and they were lessons not to be superseded for a long time by others learned in the school of personal experience.

An example of this academic learning is the long ascendancy the ram enjoyed after the events of the action fought off the island of Lissa in the Adriatic in 1866. This was the only battle in the steam age in which ramming tactics were deliberately used, though, as we have seen, Hampton Roads four years earlier revived the importance of this ancient form of offensive action. It is, therefore, worthwhile looking back to this episode. The point at issue was the control of the Adriatic at a time when Italy was backing Prussia in her war against Austria in the hopes of gaining Venice as her share in the spoils of victory. Italy had the more powerful fleet, comprising twelve armored ships, varying from the large American-built *Re D'Italia* and *Re Di Portogallo* to three ships with built-in rams, *Formidabile*, *Terribile*, and *Affondatore*, while the Austrian fleet, under von Tegetthoff, seemed very inferior, on paper at any rate. In the outcome, the determination of Tegetthoff turned the tables on the elderly and rather vacillating Count Carlo Pellion di Persano, and the particular incident that made such an impression on naval opinion throughout the world was the ramming and sinking of the *Re D'Italia* by Tegetthoff's *Ferdinand Max,* which, though without an actual ram, drove her stern into the enemy's flank at a speed of 11½ knots. Though the whole action was inconclusive, especially as it was fought when the war had virtually ended, Lissa was important for two reasons: "it showed the effectiveness of the ram at a time when armour had won an ascendancy over the gun," as one modern naval historian has put it, and because it "emphasized the importance of a clear field of fire directly ahead for the main armament," it gave another good reason for the abolition of sailing rig.[5]

In spite of this bewilderment, Britain began to feel that war was, after all, inevitable and gradually woke up to her naval responsibilities. Professor Marder of the University of Hawaii has observed that "the ironclad age, by initiating the policy of 'going one better' in warship design, gave a tremendous impetus to naval rivalries," and this seems as accurate an appreciation of, as it is a succinct comment on, the spirit of the age.[6]

The great naval expansion in both France and Russia in the 1890's gave a sense of urgency to this new attitude, but in 1889 it had already shown itself to be growing up, with the official acceptance of the "two-power standard," which enunciated that the establishment of the Royal Navy "should be on such a scale that it should be equal to the naval strength of any two other countries," a standard which was confirmed by successive governments on into the twentieth century.[7] The effect of Mahan's widely translated books on sea power, published in the early 1890's, and the tumultuous welcome he received in high places when visiting Britain soon afterward showed that public views about a strong navy had changed at last, and it is not insignificant that nearly two and a half million people visited the Royal Navy exhibition in 1891. The Naval Defence Act of 1889 led to the whole philosophy of "navalism," which meant the maintenance of a strong and up-to-date navy, and the "blue-water" school of thought achieved a considerable following from 1884 onward, maintaining that the existence of a mighty and ever-watchful navy was the only sensible defense against invasion and that to spend money on military co-responsibility in this was a wrong reading of the principles behind the strategy.

One last event must be mentioned here because of its important effect on public thinking in the early years of the twentieth century, and not merely in Britain. This was the Russo-Japanese War of 1904–1905, the first occasion on which ironclads were ever engaged on anything like equal terms. But this was true of the early stages of the war only, since the result of the battle off Tsushima Island was dramatic and unexpected: "an Eastern Power had proved that she could man and train a fleet equal to anything afloat,"[8] a historian has written, and he reminds us that during the next thirty-five years, Japan was to build up her sea power to such an extent that she could "challenge even the might and efficiency of the United States." Rozhestvensky's defeat, with the loss of fourteen battleships and five armored cruisers, reduced Russia to a third-class naval power. This has tended to obscure the fact that the Japanese torpedoes were less successful in the early stages of the war than they should have been and that the really significant lesson to be learned from Tsushima was that the big 12-inch guns had been responsible for the Russian annihilation. Mixed armaments of smaller guns were only effective at a comparatively limited range, say about 3,000 yards, and were hard to control owing to their different ranges and speeds. Once it was accepted that a more powerful gun could deliver its projectiles effectively and speedily enough to engage targets at a range outside that of the guns below it, it followed that the large battery of medium guns was likely to be less efficient than one of a few large guns.

We can now return to the development of the British all-big-gun ship during Fisher's tenure of office as First Sea Lord. Two types of ship were introduced in the 1905–1906 program, the battleship and the armored cruiser, later called the battle cruiser. The battleship took the honored name of *Dreadnought,* for among her seven predecessors, the first had fought against the Armada and the fifth at Trafalgar, and this became the name given to this class of ship all over the world. Both Fisher's new ships came to be called "capital" ships from about 1909 onward, the old name that in Stuart times, as we saw earlier, represented the ship fit to lie in the line of battle. The *Dreadnought* was launched by King Edward VII on February 10, 1906, an event that aroused great national enthusiasm and not a little controversy as well. She was ready for trials a year and a day after her keel plate had been laid, a great achievement on the part of all those concerned in her construction and one made possible by the diversion of the main armament of the *Lord*

Nelson to her. She was somehow thought to be a symbol of the new maritime age that lay ahead. Her new features were her armament of ten 12-inch guns, two in each of the five turrets, as opposed to the mixed primary armaments of 12-inch and 9.2-inch guns in the *King Edward* and *Nelson* classes; her speed of 21 knots, which was 2 knots faster than that of any battleship then building or already afloat; her lack of any secondary armament, though there were twenty-seven quick-firing 12-pounders to deal with torpedo attacks; and lastly, she was the first turbine-engined big ship in any navy. This last fact meant that she was by far the most efficient battleship in the world, since the turbines dispensed with those wearisome days spent in overhauling a ship's machinery after even a single day's steaming at high speed.

The armored cruisers were, in a way, an even more startling novelty. Three of them, *Invincible, Inflexible,* and *Indomitable,* with a main armament of eight 12-inch guns each, were in the 1905–1906 program with the *Dreadnought,* and they were designed to achieve a speed of more than 25 knots, which meant medium armor protection of only 7-inch thickness—in fact, that of the 1906 *Minotaur* cruiser. They were intended to be fast and strong enough to reconnoiter in the face of enemy cruisers and to catch and destroy the fastest armed merchant raiders, among which were some of the German transatlantic liners which could make 23 knots and were known to be likely to carry guns for commerce destruction in wartime. Thirdly, but only in the last resort, they were to be able to reinforce the van or rear squadrons of a battle fleet in action, though they were not expected to stand up to a battleship unless she was already engaged. This appreciation of their use in war was not really anything very new, since, cruisers were, quite simply, faster but less powerful than battleships—an accepted part of pre-dreadnought doctrine, though Fisher may have planned to use them as the Japanese armored cruisers under Rear Admiral Dewa had been used, that is, independently of the heavy ships so as to make the most of their superior speed.

Fisher and his committee on design, made up of civilian and naval members in equal numbers, seem to have arrived at the idea of the *Dreadnought* because they saw that the advent of long-range shooting would soon make all existing battleships obsolete in any case. This was the considered opinion of Bacon too, and it helps to explain how Fisher combated the most frequently raised objection that the *Dreadnought*

virtually meant the end of Britain's superiority in number of warships—
about 3 to 1 over Germany at the time—and the necessity of starting to
build up the fleet all over again. Fisher knew, too, that Germany,
Japan, and Russia were thinking of the all-big-gun ship. In more detail,
long-range shooting had developed for two reasons: because the menace
of the torpedo made it a necessity and because improved range-finding
instruments made it practicable. Other considerations that must have
influenced him have been listed very clearly by Professor Marder[9] and
include the fact that uniform armaments of big guns firing salvos made
spotting at long range easier and that the destructive power of even one
12-inch gun was greater than that of several 6-inch guns. Again, since
torpedo warfare made close-range fighting tactically undesirable, there
was no need to concentrate on a secondary armament, and this was
another argument for relying on the 12-inch gun alone, which was the
most accurate gun at long ranges, anyway, since it had a greater hitting
probability owing to the flatter trajectory of its shells. Fisher's belief
that speed was tactically more important even than gunpower was based
on his assumption that the fast ship could choose her ranges.

The controversy that arose over the *Dreadnought* program and the
criticism of influential men, ranging from Admiral Sir Cyprian Bridge
and Sir William White, who was Director of Naval Construction, 1885–
1902, to the less responsible utterances of Lloyd George, who dismissed
Dreadnought as "a piece of wanton and profligate ostentation," are past
history; but a study of it is instructive, nevertheless, in that it tells us
something of the attitudes of experts at that time. One main criticism
was that it was unwise for Britain to take the lead in ship construction;
rather, she should counter the lead of others with something better,
which her superior shipbuilding facilities, it was thought, could produce
quickly enough.

Four other criticisms were equally valid, though Fisher himself was
able to counter three of them to his own satisfaction. First, there
was the complaint that Britain was, so to speak, putting all her eggs "into
one or two vast, costly, majestic but vulnerable baskets"—the phrase
was White's—and that larger ships meant that there must be fewer of
them, too few to meet the commitments of Empire and trade protection.
It was thought too that it would be necessary to enlarge dry docks and
harbors generally, and we are reminded of the complaints Trinity
House placed before King Charles I when the plan to build the *Sovereign*

of the Seas became known. Fisher's answer to the last part of this criticism was typical of the man: " . . . docks and harbors exist for our ships, not the ships for the docks," he wrote tartly. "If the necessity for larger ships be shown, the expenditure which they entail must be faced, for otherwise, if we continue to build ships only because they will go into the existing docks, we shall not require any docks at all—in the day of action our ships will all go to the bottom."[10] The official answer to this was simply to point out that there was a growing tendency toward larger ships in every navy and that for a mere increase in displacement of 1,500 tons over the *Nelson* class, there was a much more powerful armament, greater seakeeping strength, greater speed, and nearly equal armor protection.

Secondly, there were critics who queried exactly this last point, feeling that protective armor had been sacrificed to increase speed and gunpower, a complaint that was to recur during the First World War and after. Yet *Dreadnought* was as heavily protected as all previous battleships had been, except the two *Nelson*-class vessels, and, indeed, she had underwater armor for the first time as a protection against torpedoes and mines.

Thirdly, many thought that armament had been sacrificed in the interests of speed. Custance in *Blackwood's Magazine* (February, 1906), for instance, argued that battles were decided by superior tactics and fighting power and that speed was not a weapon but only enabled a fleet to withdraw, a very negative form of protection. Fisher's answer was that *Dreadnought* was equal to two and a half existing battleships and that speed enabled a commander "to force or decline an action" once he was in touch with the enemy, and he quoted cases from the Russo-Japanese War showing that the Japanese could maintain contact with the Russians when the latter withdrew, even though forced to cover much greater distances in the process.

Fourthly, there was the question of dispensing with the secondary armament. Influential opinion in Britain thought that there was no justification for this, and in support of this view the fact was cited that the Japanese, even after their victory, were equipping their new battleships with 6-inch guns. To this opinion Fisher deferred, and all subsequent battleships after *Dreadnought* herself had 4-inch guns; and, later still, in the 1911–1912 program, after Fisher had left the Admiralty, 6-inch guns were introduced in the *Iron Duke* class.

The supremacy of these great battleships proved to be of short duration, and in this period the battle of Jutland in the early summer of 1916 was indeed the climax. "Never again," as a historian has written, "would long lines of the steel-clad Leviathans move ponderously into action and prepare to fight it out in an exchange of shell fire,"[11] for soon afterward, the developments in the submarine and in aircraft changed the whole nature of naval warfare; and after the war was over, the great naval powers agreed to restrict the number and size of their capital ships.

In the eight years between the completion of *Dreadnought* and the outbreak of war in 1914, other countries followed Britain's lead. Germany launched her first dreadnought, the *Nassau,* in March, 1908, and, two months later, her first battle cruiser, the *Von der Tann.* The appointment of von Tirpitz as Secretary of State for Naval Affairs in 1897 had led to the idea of building up a strong navy, as can be seen in the provisions of the act of 1900 that authorized four squadrons with eight battleships in each, together with a suitable number of cruisers and torpedo craft. The *Kaiser Barbarossa,* launched in 1900, was not unlike French ships of the period in construction, and she was fitted with a formidable mixed armament of four 9.5-inch, fourteen 6-inch, and fourteen 3.5-inch guns, as well as five torpedo tubes, a general practice beginning at about this time. Russia and Italy followed suit with dreadnoughts in 1909, the *Gangut* and the *Dante Alighieri.* Both battleships had twelve 12-inch guns in triple turrets on the center line, a refinement that was followed by the United States, Austria, and France soon after.

It would be incorrect, however, to give the impression that the United States was a mere imitator. As was mentioned earlier, the *South Carolina* and *Michigan,* though not completed till 1909, were authorized in 1905. With their eight 12-inch guns and secondary armaments of 14-pounders, they were undoubtedly dreadnoughts and were some of the concrete results of Theodore Roosevelt's "big-navy" policy. They were also the first battleships to have superimposed turrets so that the fire of all their big guns could be brought to bear on either beam. Various factors had contributed to an awakened interest in the navy in the United States, but among them stand out, first, the new responsibilities in the western Pacific as a result of the Spanish-American War, and, secondly, the assassination of President McKinley in 1901, which brought Vice-President Roosevelt into office.

Roosevelt was an admirer of Mahan, and his personal enthusiasm for developing American sea power at this time soon led to impressive practical results. During his first term, Congress authorized ten first-class battleships, four armored cruisers, and seventeen other vessels, such as scout cruisers, which were the forerunners of the light cruisers of today. The last eight pre-dreadnought battleships to be built were the *Connecticut* and *Louisiana* of 1902; the *Kansas, Minnesota, Vermont, Idaho,* and *Mississippi* of 1903; and the *New Hampshire* of 1904, all of which had a main armament of four 12-inch and eight 8-inch guns. The remaining two battleships were the *South Carolina* and *Michigan* of 1905, already mentioned as being the pioneers of the new all-big-gun ship. There were two classes of armored cruisers: the larger had four 10-inch guns, and the smaller four 8-inch, and both were capable of making just over 22 knots.

The *Delaware*, authorized in 1906, was the first dreadnought to be completed, and she was a veritable leviathan, with twice the displacement of the *Oregon*, hitherto the greatest American battleship. Moreover, she was nearly 5 knots faster and carried two and a half times as many big guns as *Oregon*, all of which were capable of longer ranges and were both more accurate and more powerful.

Roosevelt's wish to order four capital ships in the next year's program led to a violent struggle with Congress, but in the end, though only two were authorized, Roosevelt could at least feel that the earlier decision to build only one such ship a year had been improved on. The four ships built in the 1908–1909 were the *Florida* and *Utah*, armed with ten 12-inch guns, and the *Arkansas* and *Wyoming*, with twelve 12-inch guns.

Thus Roosevelt's terms of office were of momentous importance in the development of the United States Navy, and they marked a stage in public awareness of matters naval that was no less significant. Not merely were great ships built, but their possible roles in any future war were studied and further decisions were made, such as the construction of the Panama Canal, thus lessening the time it would take for the Atlantic and Pacific fleets to join each other if need be. Officer training and general naval experience were improved considerably by the much publicized "globe encircling parade"[12] made by the Atlantic fleet in between December, 1907, and February, 1909, so that when the Democrat caucus in the House of Representatives nearly brought Taft's naval program to a halt during his presidency in the years leading up to the outbreak of the First World War, there was, nevertheless, a firmly established and commonly accepted basis of naval expertise on which to build. Taft's construction program can be seen, however, to be a top-heavy one, since it was something of a compromise. He was compelled to sacrifice destroyer flotillas and the building of scout cruisers in order to make Congress accept his intention of keeping up with foreign navies by building capital ships regularly.

In general, the last years before the war can be seen as the platform on which the two rival schools of thought contended for the favors of the nation: those who held that the American navy should be equal to the German navy in the Atlantic and the Japanese navy in the Pacific and those who held that the existing navy was good enough as it was. Three more battleships were built under an act of 1914: the *New Mexico,* the second *Idaho,* and the second *Mississippi,* the last two replacing the two slow ships of these names in the 1903 program, which were obsolete even before they came into service. All three 1914 ships were capable of making 21 knots and were each armed with twelve 14-inch guns.

When we realize that Congress also authorized fifty-one submarines between 1900 and 1914, we can see that the United States Navy had rapidly grown to maturity, though we must not ignore in all this activity the revival of the theory of passive coastal defense, in which was blended an unstated isolationism based, understandably enough, on the fact of geographical remoteness.

Before we look at the performances of these great battleships in war, we must note some of the early improvements on the original *Dreadnought.* Many of them are associated with the pioneer work undertaken by Sir Percy Scott in the field of gunnery control. In lay terms, they can best be explained as the introduction of salvo-firing and spotting tops, that is, the bracket system of firing and the electric transmission of information to gunsights from a central station. Scott's central gun director disposed of the inevitable lack of coordination when each turret fired independently and also enabled the director layer to fire all the turrets simultaneously. This was a great improvement, but the Admiralty was slow to accept it, and it was not till Jellicoe insisted on its being fitted in *Thunderer* in 1911 that its advantages were tested. Even then it had not been fitted in all the ships that fought at Jutland five years later.

Another improvement was the introduction of larger guns, 13½-

inch in the *King George V* class of 1910 and 15-inch in the *Queen Elizabeth* class of 1912, which meant that with the reintroduction of secondary armaments, as already noted, the striking power of these ships was considerable. All gun turrets were soon placed on the center line, an American innovation, as we saw above, and some of them were superimposed on others so that all the big guns could be used on one or other broadside at the same time. Lastly, the introduction of oil fuel must be mentioned, as it marked a new stage in the history of the mobility of the warship. The United States battleships *Oklahoma* and *Nevada* of 1911 were fitted for oil only, and Britain had already adopted oil for destroyers and submarines, but the decision "to change the foundation of the navy," as Professor Marder puts it,[13] did not take effect until after the Royal Commission on Fuel Oil, presided over by Fisher, had made its first report.

The first action in which dreadnoughts and battle cruisers were involved was the battle off the Falkland Islands in December, 1914. The German Pacific Squadron under Vice Admiral Graf von Spee had sunk the British pre-dreadnought cruisers *Monmouth* and *Good Hope* off Coronel on the Chile coast two months earlier. Fisher, back at the Admiralty as First Sea Lord, had taken the risky but justifiable step of ordering two British battle cruisers, *Inflexible* and *Invincible,* under Admiral Sturdee, to the South Atlantic to remedy this defeat and one other, the *Princess Royal,* to watch the Panama Canal. The battle off the Falkland Islands was one-sided, for, just as Cradock had been outgunned by von Spee's armored cruisers *Scharnhorst* and *Gneisenau,* so these vessels were themselves outclassed by *Invincible* and *Inflexible.* Yet when the action was studied more closely, it was found that at their effective range of 14,000 yards, these battle cruisers had scored a low rate of hits. Also, the effect of the 12-inch shells themselves was disappointing, since it took two and a half hours to sink the *Scharnhorst* after she had been engaged, which suggested that fire control and target practice needed improvement. Strategically and tactically, the new dreadnoughts had proved themselves, of this there can be no doubt, but there were technical defects that undoubtedly reduced their efficiency.

Two other engagements in the first year of the war are instructive, though both show how much there was still to be learned about the handling of capital ships under modern conditions. The first was in January, 1915, when Beatty's five battle cruisers, *Lion, Tiger, New Zealand, Princess Royal,* and *Indomitable,* met Hipper's three battle cruisers, *Seydlitz, Derfflinger,* and *Moltke,* and the armored cruiser *Blücher* off Dogger Bank. The Germans had hoped to lure the Grand Fleet south from Scapa Flow and enforce on them the task of conducting a close blockade, with all its attendant dangers of mines and torpedo warfare. The result was a British strategic success, in that it stopped the Germans from sending detached squadrons across the North Sea on minor raiding operations, but tactically it was disappointing. Beatty started with the element of surprise, and he certainly had superiority in guns, but mistaken signals and ineffective gunnery robbed him of the initiative, and though the *Blücher* eventually sank, it was only after she had been torpedoed seven times and had received more than seventy hits from heavy shells. Hipper's flagship, *Seydlitz,* was later severely damaged when a shell penetrated the after barbette and exploded inside the turret, setting fire to the ammunition stacked ready for loading into the guns. Both gun crews in the turret were destroyed, but the vessel was saved by the heroism of three members of the crew who managed to flood the magazines. The Germans learned the lessons of this engagement more quickly than the British did and, immediately afterward, modified their arrangements for handling ammunition. Antiflash precautions, such as metal containers for all cordite charges waiting to be loaded, were introduced, for it was realized that after the charges left the magazines they became a great liability, since if hit, not merely would they explode, but the flames could easily penetrate down into the magazine.

The Dardanelles campaign of 1915, perhaps one of the most dramatic failures in modern warfare, since its success might have altered the whole course of twentieth century history, brought home only too clearly a lesson that should not have been forgotten. This was the axiom that it was fatal to expect ships to destroy well-built land fortifications unaided. This had been feasible for only the very short period between the introduction of armor and the universal use of explosive shells, and perhaps the bombardment of the Kinburn forts was the only exception. In 1915, it was clearly wrong to expect Carden's ships to force the straits unaided, yet this was what happened two months before the expeditionary force arrived. Even the *Queen Elizabeth's* impressive bombardment of Chanak at 14,000 yards could achieve little of lasting value beyond the lucky accident of blowing up a barracks, so it is hardly surprising that one of Fisher's last acts before his resignation as First Sea Lord was to ensure that this new battleship was recalled.

It is not intended to attempt any reassessment of the Battle of Jutland here, since it would be impertinent to treat the still growing literature on this single action in anything but great detail. Rather, it is intended to see whether this action, the one really full-scale one during the war, contributed in any way to the evolution of the warship. A fair summary of the many criticisms leveled against the senior commanders on both sides is found in one historian's reference to "an all but universal unfamiliarity . . . with the way in which a major modern battle, fought with modern weapons, would go,"[14] and this would seem a wiser comment than many other more detailed ones. Whether, for example, Jellicoe was too cautious need not concern us here, but it would seem that he was right to assume that the enemy might use submarines and mines more than he did and that therefore caution was wise. As it turned out, the battle was fought between big ships fighting on much the same terms as in the great engagements of the past, that is, unhampered by any other tactical considerations, such as aircraft or effective wireless telegraphy.

Yet, looked at in another way, the whole setting was very far removed from the battles of the past. Owing to low visibility, no two commanders saw the action from the same viewpoint—in passing we can recall Thucydides' caveat on the reliability of witnesses—and "although 250 ships took part, there were never more than three or four enemy capital ships in sight at the same time from any point in the British line."[15] This seems a far cry indeed from the close-line actions and melees of the eighteenth century, and when Sir James Thursfield, a senior naval press correspondent, wrote to congratulate Jellicoe, after the Jutland despatches had been published, on his feat of joining up the Grand Fleet with the battle-cruiser fleet in face of the enemy, who was already engaging the latter, it was perhaps only a graceful compliment to mention the battles of Quiberon Bay and Cape St. Vincent as precedents for such deployment, though it was perceptive of him to have selected this maneuver for special praise.[16] Frothingham, the American naval writer, made the same point when he stated that the British problem was to unite the two parts of a superior force and impose that force on the enemy. The picture conjured up in the mind's eye when he writes of "long miles of battle lines wreathed in mist and smoke" is matched by his awareness of the "great areas of manoeuvre" that confronted both Jellicoe and Scheer, and it seems that, on the whole, the Grand Fleet was less well prepared than the German High Seas Fleet for coping with sea warfare on such a scale.

Another point that showed up was the failure by the light cruisers on both sides to keep in touch with the enemy. Perhaps again the rigid system of fleet control, worked out on British prewar exercises, was at fault in that it provided situations that were unrealistic in war. Beatty's views on the use of light cruisers are interesting. In his orders he expressly stated that "an enemy force, once brought into action, should not escape in fog, under a smoke-screen, or in gathering darkness," so subordinate leaders were encouraged to anticipate orders and to "act in the spirit of the Commander-in-Chief's requirements," since this could be summed up in the coordination of the two principles "locate and report" and "attack and destroy."[17]

A more difficult criticism to meet is the commonly expressed one that British battle-cruiser gunnery was of a low standard, especially as the German official history (Appendix 8 of that account) showed that the actual hits received by their battle cruisers were higher than those they inflicted on the British battle cruisers and that the Queen Mary and the Invincible were shooting admirably right up to the time they blew up. It may be that defective design rather than the quality of the actual shooting was at fault.[18] It is worth noting, too, that the German capital ships were designed as "unsinkable gun platforms" and were carefully tested with this end in view. Von Tirpitz argued that as long as a ship could reach harbor, she could always be repaired, and it is interesting to see that Jellicoe, in his despatch, ascribed the British losses to "indifferent armour protection . . . particularly as regards turret-armour and deck-plating." Lastly, it seems generally agreed that the German fleet enjoyed a superiority in other directions: in the higher quality of their optical instruments, in magazine protection from cordite flash—a lesson they learned after the Dogger Bank action—and in such things as the watertight subdivision of their ships, as well as better shells.

Jutland can be seen as a tactical victory for the Germans in that higher losses were inflicted than were sustained, but since Britain remained predominant at sea and the German fleet virtually never again emerged in force, she can be seen to have won a strategic victory in the end. The Germans turned their attention to submarine warfare, though it was, of course, only after the war was over that it could be known that no further action involving numbers of capital ships was to take place. To the men who were building these great ships, as well as to those who manned them, it must have been something of an anticlimax to find that they were not to be the protagonists in the struggle.

The importance of the remaining part of the First World War centers, for our purposes, around the submarine, the destroyer, and the embryonic aircraft carrier, and these types of warship will be discussed in the next two chapters. It is necessary now, however, to complete the history of the capital ship, and this will involve glancing ahead to the Second World War, with its great climax in the struggle between the United States and Japan in the vast expanses of the Pacific, which proved the aircraft carrier to be the only really battle-winning great ship.

The Washington Treaty of 1922 was perhaps too idealistic, since it assumed that wars would never again be fought on the scale of the one just experienced and that therefore even countries like Britain, totally dependent on sea power to protect herself and her trade routes, could do without a strong navy. The agreement by the great powers to reduce their battle fleets meant, therefore, a greater sacrifice to Britain than to the other countries, since it meant the end of the two-power standard and, in fact, the beginning of a new phase in which the leading navies virtually started again on an almost equal footing. One clause of the treaty is of particular importance—that which limited the size of capital ships so that any warship of more than 10,000 tons displacement could be so described. These voluntary limitations in size and number, combined with the great developments in submarines in the First World War and onward and aircraft and carriers in the Second, led in the end to the dethronement of the battleship from her position as the unrivaled queen of the battle fleet.

Though the Washington Treaty prevented the creation of disproportionately large ships and navies, it did not prevent plans for modernization in those fleets. Britain built seven battleships in the twenty years between the wars, four of them in the 1937 program, the *King George V*-class vessels.

These had four 14-inch guns in each of two turrets and two in another turret superimposed forward. Antiaircraft weapons were now seen to be necessary, so the secondary armament of these ships, the sixteen 5.25-inch guns, were given an elevation of 60 degrees, and there were sixty other specifically antiaircraft guns—2-pounders, Oerlikons, and Bofors—in each ship as well. The guns themselves were improvements on their predecessors, since they were all-steel weapons and had increased ranges, though it is probably true to say they were inferior to those in American and German ships. Electric welding, replacing the less efficient riveting, was another improvement in construction, and by the end of the interwar years, the "Asdic" antisubmarine detection equipment was a distinct improvement on the old hydrophone listening apparatus, while the development of radar for air warning was sufficiently advanced for its potentialities as a ship-detecting device to be appreciated.

Nevertheless, when war broke out in September, 1939, Britain found herself short of tough medium-sized warships able to cross the Atlantic without refueling, for instance, and fast enough to destroy enemy U-boats, a deficiency that was not remedied until the frigate program of 1941 took effect. The long years in which rearmament had been frowned on could be seen now as a period of stagnation rather than as the dawning of a new era of international peace, and it was a sobering thought that the only new battleships being built at the outbreak of war, the four *King George V* class mentioned above, were not to be ready before 1941.

Of the six aircraft carriers, only the *Ark Royal*, completed in 1938, was new and specially so designed, and the completion date of six others, laid down in the last two years before the war and planned to displace 23,000 tons and to operate between thirty-five and fifty-five aircraft each, was still far in the future. Two-thirds of the sixty-three heavy and light cruisers had been completed between the wars, and nineteen more were being built in 1939. In the smaller categories of warships, the situation had always been better, and the decision to rearm in 1937 had borne fruit. About two-thirds of the 168 destroyers available in September, 1939, were reasonably modern, as all through the 1930's the Admiralty had managed to persuade the British government to authorize a flotilla in each annual naval program. Most of the sixty-nine submarines, too, were comparatively new.

There were also some new war vessels, notably the antiaircraft escort ships, designed from converted 1914–1918 light cruisers. There were other escorts, too, ships displacing around 1,200 tons, specially built for the purpose and generally known as sloops. By 1939, there were fifty of them, and though they were slow, their powers of endurance justified their existence. Finally, 140 corvettes were authorized in 1939 and 1940. These were again, small escort vessels, designed on the lines of whale catchers, with considerable endurance but not fast enough to deal with surfaced submarines.

Though Germany was prevented from having any battleships by the terms of the Washington Treaty, when Hitler came to power and the treaty became more and more ineffective, she was able to take advantage of the most up-to-date designs, and she was not inhibited by the limits on displacement figures. In fact, the *Tirpitz*, displacing 42,000 tons, though officially only 35,000, was the largest capital ship in any navy until the American *Missouri* and the Japanese *Yamato* and *Musashi* were completed. She and her sister ship, the *Bismarck*, were on the stocks at the beginning of the war, and they carried eight 15-inch guns and could make a speed of 30 knots. Germany's pocket battleships, the *Graf Spee*, *Admiral Scheer*, and *Lützow*, belong to the pre-Hitler years, when lip service was still being paid to the limitations imposed by the Washington Treaty—though, in fact, these ships displaced 14,000 tons. They were armed with six 11-inch, eight 5.9-inch, and six 4.1-inch AA guns and carried two seaplanes on catapults. The battle cruisers *Scharnhorst* and *Gneisenau* were in commission at the beginning of the war, and so was the heavy cruiser *Admiral Hipper*; there were also four other heavy cruisers being built, the *Prinz Eugen*, the *Blücher*, sunk in the Norwegian campaign, the *Seydlitz*, and the *Lützow*. This last ship was handed over to the Russians early in 1940 as part of the payment for Stalin's participation in the Russo-German pact of the previous summer. She should not be confused with the pocket battleship of this name that was originally known as the *Deutschland*.

If it is possible to summarize the aspects of the Second World War that reveal most clearly the last stages in the story of the all-big-gun ship, the following might be selected, and it is against such a background that we can see the final act being played.

In the first instance, all countries with fleets thought their capital ships useful for three main functions—commerce raiding, protection, and the covering of opposed landings. It was, of course, expected that at some date in the future, battleships would meet each other in more or less conventional circumstances; but, in fact, this did not happen in the way anticipated. The Japanese and American fleets, considerable as they were, did not meet as such, as we shall see; and, again, in the Mediterranean, the Italian fleet, with its four up-to-date battleships, *Andrea Doria, Caio Duilio, Conte di Cavour,* and *Giulio Cesare,* and its two modern battle cruisers, *Littorio* and *Vittorio Veneto,* and the *Zara*-class cruisers—all of which were powerful and fast and in some ways more than a match for the British—could never be brought to action as a fleet.

Secondly, we can learn something from the attitude of the German Admiralty in 1939. In spite of Hitler's alarmingly efficient and coordinated attack on Poland, the German navy was not ready to conduct naval warfare on any scale, so the inevitable role for her few capital ships could only be the *guerre de course,* the attack on enemy trade and shipping routes, a task in which she succeeded remarkably well. The battleship *Tirpitz,* for example, exercised by herself the traditional defensive strategy of "a fleet in being," and the fact that she might have emerged from her various hideouts in the Norwegian fjords at any time up till the autumn of 1943, when she was at last seriously damaged by Lieutenant Place's midget submarine, meant that a great many reconnaissances and other operations had to be set in motion to neutralize threats to the Russian convoys at a time when sufficiently large escort forces could not be spared. The *Tirpitz,* in fact, pinned down several ships of her class for three years and so contributed to the problem of providing carrier support for the *Prince of Wales* and the *Repulse* on what turned out to be their last journey to the Far East. It may be far-fetched to claim that these two capital ships would not have been sunk within an hour of each other off the east coast of Malaya during the fatal month of December, 1941, if they had had such support; but it seems clear, in retrospect, that its absence, together with the lack of sufficient shore-based fighter cover (because of the loss of the airfields in North Malaya) meant that a weak and unbalanced force would run into trouble.

Thirdly, it is convenient to see the Japanese attack on Pearl Harbor on December 7, 1941, as the opening of a second and completely new stage of the war at sea. It was a good omen for the future that the

American carriers *Saratoga, Yorktown, Hornet, Lexington*, and *Enterprise* were not there to be destroyed, since it was the carrier above all fighting ships that proved herself to be the preeminent battle winner during the remaining years of the war. It is, moreover, a proof of the speed at which new ideas lead to concrete results in wartime, when we remember the comparative scarcity of these vessels in 1939.

There were, of course, carrier enthusiasts who saw the shape of things to come, but the more conventional attitude at the beginning of the war, certainly in both America and Britain, was to consider the carrier to be subordinate to the capital ship with her guns. Even the Japanese were building battleships right up to the time of the attack on Pearl Harbor, though they must have been thinking of the carrier fleet as their only practical main force. It is, however, significant that they laid down no more battleships after Pearl Harbor; in fact, the British *Vanguard*, laid down in 1944, was the only capital ship to be built by any navy after that date.

NOTES

[1]See A. J. Marder, *The Anatomy of British Sea Power*, p. 516.

[2]See F. Jane, *The British Fighting Fleet*, p. 309.

[3]Penrose FitzGerald, *Memories of the Sea*, London, 1913, p. 298.

[4]See the *Daily Telegraph*, London, Dec. 29, 1896.

[5]See D. Macintyre, *The Thunder of the Guns*, p. 41.

[6]Marder, *op. cit.*, p. 9.

[7]See *Hansard*, Mar. 7, 1889, 3rd series, cccxxxiii, 1171.

[8]Oliver Warner, *Great Sea Battles*, Weidenfeld & Nicolson, London, 1963, p. 249.

[9]See A. J. Marder, *From Dreadnought to Scapa Flow*, pp. 56–70.

[10]*The Modern Battleship*, Admiralty memorandum, October, 1906. This part was almost certainly written by Fisher himself.

[11]Macintyre, *op. cit.*, p. 239.

[12]Harold and Margaret Sprout, *The Rise of American Naval Power*, p. 278.

[13]Marder, *From Dreadnought to Scapa Flow*, p. 269.

[14]Michael Lewis, *The Navy of Britain*, pp. 607–608.

[15]W. S. Chalmers, *The Life and Letters of David Beatty*, p. 265.

[16]See R. Bacon, *The Life of John Rushton, Earl Jellicoe*, pp. 322–323.

[17]Chalmers, *op. cit.*, p. 272.

[18]Chalmers, *op. cit.*, p. 270.

United States ship *Kearsarge,* laid down in 1898. *The Bettmann Archive, Inc., New York*

United States ship *Louisiana*, laid down in 1903. *Brown Brothers, New York*

These two battleships and the *Connecticut* (page 260) were among the last pre-dreadnoughts built in the United States.

HMS *Dreadnought*. The building of this battle-ship had a great effect on all subsequent warship construction. She was launched at Portsmouth in 1906. She was 526 feet in length, displaced 20,700 tons, and her principal armament was ten 12-inch guns in five turrets. She could achieve a speed of 21 knots. She did not, after all, play a great part in the war with Germany, but she did succeed in ramming and sinking a German U-boat. *Science Museum, London*

(Above) United States ship *Delaware. Brown Brothers, New York*

(Top left) The United States ship *South Carolina* was authorized in 1905. With her sister ship *Michigan*, she was to be far larger and more heavily armed than any previous battleship. This fact convinced Fisher that Britain must build "dreadnoughts," and so began the short-lived era of the all-big-gun capital ship. *The Bettmann Archive, Inc., New York*

(Left) United States ship *North Dakota. The Mariners Museum, Newport News, Virginia*

(Left, top and bottom) These two battleships built in 1907 were the first American dreadnoughts, since they were completed before the *Michigan*.

United States ship *Wyoming,* one of the four "dreadnoughts" built in the 1908–1909 program. She and her sister ship *Arkansas* had twelve 12-inch guns; the other two, *Florida* and *Utah,* had ten. *Brown Brothers, New York*

(Right) HMS *Lion,* battle cruiser launched in 1910. Nicknamed "the Splendid Cat Class," *Lion* and her sister ships *Princess Royal* and *Queen Mary* had larger hulls in order to carry their heavy armament (including eight 13.5-inch and sixteen 4-inch guns) at the required speed of 27 knots. *Lion* was Beatty's flagship and took part in the Dogger Bank action in 1915. She was badly damaged at Jutland in 1916 and was lucky to escape complete destruction. *Imperial War Museum, London and National Maritime Museum, Greenwich*

Germany's first dreadnought battleship, *Nassau,* launched in 1908. *Imperial War Museum, London*

(Left) HMS *Iron Duke,* launched in 1912, was known as a super-dreadnought because her main armament included 13.5-inch guns. She was Jellicoe's flagship till after Jutland. *Oscar Parkes Society, National Maritime Museum, Greenwich*

(Bottom left) HMS *Barham,* launched in 1914, saw service in both World Wars. She and her four sister ships in the *Queen Elizabeth* class were outstanding examples of the battleship. She took part in the Battles of Jutland and Cape Matapan, but she was torpedoed and sunk in November, 1941, between Crete and Cyrenaica. *Oscar Parkes Society, National Maritime Museum, Greenwich*

(Below) The battle cruiser HMS *Renown* in a storm. This photograph was taken from the following aircraft carrier *Ark Royal* when both ships were in Admiral Somerville's "H" Force based on Gibraltar in 1940–1941. *National Maritime Museum, Greenwich*

Ships of the British Atlantic Fleet in 1925. The leading battleship, HMS *Rodney*, *Science Museum, London*

took part in the sinking of the German battleship *Bismarck* in May, 1941.

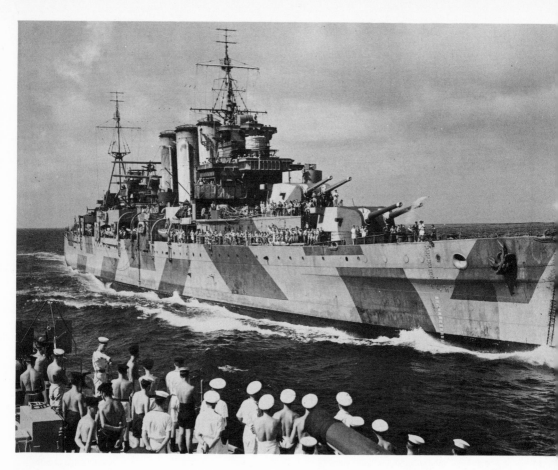

(*Left*) HMS *Devonshire*, British battle cruiser, photographed in the Indian Ocean in 1942. *Imperial War Museum, London*

(*Bottom left*) HMS *Prince of Wales*, battleship launched in 1939 and sunk by Japanese aircraft off east coast of Malaya in 1941. *Imperial War Museum, London*

(*Right*) HMS *Duke of York*, battleship of 1940. *Imperial War Museum, London*

(*Below*) HMS *Hood*, battle cruiser, completed in 1920, sunk by the German battleship *Bismarck* in May, 1941. *Imperial War Museum, London*

The German pocket battleship *Admiral Graf Spee*. Her captain was ordered to scuttle her rather than risk her internment as a result of the River Plate action in December, 1939. *Imperial War Museum, London*

(Top right) The 35,000-ton cruiser *Vittorio Veneto*. One of Italy's four greatest warships in World War II, she took part in the actions off Cape Spartivento and Cape Matapan in 1941 and experienced the British Fleet Air Arm attack on Taranto in November, 1940. *Imperial War Museum, London*

(Right) German pocket battleship *Admiral Scheer*. She was one of the first major warships to leave German waters in the autumn of 1940 to attack British trade routes. *Imperial War Museum, London*

(*Above*) The German battleship *Tirpitz*, launched 1939, the largest capital ship in any navy until the American *Missouri* and the Japanese *Yamato* were completed. Though she fired her big guns only once at an enemy target, she influenced British strategy considerably between January, 1942, and November, 1944. *Imperial War Museum, London*

(Above) United States ship *Missouri*, battleship of the *Iowa* class, launched in 1944. She was Admiral Halsey's flagship, and it was on board this ship that the Japanese surrender ceremony took place. *Brown Brothers, New York*

(Left) United States ship *Missouri*. The 16-inch guns in her forward turret are firing, and the six projectiles can be seen in flight. Note the effect of the blast from the guns on the water. *Brown Brothers, New York*

The Japanese battleship *Yamato*, completed in 1942. Fully loaded she displaced 70,321 tons and was armed with nine 18-inch guns, the largest ever to have been mounted in a ship. She carried seven aircraft, which could be launched from catapults. She was sunk in April, 1945. *Imperial War Museum, London*

HMS *Vanguard*, Britain's last and largest battleship, launched in 1944 and completed in 1946. She was scrapped in 1960. *Admiralty and National Maritime Museum, Greenwich*

United States nuclear-powered attack submarine *Triton*, commissioned in 1959. The world's largest and most powerful submarine and the first to be powered with two nuclear reactors, she circumnavigated the globe submerged in eighty-three days in 1960. *Submarine Library, General Dynamics Corporation, Groton, Connecticut*

XII

 The Submarine in War

THERE CAN be little doubt that the acceptance of the submarine, her development, and the ways in which she was used during the First and Second World Wars constitute an important stage in the evolution of the warship. Therefore, though we have already seen something of the early history of submarines, it is right that they should have a chapter to themselves.

The first British submarine, a boat a mere 60 feet in length, was built to Holland's American design, as we have already noted, and was launched in October, 1901. At this time, even in important naval circles, the whole concept of submersible warships was still suspect. It was thought by some that the submarine was a mere toy and not worthy of serious consideration, while even a future First Sea Lord, Sir A. K. Wilson, thought it to be "underhand, unfair and damned un-English." Luckily, however, the submarine found a protagonist in Fisher, who had the vision to realize that they would revolutionize naval tactics. "The present battle formation of ships in single line presents a target of such length," he wrote characteristically, "that the chances are all in favour of the Whitehead torpedo hitting some ship in the line even when projected from a distance of several miles."

A few years later, and after submarines had been successfully tested on maneuvers, Fisher pressed his argument more strongly, and this time he was determined to convince the British Admiralty, which had come to accept the defensive role submarines might play, that they could also be used offensively, provided that enough of them existed. In a letter to the then Comptroller of the Navy, he talked of the "essential, imperative, immediate, vital, pressing, urgent (I can't think of any more adjectives) necessity for more submarines at once," and the letter closes with the following words, many of them heavily underlined: ". . . in all seriousness I don't think it is even *faintly* realized the *immense impending revolutions which the submarines will effect as offensive weapons* of war."[1] It is this "impending revolution" that we must now examine.

Technically, the early development of the submarine was "groping and erratic";[2] but in the first years of the twentieth century, progress was made with the introduction of more uniform designs and an increased displacement. However, by the time Fisher was writing the words quoted above, the latter still did not exceed 300 tons, and submarines were not used at all in the Russo-Japanese War of 1904–1905. The chief designs after the original Holland A class, developed by the United States Electric Boat Company, were the American *Cuttlefish* (1904) and *Octopus* (1905–1909) classes; the British Holland type, developed by Vickers; the type built by the Whitehead Company in Fiume; the Lake type favored by Russia; the French Laubeuf type; the Italian Laurenti type; and the Germania type begun at Kiel in 1906.[3]

From these, the early experiments of the two principal belligerents in 1914 can be selected for closer examination. For example, the British D class of boat, made by Vickers between 1906 and 1911, displaced 540 tons, had an armament of three torpedo tubes and a quick-firing gun, and was fitted with diesel engines. Its seagoing capabilities were not entirely satisfactory, since it still depended on a parent ship, so the next class was planned to surmount this. In consequence, the displacement in the E-class submarine, built between 1912 and 1918, was increased to 780 tons, the armament was five 18-inch torpedo tubes, with two light 3-inch guns, and these vessels had a radius of 3,225 miles, since they could carry 42 tons of oil. There were further classes, but they were chiefly modifications on the E class—the G, for instance, differed in that there was a double hull, and the K class, in which steam power was used for the first time, was intended to have sufficient speed to maintain station when cruising with the Grand Fleet.

The Germans developed their submarines, the *Unterseeboote*— hence the name U-boats, though they were also known as Krupp boats for a time—some years after other countries. The *U 1*, displacing only 200 tons, was a variation on the French Laubeuf type, with a circular "strength hull," cylindrical at the middle but tapering toward each end. The first fifteen were 110 feet long and each carried 12 mines in six vertical tubes. Numbers 16 through 79 were 162 feet long, had three torpedo tubes, and carried 18 mines. The German navy had thirty-eight submarines at the outbreak of war in 1914, but the last six to be laid down were probably not completed. During the war, Germany built about three hundred U-boats of all classes, with an average displacement between 550 and 850 tons.[4] Two further developments must be noted: the much heavier *Tauchkreuzer*, or submersible cruiser, armed with two 6-inch guns and six torpedo tubes and designed for commerce destruction in 1916, but she was not ready for action till 1918; and the mine-laying submarine, first built in 1915, the UC-boat, which carried her twelve mines in six wells forward. These vessels were small enough to be transported by rail, since they were only about 11 feet long—indeed, one of them, built at Bremen, was conveyed overland to Pola on the Adriatic.

The successes both sides were to have in the First World War must not blind us to the experimental nature of these craft and therefore to the extreme courage and devotion to duty of those who manned them. Of the 372 that Germany owned at the outbreak of war and built during it,[5] 178 were sunk, according to one authority, and 15 more were scuttled to avoid capture; while on the British side, 54 out of a total of 203 were lost, including 26 out of the 56 E-boats, and one-third of the men serving in submarines did not survive the war.

When the time came to assess the value of these latest additions to a battle fleet, it was found that there were a number of conflicting opinions about them, though it was not doubted that individual submarine commanders had acquitted themselves with distinction and that the vessels had, on the whole, proved themselves both efficient and wonderfully adaptable to the changing conditions of modern warfare. The weaknesses should perhaps be listed first, so that we can see the successes in better perspective. First, it was felt by many that the threat the submarine offered had been successfully met by the coordinated effect of one or more of the following: systematic patrolling; air reconnaissance; the convoy system; the arming of merchantmen so that U-boats could attack them only when submerged, that is, when traveling at their slowest; and, finally, such devices as the depth charge, listening apparatus, the American "antenna" mine, and netting. The transportation of more than two million American troops across the Atlantic in 1917 and 1918 without loss gave substance to the claim that the menace had been successfully countered. It was also well known that it was a difficult feat for a submarine to torpedo a moving vessel except at very short range and that if the first torpedo from a very limited supply missed its mark, it was very unlikely that there would be a second chance. The forthright opinion of Professor Hovgaard (see footnote 6 and Bibliography), expressed in 1920, might be taken as typical of those held by many others: "Capital ships," he wrote, "properly guarded by patrol vessels and aircraft, equipped with the latest means of detection of and attack on submarines, and provided with modern systems of internal protection, do not necessarily run any greater risk from submarine attack than from other dangers incidental to naval warfare."[6]

Another serious handicap was the difficulty of maintaining efficient communications, especially when submerged for long periods. The following incident shows how traditional methods had still to be relied on. In August, 1915, the commander of the British submarine *E 6* wished to send important information from Heligoland Bight and found that he was out of telegraphic range. He therefore sent off four pigeons, each with a copy of the message, at 4 A.M. "They had to fly 120 to 140 miles, about WSW wind SSE, about 15 miles per hour, to their traps," this officer wrote, "be found there by their owners, the message removed and taken to the nearest post office; telegraphed from there to Admiralty, decoded and transmitted to HMS *Maidstone* at Harwich, and again decoded." The message was finally received by the addressee at 3:30 P.M.[7] and the officer was Lieutenant Commander C. P. Talbot, later to become Flag Officer, Submarines. Later, all manner of devices were experimented with, but on the whole, they were disappointing. The Fessenden electric gear, for instance, which vibrated and sent out sonic waves into the water and enabled submarines to communicate with each other, even when submerged, had a range of only two to three miles, and enemy listening equipment in range could pick up the signals equally well.

On the other hand, it was appreciated that the strategic value of the submarine was out of all proportion to its size and cost. Episodes in the

Baltic and in the Sea of Marmora showed this very clearly. *E 9*, for instance, traveled seven thousand miles in two months, sinking four ships and damaging a fifth during that time. This was in the Baltic, and the captain of this boat, later Admiral Sir Max Horton, Flag Officer, Submarines, 1940–1942, and Commander in Chief, Western Approaches, 1942–1945, was told that the German Baltic fleet feared his activities more than those of the whole Russian fleet.[8] Again, when the British submarine *B 11* entered the narrows of the Dardanelles on December 13, 1914, she dived under five rows of mines and sank the Turkish battleship *Messudieh* and escaped after having been at one time submerged continuously for a period of nine hours. Indeed, for the loss of five of their number, British submarines sank 2 battleships, 1 destroyer, 5 gunboats, 9 transport vessels, 30 steamers, 7 supply ships, and 188 sailing vessels during 1915 in the Dardanelles campaign, thus completely dislocating the Turkish supply routes.[9]

The great endurance of these small craft must be mentioned next. *E 11* and *E 12* were able to operate for forty days in the Sea of Marmora in 1915 without maintenance, and both these submarines were still in existence at the end of the war. This was equally true of the German U-boats, as it seems to have been normal for them to spend twenty-four days on continuous service, followed by twelve days at the base. *U 41* left Wilhelmshaven on April 25, 1915, reached the Dardanelles on May 25, and torpedoed the *Triumph* the following day and the *Majestic* the day after. Again, in the last months of the war five U-boats operated off the coast of America. Though impressive, such a feat was of little strategic use, as Germany needed to concentrate all her available U-boats on the ocean lanes to the south of Ireland, where the various trade routes began to converge on Britain. It was perhaps more in the nature of a propaganda measure intended to persuade the Americans to keep their destroyers in their own waters.[10]

Right from the beginning, the hitherto untried British submarine succeeded in putting herself on the map. Submarines escorted the successful transportation of the British Expeditionary Force to France in August, 1914, and were given the task of watching the German bases when the strategy of close blockade by cruiser patrols was abandoned. The exploits of *E 9* in Heligoland Bight, leading to the destruction of the light German cruiser *Hela* at a range of 600 yards, and soon after, of the destroyer *S.116*, both within a few miles of the coast, showed what sort of offensive action submarines could take. Indeed, even as early as October, 1914, the First Lord sent a characteristically worded minute to the First Sea Lord that began with the encouraging phrase "please propose without delay the largest possible programme of submarine boats to be delivered in from twelve to twenty-four months from the present time." Submarine production was to be worked to the "absolute maximum," and the Third Sea Lord's department was warned that it was "not to be deterred by the kind of difficulties which hamper action in time of peace."

Germany's decision to starve Britain into submission by intensifying the blockade by submarine began as early as February, 1915, and was later extended to the Atlantic approaches, so that the zone in which these vessels operated was about three hundred miles wide and stretched from the Arctic Circle to about Madeira. By 1917, this aspect of the war had become "unrestricted"; that is, all merchant ships were equally vulnerable, and as U-boats could not bring their captives to shore, it became a very literal form of commerce destruction. Yet there were never really enough U-boats available, though their successes were real enough. One authority has stated that only about 12 per cent of the 110 to 150 U-boats available in 1917–1918 were actually on duty at any one time,[11] though it would seem that this figure is much too low, and the Germans were compelled to use smaller boats for Baltic and North Sea patrols, while they concentrated their main effort on shipping in the western approaches.

Rear Admiral William S. Sims was sent to Europe in 1916 to act as the senior naval liaison officer once it became clear that the United States would join the Allies if Germany extended her U-boat war to all merchant shipping. He appreciated the fact that fighting the submarine was "the most baffling problem presented by the war." Later he became commander of the American naval forces operating in European waters, and in his book, *The Victory at Sea*, published exactly two years after the armistice, he has made some interesting observations on the difference between British and German submarines, though not everyone today would agree with his assessment.

In this context, it is instructive to look ahead and consider the views of Grand Admiral Dönitz. In his *Memoirs*, published after the Second World War, he corrects the landsman's idea that a submarine was an *under*water vessel, stressing that up to 1944, submarines of all nations spent most of their time on the surface. They were, he says, "*diving-vessels*, that is to say surface vessels capable of disappearing from view by diving," but once they were submerged, they were more or less stationary and "their effectiveness was reduced . . . to that of a mine." In consequence, their proper role was to take the offensive on the surface, not to adopt the tactics of a wild beast that crouched in the undergrowth waiting for its quarry to run into its jaws.[12]

The convoy system, introduced rather tardily we may think today, eventually defeated the U-boat threat, and an analysis of losses during the war shows that 44 were sunk by mine; 38 by rudimentary depth charge, first used in 1916; 19 by submarine; 16 by gunfire, and lesser numbers by other causes.

Before we leave the First World War, mention must be made of the American invention of the antenna mine, which made the Northern Barrage project a reality. These mines were invented by Ralph C. Browne, an electrical engineer from Salem, Massachusetts, and their virtue lay in the fact that they were much more economical than any other type of mine. They had copper wires attached to them that could detonate the mine if touched by a ship. The Barrage project was the plan to close the northern entrances to the North Sea, a distance equivalent to that between New York and Washington, with a continuous minefield. Before the invention of the antenna mine, it was not considered feasible, but now that a quarter of the hitherto agreed number of mines seemed sufficient, the American and British governments adopted the scheme, and during the summer of 1918 the mines were being laid from bases at Inverness and Invergordon. The nine minelayers were originally coastal vessels—two of them were the *Bunker's Hill* and the *Massachusetts*, which had run between Boston and New York—but they were mostly renamed to suit the occasion and bore such names as *Shawmut, Canandaigua, Saranac,* and *Quinnebaug*. They had also been altered structurally, since three decks for carrying mines were installed and elevators introduced for the first time to convey the mines as rapidly as possible to the launching track. Nevertheless, it must be admitted that this admirable project was not entirely successful, since the Allies lost a great many ships in the barrages.

The destroyer played an important part in the First World War. It was necessary to destroy torpedo boats with a similar type of ship, but one that was larger, faster, and more seaworthy. For her own protection, as well as in the interests of economy, she was equipped to fire torpedoes so that she could attack ships larger than herself. We saw in an earlier chapter that the Yarrow Company's *Havock* and the Thornycroft Company's *Daring*, both built in 1893, were the first British destroyers. During the next decade, there were setbacks, and it was found difficult to increase both displacement and speed until the introduction of the turbine engine. The strongly built *River* class of 1902–1906 could make 25 knots and had a radius of 1,300 miles when traveling at half speed. The *Cossack* class of 1907 was the first real "oceangoing" destroyer, with a speed of 35 knots, though this was later reduced. Britain built 280 destroyers during the First World War, and among them a new type was introduced as a link between the destroyer and the light cruiser. These flotilla leaders, as they were called, were built in various classes: the first was the *Swift* on 1907, a type that was repeated in the *Faulknor* and *Broke* of 1914, for instance, and in several others that gradually attained a higher speed and heavier armament.

In the United States, destroyers of the *Duncan* class of 1912, the *Jacob Jones* class of 1915, and the *Sampson* class of 1916 were similar to the British but had, on the whole, a more powerful armament. In France, the destroyer had a noticeably lower freeboard, while in Germany the *Torpedo-Divisionsboot*, the equivalent of the flotilla leader, was built much earlier than elsewhere. She was smaller than her British counterpart, however, and had, relatively speaking, more punch in her torpedo armament than in her guns.

Active service proved the efficacy of the destroyer in two main roles: in protecting and escorting battleships and in hunting out and destroying U-boats. During the Dardanelles campaign, there were occasions when battleships not actually required for shore bombardment had to make for shelter, and as one war correspondent expressed it, " . . . for a period of nearly two months the care of the narrow waters and the duty of protecting the transports and covering the flanks of the army fell to the destroyers."[13] At the Battle of Jutland, destroyers were used as a screen for capital ships, for protection against other destroyers and U-boats, and for direct attack against capital ships. Guarding lines of communication, surprise night bombardments, and even ramming submarines were other tasks that came their way; but it seems that in whatever role they were employed, the gun was the main offensive weapon and the torpedo secondary to it. Five 4.7-inch guns were mounted in the British flotilla leader *Shakespeare* of 1914, and this caliber of gun thoroughly justified itself and was retained throughout the war. In conclusion, it is interesting to note that 68 out of the 354 United States ships in European waters at the end of 1918 were destroyers.

At the end of the war, the L class was the most up-to-date British submarine. She was half as large again as the E, was more efficient, and was armed with six 21-inch torpedoes and one 4-inch gun. There were also a few R-class submarines, designed to deal with other submarines, and they could make 15 knots when submerged, which was twice their surface speed. In the early postwar years, experiments were carried out with the object of building a satisfactory fleet submarine, but the *K 26* was no more successful than other K-boats had been, and she was soon abandoned. The *X 1* was an attempt to build the largest submarine possible so that she could take on the additional task of surface raiding. She was armed with four 5.25-inch guns in twin turrets, but she too was a failure, probably because the development of submarine engineering had not yet caught up with the new designs.

It was therefore natural that when Britain started building submarines seriously in the middle 1920's and onward, she gave up experimenting and producing "freaks" of doubtful value and concentrated on two types of patrolling vessels, a larger O class—though from this time onward, names were introduced in place of letters and numbers—and a smaller one. The *Porpoise,* in service by 1931, was the first special mine-laying submarine. From then on and into the Second World War, submarines became much more standardized: they were usually double-hulled, with the thin outer hull containing the principal ballast tanks, and the torpedoes were the 21-inch type. The improvements during these years were in the fittings and especially in the listening devices.

Most larger submarines were equipped with Asdic, as sonar control was then called in Britain, a British invention that was undergoing great development at this time. It was clear, too, that radar would soon become available. This happened early in the war, and the detection range of a surfaced submarine was considerably increased and, in consequence, the time a submarine could spend on the surface recharging batteries was reduced, especially as darkness no longer provided adequate security. These advances in antisubmarine weapons led designers to experiment with stronger hulls that would enable submarines to dive deeper and thereby increase the chances of a depth charge missing its mark.

The performance of submarines in the Second World War can best be illustrated by the events of the Battle of the Atlantic, which began on the day the war was declared and continued till May 4, 1945. It was a grim and somber period, lit up only by deeds of great individual bravery and an enduring devotion to duty displayed by both sides in the struggle. As in the First World War, Germany nearly succeeded in her task of breaking Britain's Atlantic supply lines, and her U-boats were modern and efficient, incorporating, almost up to the end, new improvements as they were made available. She started with 57 operational boats, but two years later she had 485 in service. At the end of the war, her U-boats had been responsible for 69 per cent of the total losses in British, Allied, and neutral shipping, yet the monthly figures were barely half those of the submarine campaign in the First World War. However, 781 U-boats were sunk, mostly by surface ships and shore-based aircraft, but also by carrier-borne aircraft and submarines; out of this total, the United States Navy and Air Force destroyed 132.

It is not our object to cover the successive stages of this great battle but rather to examine the problem set by the new type of warfare, remembering that new tactical uses for submarines evolved parallel to the development in antisubmarine weapons.

As we shall see in the next chapter, the carrier-borne aircraft was perhaps the greatest antisubmarine weapon of all, and ever after the successful sinking of *U 64* by a Swordfish aircraft catapulted from *Warspite* in the second Battle of Narvik in April, 1940, it was clear that therein lay a major threat to submarine activities. Here, however, we must note more detailed items that, taken together, added up to a major counteroffensive. There were three types of depth charge, on which the surface vessel relied almost entirely. They contained 250 pounds T.NT., 290 pounds amatol, and 300 pounds minol, respectively, and could be set to detonate at depths varying between 50 and 500 feet. Later, a slightly lighter version of this type of charge was supplied to aircraft containing 185 pounds Torpex explosive, and it had a special head and "break-off" tail to ensure the required trajectory both in the air and in the water. "Snowflake," which was a brilliant form of illuminant, net defenses, and the "Hedgehog" weapon were other experimental devices that were tried out. The "Hedgehog" was a weapon designed, in 1942, to reach a U-boat with which the warship was still in sonar contact. It was a salvo of twenty-four charges, each of which contained about 30 pounds of explosive, and was fired ahead of the ship from a twenty-four-spigot mortar. It was a great improvement on the original depth charge, but to ensure a kill, a direct hit was necessary. It led to the invention of the "Squid," a three-barreled mortar which fired a pattern of charges ahead of the ship and which could be set to explode at any depth. A new explosive called Minol, twice as powerful as Torpex, began to be used about halfway through the war; it could crack the hull of a U-boat more effectively than ever before.

By the early summer of 1943, the U-boat had been forced onto the defensive, but the Germans had perfected at about the same time their most successful methods of defeating the Allied antisubmarine measures. These were a search receiver known as *Hagenuk,* which defeated aircraft radar for a time, and a development of the Dutch-invented *Schnorchel* ventilating apparatus, which eventually made surfacing to recharge batteries unnecessary, since air could be drawn through a tube down to the diesel engines and the exhaust gases expelled.[14] The German acoustic torpedo should also be mentioned. It was homed onto its target by the sound of a ship's propellers and was used mainly against escort vessels. It was, however, countered by a noise-making device towed by escort ships to attract torpedoes. Among the better known antisubmarine measures, we should notice the improved technique of the convoy system, which favored evasive routing, and the inclusion of specific rescue ships. Details such as the provision of automatic radio sets in lifeboats and red lights on life jackets assisted in rescue work and helped to maintain morale; but perhaps, above all, emphasis should be placed on the decision made at the Atlantic Convoy Conference held at Washington in March, 1943, to pool Allied resources, to standardize procedure, and to use aircraft operating from escort carriers for antisubmarine duties and for closing the Atlantic gap, that is, the area between the shore-based aircraft's sphere of activity on each side of the ocean.

The Battle of the Atlantic was, in Churchill's phrase, "a war of groping and drowning, of ambuscade and stratagem, of science and seamanship," and in it a prominent part was played by the submarine. In these boats, the crews demonstrated the growing efficiency of this type of warship, practising the art of underwater attack, limiting the necessity of surfacing to the minimum, and using to the best advantage their increasing knowledge of the new tactical weapons that had so recently come into their hands. To the historically minded among those who took part in the continuous sixty-eight months of this tensely fought aspect of the war at sea, it must have seemed a long time since Fulton's *Nautilus* blew up the *Dorothy* brig off the Sussex coast and so great a sailor as St. Vincent could criticize the younger Pitt for encouraging "a mode of warfare which those who commanded the sea did not want and which, if successful, would at once deprive them of it."[15]

NOTES

[1]See article by Lt. Comdr. Peter Kemp in *The Times,* London, Sept. 30, 1961.

[2]William Hovgaard, *Modern History of Warships,* p. 296.

[3]*Ibid.,* pp. 297–306.

[4]See *Jane's Fighting Ships,* 1918.

[5]See P. K. Kemp, *HM Submarines,* p. 131.

[6]Hovgaard, *op. cit.,* p. 325.

[7]See F. W. Lipscomb, *The British Submarine,* p. 88.

[8]See W. S. Chalmers, *Max Horton and the Western Approaches,* Hodder & Stoughton, London, 1954, pp. 17–18.

[9]Lipscomb, *op. cit.,* p. 93.

[10]See William S. Sims, *The Victory at Sea,* p. 269.

[11]Hovgaard, *op. cit.,* p. 323.

[12]See Karl Dönitz, *Memoirs,* translated by R. H. Stevens in collaboration with David Woodward, Weidenfeld & Nicolson, London, 1959, pp. 127–128.

[13]E. Ashmead-Bartlett, letter in *The Times,* London, Oct. 19, 1915.

[14]Dönitz, *op. cit.,* p. 353.

[15]Kemp, *op. cit.,* p. 21.

British Submarine *E 7*. Fifty-six E-class submarines were built between 1912–1918. Their displacement of 780 tons and their general performance were great improvements on those of the earlier classes. They had five 18-inch torpedo tubes and a radius of more than three thousand miles, since they could carry 42 tons of oil. *E 7* saw action in Heligoland Bight and in the Dardanelles, where she was sunk in September, 1915. *Imperial War Museum, London*

British submarine monitor *M 1* (ex-*K 18*), July, 1917. Three of these boats, each armed with a 12-inch gun, were laid down during the war but were discontinued in accordance with the terms of the Washington Treaty of 1922. The submarine dived to about 20 feet with the gun laid to high-angle elevation so that its muzzle was above water. *M 1* was sunk in a collision in 1925. *Imperial War Museum, London*

(Top left) USS *Shawmutt.*

(Left) USS *Canandaigua.*

(Left, top and bottom) Originally intended for coastal defense, these two ships were among those converted into minelayers and were used in the project of laying antenna mines in 1918 to block the northern entrances to the North Sea when the German U-boat threat was at its height. *The Mariners Museum, Newport News, Virginia*

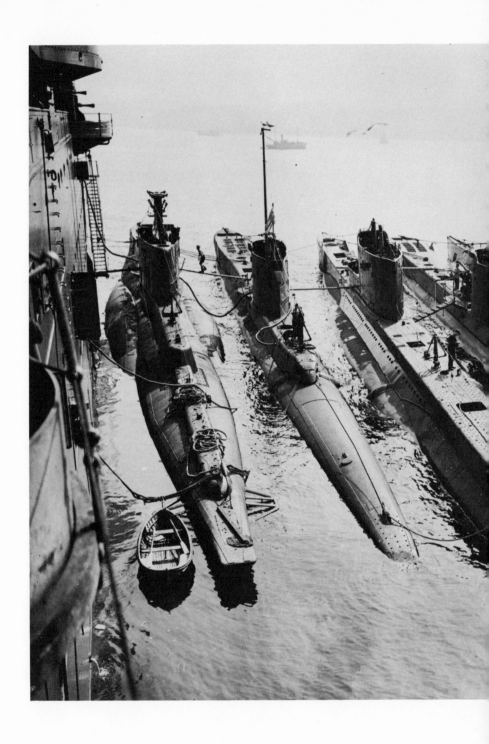

British submarine
flotilla alongside
a depot ship, World
War II. *Imperial War
Museum, London*

(Above) HMS *Graph,* ex-German U-boat *U 570,* World War II. *Imperial War Museum, London*

(Left) British midget submarine—about the size of an ordinary torpedo—known as a "chariot." She had an electric battery-fed motor and was driven by two men in diving suits. Their task was to fix the detachable warhead of a torpedo onto the underparts of an enemy ship. The Italians first developed this device. *Imperial War Museum, London*

United States atomic submarine *Nautilus,* commissioned in 1954. Her bulbous prow enables her to travel faster underwater than on the surface. She has a diving depth of 700 feet and is propelled by atomic power, diesel, or electric motors. *Science Museum, London*

HMS *Indomitable*, aircraft carrier completed in March, 1940. Her flight deck was 753 feet long by 95 feet wide, and she could accommodate more than sixty aircraft. She was scrapped soon after the end of World War II. *Imperial War Museum, London*

XIII

The Aircraft Carrier

SINCE the end of the Second World War, the combination of aircraft and suitable ships from which they can operate has been accepted so irrevocably that it seems difficult to recall the days when this cooperation did not exist. Yet the early days of this partnership are well worth studying, not merely because they show instances of the solution of an entirely new set of problems, but also because they show us the slow dawning of a realization that perhaps herein lay the future of naval warfare. Governments tended to be cautious, suspicious, sceptical, or frankly incredulous, so that the ultimate success of what could already be called the naval air arm even in the First World War was a triumph of individual heroism and determination as well as a victory over certain technical difficulties.

The early dirigibles were self-propelled balloons filled with gas and shaped like cigars or cucumbers with small carriages suspended below them that contained the power plant and accommodation for passengers. They could be directed by rudders, and they were either rigid, semirigid, or nonrigid. From them developed the "kite balloons," nonrigid and sausage-shaped, that were used on board warships as elevated observation posts. Dupuy de Lôme, whom we have met already in these pages, made one of the earliest dirigibles in 1871. It had a volume of 122,000 cubic feet and was propelled by a two-bladed screw worked by a team of eight men. Though successful in its initial trials, it was unquestionably slow, and it was not until petrol- and light-oil engines had been invented that the project became really practicable. Of the early types of airships, Count Ferdinand von Zeppelin's aluminum-framed vessels were the most famous as early as 1913, though freak weather conditions brought disaster in their early trials.

The next stage after the airship was the airplane. The exploits of the Wright brothers in the early 1900's and of the French aeronautical pioneers—Farman with his "pusher" biplane and Blériot with his tractor monoplane—led to the first seaplane, that of Henri Fabre, produced in 1910, though it was not till Glenn H. Curtiss produced one in the following year that the seaplane was fully accepted. In 1912, Curtiss' fourth seaplane, the *Triad,* was adopted by the United States Navy, and two years later his *America* was designed for crossing the Atlantic. This plane had a radius of thirteen hours and could travel at a speed of 50 knots and so was equal to the best planes anywhere. It was soon appreciated that seaplanes were cheaper and handier than dirigibles because they were smaller, but a drawback was that they were slower and had a smaller carrying capacity than ordinary planes because of their floats. Originally, they were started on their flights by being put overboard on cranes, becoming airborne after a short run in the water. Later, when planes could take off direct, it was realized that the more difficult problem was the landing. The first flight from a moving vessel took place during the naval review at Weymouth in 1912 when a biplane took off from the forecastle of the British battleship *Hibernia* when she was traveling at a speed of 10½ knots.

All these developments brought nearer the invention of the aircraft carrier. Once again, the French were the pioneers, as their cruiser *Foudre* was fitted out to carry aircraft for maneuvers in the Mediterranean in 1913. She carried two planes: one was launched from a runway, while the second was hoisted out like a ship's boat. Both were hoisted in again by means of cranes. The first British ship to be improvised as a carrier was the old cruiser *Hermes.* She was fitted to carry two seaplanes that could be launched on trolleys from a short deck built forward from her bows. This was in 1913, and this vessel became the parent ship of the Royal Naval Air Service, officially established on July 1, 1914, though she was torpedoed four months later, a particular tragedy since it meant that the flight deck was hardly tested in action.

But it is more accurate to say that the first real British carrier was the oil tanker taken over in 1914 by the Admiralty while she was still being built and completed as a carrier for seaplanes, with hangar space below-decks and cranes for hoisting her ten planes onto and off the water. She was called the *Ark Royal,* an honored name, as the original ship to bear it was Howard of Effingham's flagship, which fought the Spaniards in 1588. Admiral Sir William Jameson, in his book about the third *Ark Royal*, makes the pleasant suggestion that perhaps the carrier's name was a graceful reference to Noah's despatch of the dove from his ark, "the first recorded use of successful air reconnaissance from afloat."[1] She made history on at least one occasion, when, a year later, her seven Sopwith Camel planes successfully bombed the Zeppelin bases at Tondern in 1918.

She was used during the Dardanelles campaign and in the immediate postwar years for dealing with danger spots in the Middle East. Her name was changed to *Pegasus* in 1935, and she was used as an experimental ship for trying out launching catapults. At this time, she could carry thirty-six planes. Luxury liners, too, such as the *Campania*, were adapted for this purpose, but experience soon showed that a long high-speed vessel was the most suitable, so the 18-inch-gunned battle cruiser *Furious* was converted in 1916 in such a way that planes could both take off and land again on her deck. Yet even she was at first unsatisfactory in that her 228-foot by 50-foot landing deck was too short, and the swirling air from the funnels provided an additional handicap. This was overcome when she was rebuilt with an unbroken deck from fore to aft, and the smoke from the funnels was led off to the sides through horizontal pipes. She was finally broken up in 1954. The British carrier *Hermes* of 1919 was built with the bridge and funnel placed on one side of the deck, and this "island" design was to become standard.

Right from early days of aircraft, it was realized that their role in war would include the detection of submarines, but soon it was appreciated that they could be used offensively, that they could destroy with bombs and even torpedoes the submarines that they detected. On the whole, however, their use in the First World War lay in the patrolling of Britain's coasts, and offensive action was limited to the bombing of submarine bases in Belgium. At this stage of aircraft development, to attack a moving ship was difficult, since it was hard to achieve the element of surprise, nor were the bombs carried powerful enough to achieve very much. When, for instance, the Turkish ship the *Sultan Selim*—the former German cruiser *Goeben*—was bombed in the Golden Horn from the height of a mere 800 feet by a naval Handley Page aircraft, she was not sunk; and she was to survive a similar attack a few months later, though on that occasion she was damaged very much more severely.

By the summer of 1918, seventy aircraft and thirty kite balloons were carried on board ships of the British Grand Fleet, and it was also accepted doctrine that aircraft were indispensable as protection to convoys against the dangers of the submarine.

The First World War taught the lesson to those prepared to learn it that aircraft must frequently operate from ships, with its corollary that the usefulness of shore-based aircraft was often severely limited. To recapitulate, the evolution of the modern carrier began with the modification of existing ships, such as cross-Channel steamers, so that they could accommodate seaplanes, though at this stage there was no need of a flight deck. Next came the real aircraft carriers that we have mentioned, such as the first *Hermes* and the *Ark Royal*, with small forward flight decks, though they were not often used for takeoff and never for landing, and the seaplane was still envisaged as the only possible naval plane. The next stage was the conversion in 1915 of the Isle of Man packet *Vindex* so that she could carry two fighters as well as five seaplanes and could launch the former from a 64-foot flight deck sited forward, though the problem of landing the planes was not yet solved. In 1916 and 1917, the modern principle of bringing the planes up from the hangar and onto the flight deck above through a sliding roof was introduced in the *Manxman,* the *Nairana,* and the *Pegasus;* and in 1917, too, great strides were made with the conversion of the *Campania* so that she could launch seaplanes mounted on trolleys and, more important, so that the size of her flight deck made eventual landing-on a possibility and not just a dream.

Takeoff and landing-on were first possible in the *Argus,* originally the *Conte Rosso,* a liner being built for Italy, because she had for the first time a flight deck from bow to stern, 550 feet in length and 68 feet wide. She was not completed in time to see war service, but she was of great importance in the early postwar years for further trials. The *Eagle,* originally the *Almirante Cochrane* and purchased from Chile; the *Furious,* on whose deck the first "stunt" landing had been made as early as 1917; and the second *Hermes,* completed in 1923 and the first ship in the world specially built as a carrier, are important names in the evolutionary process we are describing. With the *Courageous* and *Glorious,* sister ships of the *Furious,* though fitted with different "arrester gear," as well as having the island bridge and funnel on the starboard side of the flight deck, it can be seen that the British navy had six carriers by 1930. But the pressing need to economize blinded the eyes of the politicians, so the Admiralty was unable to build up the balanced fleet required. It was not until 1937, the year in which the third *Ark Royal*, designed to carry seventy-two aircraft, was launched, that the Admiralty was empowered to build more carriers. The *Illustrious*, *Victorious*, *Formidable*, and *Indomitable* were ordered in that year and the *Implacable* and *Indefatigable* in 1938.

Meanwhile, the United States had laid down two carriers, the *Lexington* and the *Saratoga*, in 1925. They were originally intended to be battle cruisers displacing over 40,000 tons, but this was disallowed by the terms of the Washington Treaty, so they were converted into carriers instead. They were colossal in every way, and they were not surpassed for nearly twenty years: in each of them the four individual funnels were encased in a single containing funnel that stood 130 feet above the water; the flight deck was 909 feet long and 105 feet wide; they could make a speed of 34½ knots; they had a main armament of eight 8-inch guns; and they could carry ninety planes and a crew of 1,788 men. They cost $45,000,000 each, and a further $15,000,000 was spent when they were modernized in 1939.[2]

By the time war broke out in 1939, the United States, Great Britain, and Japan alone had appreciated the likely developments in any future war and had taken steps to equip themselves with carriers as best they could. Indeed, they can be said to be the only countries to have taken the carrier seriously. The American navy had six, the British thirteen, and the Japanese ten, with five more being built. It should, however, be noted that six of the British carriers were still uncompleted and that the *Ark Royal* was the only really modern one among them; also, they could only carry about half as many aircraft as the American and Japanese carriers. In other navies, little progress had been made: the carrier being built in Germany at the beginning of the war was never completed; the French had only one, and she was twenty years old; and the Italians had none at all.

The tactical use of carrier-borne aircraft had to be adapted to the circumstances obtaining at any given time and also to their availability. It was appreciated in Britain that the Germans would concentrate again on the long-range U-boats that had so nearly been successful before and, banking on a short war, would hope thereby to dominate the scene, together with their battleships and cruisers and shore-based long-range bombers, before the enemy could build up her carrier force. The western approaches to Britain, in any case, were likely to bear the brunt of the attack on seaborne trade, so it is interesting to see, in the very first year of the war, the idea taking shape of a carrier, escorted by a "hunting group" of four destroyers, being stationed at a key point in order to keep that area clear of U-boats. Unluckily, the first tryout of this scheme led to the destruction of the carrier *Courageous,* so it was discontinued, though it was revived later when the smaller and therefore more quickly constructed escort carriers were brought into use.

It is not intended to do more here than show very briefly how the new carriers and their aircraft were gradually integrated into the fleet and came to assume a more and more important role. This can be conveniently studied in two stages, taking the attack on Pearl Harbor as the approximate dividing point. In the first stage, we shall consider developments in the British fleet; in the second, those in the fleets of the United States and Japan.

The sinking of the German cruiser *Königsberg* at Bergen during the Norwegian campaign in 1940 by British Fleet Air Arm Skuas was a fully naval affair, though these aircraft were not, in fact, operating from a carrier, since *HMS Sparrowhawk* was a shore station in the Orkneys. Toward the end of that year, the attack on Taranto, the Italian naval base only twelve hours from Malta by sea, affected the balance of naval power throughout the Mediterranean. Twenty-four torpedo-carrying Swordfish from the carrier *Illustrious,* as a result of great determination and meticulous practice in preparation for a difficult and novel task, sank an Italian battleship, the *Conte di Cavour.* Two others, the new *Littorio* and the older *Duilio,* were severely enough hit to be out of action for some months. A cruiser and two destroyers were also hit, and the seaplane base and oil-storage depot there were badly damaged. Only two Swordfish were lost in this daring raid, which Admiral Cunningham described later as an unsurpassed example of economy of force.

In March, 1941, the Battle of Cape Matapan showed a good example of the growing coordination between naval aircraft and surface ships, illustrating how the former gave the latter added flexibility. Though the Italian battleship *Vittorio Veneto* escaped on this occasion, the cruisers *Zara, Fiume, Pola,* and two destroyers were sunk; and the importance of the action to the British was that never again did the Italian fleet challenge them, so that it led to the eventual recovery of that supremacy in the eastern Mediterranean so vital to British interests, especially as a very short time after the battle, Greece and Crete were to be overrun by the Germans.

Two months later, the sinking of the 42,500-ton battleship *Bismarck* marked the end of one strand of German naval strategy, since never again were battleships or, indeed, any large warships sent out against the convoy routes. Here again the Swordfish aircraft from the carriers *Ark Royal* and *Victorious* showed their value as a striking force at sea, and it is certain that without them the *Bismarck* might have reached Brest and safety.

The defense of Malta and of the Russian convoys, especially during the first three years of the war, the gallant though unavailing defense of Crete in 1941, and the close support given to the army, first in the Madagascar landings and then on a far greater scale in the North African and Salerno landings, all illustrated the now accepted axiom that command of the sea also implied command of the air above those seas. All of these operations showed a new dimension, so to speak, in naval warfare, that in which carrier-borne aircraft could give protective cover, could conduct tactical reconnaissance, and could smother opposition while a military landing was in progress, as well as conduct the more conventional, though no less important, task of preventing U-boats from interfering.

Lastly, mention must be made of the convoys and their protection against the threat of the U-boat. Inevitably, this overlaps to some extent with the subject matter of the previous chapter, but there are still a few general points to be made. The Battle of the Atlantic began, though apparently by accident, with the sinking of the Donaldson liner *Athenia* two hundred miles west of the Hebrides, on the very day that Britain declared war on Germany. After that, it continued with mounting intensity, only slackening in the middle of 1943. The task of the navy, therefore, was to keep open the Atlantic sea-lanes and to pay particular attention to the gap between the shore-based air cover radiating out on each side of the Atlantic Ocean. Air patrols over the convoy gave their most effective protection, since they forced the U-boats to remain submerged and therefore slowed them down. After the fall of Norway and France, the U-boat campaign was intensified, since the conquest of those countries provided Germany with many new bases. For a time, the escort carrier provided the answer. She developed from the merchant aircraft-carrier ship ("macship"), the first of which, the *Audacity,* formerly the *Empire Audacity* but originally the German ship *Hannover,* was provided with a flight deck 400 feet by 60 feet. In a short fighting career of five months, she was able to show how Focke-Wulf aircraft could be beaten off by her six American-built Martlets, which also flew antisubmarine patrols. Nevertheless, the carrying capacity was inadequate, so the escort carrier was evolved with more aircraft that not only could bring greater striking power to bear, but also could cover wide areas of ocean and could call on smaller warships—frigates and corvettes, for instance—to deal with the U-boats they detected. Soon the numbers of very long-range aircraft were increased and the escort carrier was no longer needed. The convoy system relied on escort groups, support groups, and shore-based aircraft such as the small and easily maneuverable plane, the Swordfish, which remained useful for this work long after it had been superseded by the much faster Barracuda in fleet actions.

We must now turn to the war in the Pacific. As was noted earlier, the Japanese built up a powerful fleet that included a carrier-borne air arm, and she was rewarded with successes in 1941 and early 1942 that were both dramatic and geographically extensive. The sinking of the unescorted British battleships *Prince of Wales* and *Repulse* by twenty-seven bombers and sixty-one torpedo planes, the attack on Pearl Harbor, and the conquest of Hong Kong, Malaya, Singapore, Siam, the Philippines, Burma, the Netherlands East Indies, and Borneo need no further elaboration to emphasize these successes; but the Japanese were well aware that in the long run, the might of America would tell against them. They saw, too, that the oil that was so essential for their ships had to be transported from great distances and that the routes for their tankers were extremely vulnerable. Japanese strategy therefore was to establish an outer defensive perimeter in the mid-Pacific, from the Aleutian Islands, south to Midway, and then southwestward to Samoa, Fiji, and New

Guinea, and to deny the Americans the use of these islands as bases from which to counterattack.

By the second half of 1942, however, the United States had delayed the Japanese advance and began the slow task of pushing them back. This is the importance of the Battle of the Coral Sea in May, as a result of which the Japanese failed to capture Port Moresby in New Guinea, and of the Battle of Midway in June and of the long-drawn-out struggles for Guadalcanal in the South Pacific, since these actions resulted in the United States moving into the area of the Ellice, Gilbert, and Marshall Islands and Japan being forced back to an inner chain of defenses far nearer to her own islands.

At Midway, Admiral Yamamoto's fleet looked formidable enough on paper, as it included his flagship, the 64,000 ton *Yamato*, armed with nine 18-inch guns, the battleships *Nagato* and *Mutsu*, with eight 16-inch guns each, and four other battleships armed with twelve 14-inch guns each. Yet Admiral Nimitz, with no battleships at all, but three carriers, the *Yorktown, Enterprise*, and *Hornet*, was able to bring about the eventual destruction of all four Japanese carriers, the *Akagi, Kaga, Soryu*, and *Hiryu*, while the Japanese battleships were powerless to support them. Yamamoto made a costly error, we can now see, when he decided to use the aircraft from his carriers to batter the island and not to attack the American carriers immediately. Perhaps he expected, as Professor Morison has suggested, that Midway would capitulate easily and that he could move his vast force there and use it as a base from which to launch an attack later on those carriers that, unbeknown to him, were already in the area.[3] But whatever his motives, the outcome of the battle marked a decisive stage in the Pacific war, since it showed how quickly the situation could be reversed if sea power did not include air power. In the remaining years of the war, aircraft carriers came more and more into the forefront, since, quite apart from other considerations, large warships could not operate among the islands of the western Pacific without their own air cover. Japan was therefore at a distinct disadvantage. She had lost four of her six fleet carriers at Midway, and only the *Taiho* of those being built was to be ready before the end of the war, and she was to be lost in her first action in June, 1944.

Guadalcanal, drawn out over several months, proved too that

battleships could do little but cover the advance of invading forces by bombarding the shore defenses or acting as carrier escorts.

In 1943, the United States was able to mount her counteroffensive, with General MacArthur, the Supreme Commander, Southwest Pacific Area, advancing on the Philippines from the south and Admiral Nimitz, Commander in Chief, Pacific Fleet and Pacific Ocean Area, driving west from Hawaii to meet him, behind a screen of carriers, and thereby cutting off Japan's communications with many of her conquests among the southern islands. Thus the stage was set for the Battle of Leyte Gulf.

By the early autumn of 1944, this counteroffensive was well advanced, and the Japanese were compelled to put their "Sho" plan into effect. This was an attempt to divert the main American carrier task force, Admiral Halsey's Third Fleet, from the Philippines by an attack from the north with all the remaining carriers she could muster, namely, her last large carrier, *Zuikaku*, and three lighter ones, the battleships *Hyuga* and *Ise*, and other vessels, all under the command of Vice Admiral Ozawa. While the Third Fleet was thus engaged, it was hoped to launch a pincerlike attack on the American landings in the Philippines by means of the coordinated arrival of several forces from Singapore and from the north, of which the most powerful was Admiral Kurita's center force, which comprised the main Japanese surface-force ships, the 64,000-ton battleships *Yamato* and *Musashi*, with their 18-inch guns, as well as several older battleships, twelve cruisers, and fifteen destroyers.

As a result of the series of actions between October 23 and 27, 1944, now generally called the Battle of Leyte Gulf, Japan lost the Pacific and was unable to halt the American advance. It was a decisive battle, therefore, and because of the number of ships engaged, one of the greatest naval actions of all time. The figures have been compared with those of Jutland, and if we use this comparison, we find that whereas in the earlier battle 151 British and 99 German ships took part, at Leyte 216 American, 2 Australian, and 64 Japanese ships engaged, not counting the hosts of amphibious craft, minesweepers, and other ancillary vessels. More important for our present purpose, at least two of the engagements, those of the Sibuyan Sea and Cape Engaño, showed the new type of naval battle emerging in unambiguous clarity, for they were essentially actions between carrier-borne aircraft, in spite of the battle as a whole revealing all the methods of conducting warfare yet invented. These two actions were fought out between carrier-borne aircraft, and it is significant that both Halsey and Kurita can be criticized for concentrating perhaps too much on destroying the enemy's carriers.

When the Battle of Leyte Gulf could be seen in some kind of perspective, it was clear that the battleship had outlived her usefulness. Halsey's battleships never succeeded in bringing their 16-inch guns to bear on Kurita's; and inevitably, after Leyte, they were being used merely as escorts for carriers or for bombardment in support of landings. The Japanese failure struck home more forcibly still: *Musashi* had been sunk by dive bombers and torpedo planes in the Sibuyan Sea, while the great *Yamato* herself missed the chance of annihilating the carrier force that was virtually within her grasp, and in April of the following year was herself bombed, torpedoed, and sunk.

After the Second World War, the lessons that it taught were studied and pondered over, and the contribution of the ship-borne aircraft was seen to have been considerable. Yet almost immediately, new challenges presented themselves, such as the jet engine, which increased the speed of aircraft by about 50 per cent and so brought in once again the problem of landing on board a ship. The angled deck provided an answer, as can be seen, for example, in the magnificent United States carrier *Forrestal* of 1955, at one time the largest warship in the world, with a carrying capacity of from 90 to 100 planes, a speed of 34 knots, and a displacement of 75,900 tons. The steam catapult, which gives additional launching power; the introduction of the helicopter, with its ability to take off and land on a small platform; and the whole question of nuclear power, both in carriers themselves and in submarines, are some of the other modern developments affecting the warship, developments which make it quite impossible to think that this chapter of our story has come to a close.

NOTES

[1]W. Jameson, *Ark Royal*, Rupert Hart-Davis, London, 1957, p. 19.
[2]See Björn Landström, *The Ship*, p. 255.
[3]See Samuel E. Morison, *History of United States Naval Operations in World War II*, Little, Brown and Company, Boston, 1955, vol. iv, pp. 78–79.

(Right) HMS *Argus*, aircraft carrier, originally the *Conte Rosso*, a liner building for Italy. She was the first ship to have an unrestricted flight deck from bow to stern; it was 550 feet long by 68 feet wide. *Imperial War Museum, London*

(Bottom right) A Sopwith *Camel* plane about to land on the flight deck of HMS *Argus*. *Imperial War Museum, London*

(Below) HMS *Ark Royal*, the first British aircraft carrier. Originally an oil tanker, she was adapted to accommodate seven seaplanes in hangars below-decks and was equipped with cranes for hoisting the aircraft onto and off the water. *Imperial War Museum, London*

HMS *Audacity*, merchant aircraft carrier ("macship"), was the first stage in the development of the escort carrier. *Imperial War Museum, London*

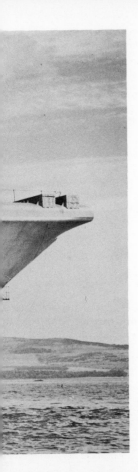

(Overleaf) United States aircraft carriers *Saratoga* and *Lexington* seen from the flight deck of USS *Ranger*. The *Saratoga* and *Lexington* were both laid down in 1925 and were originally intended to be battle cruisers. They could each carry ninety planes, and their flight decks were 909 feet long. *Culver Pictures, Inc., New York*

(Left) HMS *Implacable*, aircraft carrier completed in December, 1942. *Imperial War Museum, London*

(Below) USS *Saratoga*, fleet aircraft carrier, completed in 1927. She is here seen at anchor in San Diego Harbor. *Brown Brothers, New York*

United States aircraft carrier *For-restal*, completed in 1955, and her five sister ships were the largest prenuclear warships in the world. Though intended originally to have been flush-decked with a retract-able bridge, she was redesigned with angled deck and "island" superstructure on her starboard side. She can carry ninety to one hundred aircraft, which can land and take off at the same time, and her deck is fitted with four large lifts. *Brown Brothers, New York*

United States aircraft carrier *Yorktown* (1936) took part in the Battles of the Coral Sea and Midway Island in May–June, 1942, though she was severely damaged at Midway and was torpedoed a few days later. *Mariners Museum, Newport News, Virginia*

Epilogue

"The sea," wrote Joseph Conrad, "has never been friendly to man. At most it has been the accomplice of human restlessness." It is in this latter role, with its ceaseless movement, that it symbolizes the evolution of the warships that have sailed upon it. Since man seems likely to continue to fight against his fellows as long as greed, jealousy, vaulting ambition, but also faith in a just cause, remain human characteristics, it is certain that he will continue to go down to the sea in ships and conduct the business of war in great waters. Equally certain is it that the ships in which he will fight will change, imitating, as it were, the rise and fall of the waves, the ceaseless ebb and flow, the very patterns of darkness and light among the moving waters.

It is for these reasons that it would be difficult to bring a book such as this to a satisfactory close, were there not developments in the years since the Second World War ended that seem to mark the end of a whole era because they show that a new, very different one is beginning. The first atom bomb was successfully exploded at Alamagordo in the New Mexico desert in July, 1945, and a month later played its grimly decisive part in ending the Japanese war. Nearly a year later, the tests carried out by the United States at Bikini Atoll showed that the new developments had considerable naval implications, since 240 ships took part—and 9 old battleships and cruisers, 2 aircraft carriers, and 37 other other warships were placed in the target area. The Monte Bello Islands off Western Australia, the Woomera rocket range and the Maralinga weapons proving ground in Australia, and Christmas Island in the middle of the Pacific Ocean mark the stages along the road which led Britain to the production of thermonuclear weapons between 1952 and 1957.

These events changed the whole nature of naval warfare and added greatly to the actual power a navy could wield, though the agreed role of that navy was somewhat obscured in the process. Stated simply, it meant that one carrier-borne aircraft alone, if armed with a nuclear weapon, could destroy a whole battle fleet of prewar ships. To this could be added the further disturbing fact that the nuclear-powered submarine, operating underwater almost limitlessly, could project missiles with nuclear warheads hundreds and even thousands of miles across the seas and into enemy territory. Furthermore, the United States Navy developed submarines that could launch Polaris missiles from beneath the sea. All this meant that navies lost one of their traditional roles: they were no longer the defensive bulwarks that they had been in the past; the nuclear-powered submarine was faster, deadlier, and therefore presented a greater threat than had ever existed before, in spite of the advances made in detection apparatus.

Let us look at the postwar developments a little more closely. Wartime experience had, as we have seen, taught the lesson that the battleship was outmoded. Britain scrapped ten of the fourteen she possessed in 1945, as well as *Renown*, her last battle cruiser; and the remaining four, *King George V, Duke of York, Anson,* and *Howe,* all built during the war, were soon to follow. *Vanguard,* laid down in 1941, was finally completed in 1946 and had the double distinction of being the largest warship ever built in Britain as well as being Britain's last battleship. She displaced 44,500 tons, had a main armament of eight 15-inch guns, a secondary armament of sixteen 5.25-inch and sixty 40-mm guns, and she could make a speed of 30 knots. She was a worthy ship to end a long succession of great ships that began with the *Henri Grâce à Dieu* and included the *Sovereign of the Seas.* By 1960, the United States and France were the only countries to have any battleships at all: the former had twelve and the latter had two.

While the number of battleships dwindled, the cruiser fared little better. Britain, for example, drastically reduced her ships in this category, building no new cruisers between 1945 and 1954, since it seemed that, eventually, fleet escort duties would be taken over by guided-missile vessels of the destroyer type. Yet in time this policy was abandoned, and by 1960, *Lion, Tiger,* and *Blake* had come into service, perhaps the last conventional cruisers to be built; and by the same year the comparative figures in cruiser strength were as follows: United States, 51; Russia, 32; Britain and the Commonwealth, 19; France, 5; Italy, 3; and China, 2.[1]

The Korean conflict confirmed the importance of naval air power and therefore of the aircraft carrier. It also showed how carrier-borne aircraft could support troops onshore. In consequence, the leading navies concentrated on these vessels, and such innovations as the angled deck, the steam catapult, and the deck-landing mirror system were introduced. The United States ship *Antietam* was the first carrier to be fitted with an angled deck, a device that went a long way to solve the problems of landing after jet propulsion had nearly doubled landing speeds.

In the 1950's, Britain built her two largest carriers, *Eagle*, completed in 1951 and now being completely modernized, and *Ark Royal*, completed in 1953. They displaced 43,000 tons and could accommodate up to a hundred aircraft each and had a maximum speed of more than 30 knots. The carrier *Victorious* of 1939 was redesigned and modernized to such an extent that when she was completed in 1957 she was virtually a new ship. Britain also built two other classes of carriers, the 22,000-ton medium fleet carrier—the *Centaur, Bulwark, Albion,* and *Hermes*—and the six light *Magnificent*-class carriers, displacing 15,700 tons.

In 1963, the United States Navy had fifty-eight carriers, of which nine had been built since the war. These last included the *Forrestal* and *Kitty Hawk* classes and the mighty *Enterprise*, the only nuclear-powered carrier in the world at the time of writing, a ship that is virtually self-supporting, since she does not need to refuel and can carry vast stocks of every kind of supply. Whether this size of ship provides a satisfactory solution for the foreseeable future is a matter for debate, but it is clear that a carrier must be able to escape from radiation fallout as quickly as possible if she is to survive a nuclear attack, so speed and maneuverability are factors of some importance.

One school of thought argues that the smaller carrier, such as the French *La Résolue* of 10,000 tons, able to carry a commando and a dozen or so helicopters, is the answer, that there should be plenty of them available, and that it is better to distribute naval eggs among as many baskets as possible. The war in the Pacific, with its vast distances and unprecedented logistical problems, taught the Americans the value of the idea of the task force with its own fleet train, and, in a manner of speaking, this idea has persisted in the growing acceptance of the concept of the commando carrier. Limited war in Malaya and elsewhere in the last decade has shown the value of being able to land troops from helicopters beyond the beach defenses in wooded or mountainous country where there are no airfields. The United States Navy is building a 10,700-ton helicopter–amphibious-assault ship with a complement of forty-five helicopters and capable of landing two thousand marines, while Britain has equipped the fleet carrier *Bulwark* for the same purpose, though her twenty helicopters can easily be adapted for an antisubmarine role.[2]

The advances in submarine construction have been, and still are, the most outstanding developments in warship design since the war. The United States nuclear submarine *Nautilus,* built by the Westinghouse Electric Corporation, underwent her final trials in 1955 and represents a personal triumph for Admiral Rickover, for, although the United States had pioneered far ahead of other countries in this direction, there was serious opposition to be overcome. This first nuclear-powered submarine has overcome most of the difficulties that have up till now confronted designers and users. *Nautilus* was found to have speed, and her bulbous prow, replacing the more conventional knife-blade one, enabled her to travel faster underwater than when surfaced. She also could dive to a depth of 700 feet, had excellent maneuverability, and could remain underwater almost indefinitely, since her reactor does not require a supply of air. She was refueled for the first time in 1957 after twenty-six months' service, during which she had traveled sixty-nine thousand miles on the original core of enriched uranium. *Nautilus* traveled submerged from near Alaska under the Arctic ice cap to near Iceland by way of the North Pole in August, 1958, and her sister ship *Seawolf* achieved the record of spending sixty days underwater very soon after. If further proof were needed of the endurance of these vessels, it can be added that the *Triton* circumnavigated the world in eighty-four days without fully surfacing. *Nautilus* was so successful that the United States continued to build along similar lines, and by 1960 there were ten submarines in service and twenty-nine more under construction, about half of which will be able to launch long-range Polaris missiles when submerged.

On Trafalgar Day, 1960, the first British nuclear submarine was launched by Queen Elizabeth II at the Vickers-Armstrong shipyard at Barrow-in-Furness, an achievement made possible by the cooperation of the United States in providing both nuclear machinery and also training facilities for personnel from the British Admiralty, Vickers-Armstrong, and the Rolls Royce Company. The new submarine was named *Dreadnought* and is the ninth British ship of that name.[3] She was not designed, however, to carry long-range ballistic missiles but rather to hunt down enemy submarines and destroy them with her torpedoes. Like the American nuclear submarines, she has great speed, and her radius of action when submerged is limited only by the endurance of the crew. In appearance she has the streamlined "teardrop" hull of the American ships and is, in fact, modeled closely on the *Skipjack*, with the same whalelike hull and a streamlined conning tower not unlike a fin.

But it is on this threshold that our journey comes to an end. The door is ajar and through it we can see, though as yet only dimly discernible, the shapes of new men-of-war, the subject matter of future histories of the warship. Though the ships will change, the sailors that make up their crews will change far less than we may expect. It will still be necessary for the gentlemen and the mariners to haul and draw together, as Drake commanded, and, in Fisher's words, for the officer, though "fed on mechanism," to be "above all things a seaman, and possess that peculiar knowledge which only wind and sea, dark nights and mist, can give."[4]

A reproduction of "The Fighting Téméraire" might have been included in this book because it illustrates the passing not merely of a ship of the line that fought at Trafalgar, but also of the wooden sailing ship herself. However it may also symbolize the end of an era in the long history of the warship. Certainly to contemporaries, and perhaps to the painter himself, it seemed like this. When Ruskin said that it was the most pathetic picture that was ever painted and that "no ruin was ever so affecting as this gliding of the vessel to her grave," he was putting words to a feeling that many must have felt at the time. It is worthwhile perhaps to consider the history of this painting. Turner had been greatly moved when he saw the return of Nelson's body in the *Victory* in December, 1805, and the finely imaginative picture of Trafalgar now in the Maritime Museum at Greenwich shows that he felt sufficiently deeply about the grandeur of that occasion to lift his portrayal of it far above the banal levels of contemporary historical painting. In 1838, Turner was traveling up the Thames in a steamboat when he saw against the background of a magnificent sunset the *Téméraire* being towed to Beatson's ship-breaking yard at Rotherhithe. According to the pre-Raphaelite sculptor Thomas Woolner, Turner immediately made sketches and in the following year the now well-known painting was exhibited, a painting that the artist would not part with in his lifetime. Yet the sunset faded into night, and the old ship was broken up— though some of her timbers survive in the church furnishings in St. Paul's, Rotherhithe.

There are several grave technical inaccuracies in the painting, but we can still experience something of Ruskin's enthusiasm when we look at Turner's masterpiece in the National Gallery in London. Listen again to what he wrote: "Under the blazing veil of vaulted fire which lights the vessel on her last path there is a blue, deep, desolate hollow of darkness out of which you can hear the voice of the night wind and the dull boom of the disturbed sea." There is an elegiac wistfulness about these words, of course, perhaps a sentimentality that is distasteful to us a century later because it may not seem to ring true, but the point is surely this: the stocky little tug reveals the power of steam, power concentrated even in a small and insignificant vessel, that is, nevertheless, sufficient to conduct a great wooden sailing ship of the line along her way and, having thus disposed of her, is free to meet the challenge of the future.

For man is, after all, adaptable to change. He always has been, and if this had not been so, most of the developments in warship design described in this book could not have happened. Admiral Mahan shows this adaptability in a passage in his memoirs that deserves to be quoted at some length. In 1868, on one of his early cruises, he saw two British ships, the *Rodney*, the flagship of the British China Squadron, and the *Princess Royal*, and he noted down the remark of one of his messmates. "Yes," this man said, commenting on the latter ship, "she possesses several elements of the sublime." Then Mahan continues, "They were certainly imposing creations with their double and treble tiers of guns thrusting their black muzzles through the successive ports which, to the number of fifteen to twenty, broke through the two broad white bands that from bow to stern traversed the blackness of their hulls; above which rose spars as tall and broad as ever graced the days of Nelson. To make the illusion of the past as complete as possible and the dissemblance from the sailing ship as slight, the smoke-stack—or funnel—was telescopic, permitting it to be lowered almost out of sight. For those who can recall these predecessors of the modern battleships, the latter can make slight claim to beauty or impressiveness; yet, despite the ugliness of their angular, broken skyline, they have a gracefulness all their own, when moving slowly in still water. I remember . . . watching the French Mediterranean fleet of six or eight battleships leaving the harbour of Villefranche, near Nice. There was some manoeuvring to get their several stations, during which, here and there, a vessel lying quiet waiting her opportunity, would glide forward with a dozen slow turns of the screws, not agitating the water beyond a light ripple at the bows. The bay at the moment was quiet as a mill-pond, and it needed little imagination to prompt recognition of the identity of dignified movement with that of a swan making its leisurely way by means equally unseen; no turbulent display of energy, yet suggestive of mysterious power."[5]

Perhaps, who knows, the vast underwater leviathans of today will also win their meed of praise from the artists and writers of the future.

NOTES

[1] See *Jane's Fighting Ships*.

[2] See B. B. Schofield, *The Royal Navy Today*, p. 95.

[3] See G. A. Smith, *HMS Dreadnought*, Holden's Press Bureau, London, 1960. This is the official handbook produced for Messrs. Vickers-Armstrong, Shipbuilders, Ltd.

[4] Minutes dated 1902, quoted in R. H. Bacon, *The Life of Lord Fisher of Kilverstone*, vol. i, p. 189.

[5] A. T. Mahan, *From Sail to Steam: Recollections of Naval Life*, pp. 28–29.

Bibliography

The references listed below by chapters serve a double purpose: they are intended to enable the reader to follow up subjects that interest him by directing his attention to what has been written; but they also allow the author to acknowledge his debt to those who have pioneered the study of the warship or have, by leaving behind them contemporary records, made such a study possible.

The author would like to list certain sources that have proved particularly valuable in the writing of this book:

R. C. Anderson, *Oared Fighting Ships,* Percival Marshall, London, 1962.

Romola Anderson and R. C. Anderson, *The Sailing-Ship: Six Thousand Years of History,* Harrap & Company, London, 1926.

G. S. Laird Clowes, *Sailing Ships: Their History and Development,* Her Majesty's Stationery Office, London, 1932, reprinted 1959.

W. Laird Clowes *et al., The Royal Navy: A History* (7 vols.), Sampson Low, Marston & Company, London, 1897–1903.

M. A. Lewis, *The Navy of Britain,* George Allen & Unwin, London, 1948.

D. Macintyre, *The Thunder of the Guns: A Century of Battleships,* Frederick Muller, London, 1959.

T. D. Manning and C. F. Walker, *British Warship Names,* Putnam, London, 1959.

S. E. Morison, *History of United States Naval Operations in World War II,* Vols. I–XI, Little, Brown and Company, Boston, 1948–1957.

F. L. Robertson, *The Evolution of Naval Armament,* Constable, London, 1921.

S. W. Roskill, *History of the Second World War: The War at Sea, 1939–45,* Vols. I, II, III, Parts 1 and 2, Her Majesty's Stationery Office, London, 1954–61.

Björn Landström, *The Ship: A Survey of the History of the Ship from the Primitive Raft to the Nuclear-powered Submarine with Reconstructions in Words and Pictures,* George Allen & Unwin, London, 1961.

The Mariner's Mirror, the quarterly journal of the Society for Nautical Research, London.

The publications of the Navy Records Society, London.

CHAPTER I   *The Ancient World*

Aeschylus, *Persae* (for an eyewitness account of the Battle of Salamis).
Anderson, R. C., *Oared Fighting Ships*, Percival Marshall, London, 1962.
Casson, Lionel, *The Ancient Mariners*, Gollancz, London, 1959.
Hale, J. K., *Famous Sea Fights*, Methuen, London, 1911.
Herodotus, *The History*.
Thiel, J. H., *Studies in the History of Roman Sea Power in Republican Times*, North-Holland Publishing Company, Amsterdam, 1946.
Thucydides, *History of the Peloponnesian War*.

CHAPTER II   *The Viking Ship*

Brøgger, A. W., and H. Shetelig, *The Viking Ships: Their Ancestry and Evolution*, Dreyers Forlag, Oslo, and Edward Stanford, London, 1950. (English edition, translated by Katherine John, 1953.)
Brøndsted, Johannes, *The Vikings*, Penguin Books, Harmondsworth, England, 1960.
Bruce-Mitford, R. L. S., *The Sutton Hoo Ship Burial: a Provisional Guide*, Trustees of the British Museum, London, 1951.
Kendrick, T. D., *A History of the Vikings*, Methuen, London, 1930.
Note: Brøgger, formerly Professor Archeology, University of Oslo.
    Brøndsted, formerly Director of the National Museum in Copenhagen.
    Shetelig, formerly Professor of Archeology, University of Bergen.

CHAPTER III   *The English Warship Before 1600*

Anderson, Romola, and R. C. Anderson, *The Sailing-Ship*, Harrap & Company, London, 1926.
Brindley, H. H., *Impressions and Casts of Seals, Coins etc., Exhibited in the Seal Room, National Maritime Museum, London,* Her Majesty's Stationery Office, London, 1938.
Lewis, M. A., *The Navy of Britain*, George Allen & Unwin, London, 1948.
Lewis, M. A., *The History of the British Navy*, Penguin Books, Harmondsworth, England, 1957.
Lewis, M. A., *The Spanish Armada*, Batsford, London, 1960.
Lewis, M. A., *Armada Guns*, George Allen & Unwin, London, 1961.
Maclagan, Eric, *The Bayeux Tapestry*, The King Penguin Books, London, 1945.

Marcus, G. J., *A Naval History of England, Vol I: The Formative Centuries,* Longmans, London, 1961.

Oppenheim, M., *The Administration of the Royal Navy, 1509–1660,* Shoe String Press, 1961. (First edition, Bodley Head, London, 1896.)

Warner, Sir George, (ed.), *The Libelle of Englyshe Polycye: A Poem on the Use of Sea-Power, 1436,* Oxford, London, 1926.

CHAPTER IV   *Galleys, Galleasses, and Galleons*

Anderson, R. C., *Oared Fighting Ships,* Percival Marshall, London, 1962.

Anderson, Romola, and R. C. Anderson, *The Sailing-Ship,* Harrap & Company, London, 1926.

Wiel, Alethea, *The Navy of Venice,* John Murray, London, 1910.

CHAPTER V   *Northwestern European Warships in the Seventeenth Century*

Boxer, C. R., article on M. H. Tromp, *The Mariner's Mirror,* Vol. XL, 1954, and on M. A. de Ruyter, *The Mariner's Mirror,* Vol. XLIV, 1958.

Corbett, J. S. (ed.), *Fighting Instructions 1530–1816,* Navy Records Society, London, Vol XXIX, 1905.

Lubbock, Basil (ed.), *Edward Barlow's Journal, 1659–1703* (2 vols.), Hurst & Blackett, London, 1934.

Margoliouth, H. M. (ed.), *The Poems and Letters of Andrew Marvell,* Oxford, London, 1927.

Oppenheim, M., *The Administration of the Royal Navy, 1509–1660,* Shoe String Press, 1961. (First edition, Bodley Head, London, 1896.)

Penn, C. D., *The Navy under the Early Stuarts,* Gieve's Publishing Company, Portsmouth, and John Hogg, London, 1920.

Wedgwood, C. V., *Richelieu and the French Monarchy,* Hodder & Stoughton, London, 1949.

CHAPTER VI   *The British Navy in the Eighteenth Century*

Corbett, J. S. (ed.), *Fighting Instructions 1530–1816,* Navy Records Society, London, Vol. XXIX, 1905.

Ehrman, John, *The Navy in the War of William III, 1689–1697,* Cambridge, London, 1953.

Hay, M. D., (ed.), *Landsman Hay: the Memoirs of Robert Hay, 1789–1847,* Rupert Hart-Davis, London, 1953.

Laughton, L. G. Carr, "Capital Ships," *The Mariner's Mirror*, Vol. XII, 1926, pp. 396–405.

Macintyre, Donald, *Admiral Rodney*, Peter Davies, London, 1962.

Merriman, R. D. (ed.), *Queen Anne's Navy*, Navy Records Society, London, Vol. CIII, 1961.

Moorhouse, E. Hallam, *Letters of the English Seamen, 1587–1808*, Chapman & Hall, London, 1910.

Ward, Edward, *The Wooden World* (1707), Navy Records Society, London, Occasional Publication No. 2, 1929. (Reprinted from 1751 edition.)

Warner, Oliver, *A Portrait of Lord Nelson*, Chatto & Windus, London, 1958.

CHAPTER VII *The American Navy in the Days of Sail*

Chapelle, Howard I., *The History of American Sailing Ships*, Putnam, London, 1936.

Maclay, E. S., *The History of the United States Navy, 1775–1894*, Vol. II, Bliss, Sands and Foster, London, 1894.

Morison, Samuel E. *John Paul Jones*, Faber & Faber, London, 1959.

CHAPTER VIII *The Nineteenth Century Revolution: Paddle Wheel and Screw Propeller*

Ballard, G. A., "The Navy," in G. M. Young (ed.), *Early Victorian England*, Oxford, London, 1934, pp. 297–344.

Bartlett, C. J., *Great Britain and Sea Power, 1815–1853*, Clarendon Press, Oxford, London, 1963.

Graham, G. S., "The Transition from Paddle-Wheel to Screw-Propeller," *The Mariner's Mirror*, Vol. XLIV, 1958, pp. 35–48.

Lloyd, C. C., *Captain Marryat and the Old Navy*, Longmans, London, 1939.

Lloyd, C. C., *Lord Cochrane: Seaman, Radical, Liberator*, Longmans, London, 1947.

Maclay, E. S., *The History of the United States Navy, 1775–1894*, Vol. II, Bliss, Sands and Foster, London, 1894.

Penn, Geoffrey, *Up Funnel, Down Screw!: The Story of the Naval Engineer*, Hollis & Carter, London, 1955.

Robertson, F. L., *The Evolution of Naval Armament*, Constable, London, 1921.

Spratt, H. P., *The Birth of the Steamboat*, Charles Griffin & Company, London, 1958.

Warner, Oliver, *Captain Marryat: A Rediscovery*, Constable, London, 1953.

CHAPTER IX   *The Nineteenth Century Revolution:*
The Ironclad Vessel and the Naval Gun

Ballard, G. A., article on the *Devastation, The Mariner's Mirror,* Vol. XXXII, 1946, pp. 2–20.
Bartlett, C. J., *Great Britain and Sea Power, 1815–1853,* Clarendon Press, Oxford, London, 1963.
Baxter, James P., *The Introduction of the Ironclad Warship,* Harvard, Cambridge, Mass., 1933.
Robertson, F. L., *The Evolution of Naval Armament,* Constable, London, 1921.

CHAPTER X   *Early Submarines, Destroyers, and Cruisers*

Hovgaard, William, *The Modern History of Warships,* E. & F. N. Spon, London, 1920.
Kemp, P. K., *HM Submarines,* Herbert Jenkins, London, 1952.
Robertson, F. L., *The Evolution of Naval Armament,* Constable, London, 1921.

CHAPTER XI   *The Twentieth Century Battleship*

Bacon, R. H., *The Life of John Rushton, Earl Jellicoe,* Cassell, London, 1936.
Chalmers, W. S., *The Life and Letters of David Beatty, Admiral of the Fleet,* Hodder & Stoughton, London, 1951.
Hovgaard, William, *The Modern History of Warships,* E. & F. N. Spon, London, 1920.
Jane, F. T., *The British Battle Fleet* (2 vols.), Library Press, London, 1915.
Macintyre, D., *Jutland,* Evans Brothers, London, 1957.
Macintyre, D., *The Thunder of the Guns: A Century of Battleships,* Frederick Muller, London, 1959.
Marder, Arthur J., *The Anatomy of British Sea Power: A History of British Naval Policy in the Pre-Dreadnought Era, 1880–1905,* Alfred A. Knopf, New York, 1940.
Marder, Arthur J., *From the Dreadnought to Scapa Flow: The Royal Navy in the Fisher Era, Vol. I: The Road to War, 1904–14,* Oxford, London, 1961.
Pears, R., *British Battleships, 1892–1957,* Putnam, London, 1957.
Roskill, S. W., *The Navy at War, 1939–45,* Collins, London, 1960.
Sims, Sir Alfred, *Warships, 1860–1960, Transactions of R.I.N.A.,* Vol. CII,

1960, pp. 613–62. (A paper read at the centenary meeting of the Royal Institute of Naval Architects on May 17, 1960.)

Sprout, Harold, and Margaret Sprout, *The Rise of American Naval Power, 1776–1918,* Princeton, Princeton, N.J., 1939.

CHAPTER XII   *The Submarine in War*

Central Office of Information, *The Battle of the Atlantic: The Official Account of the Fight Against the U-Boats, 1939–45,* Her Majesty's Stationery Office, London, 1946.

Hovgaard, William, *The Modern History of Warships,* E. & F. N. Spon, London, 1920.

Kemp, P. K., *HM Submarines,* Herbert Jenkins, London, 1952.

Lipscomb, F. W., *The British Submarine,* A. & C. Black, London, 1954.

Roskill, S. W., *The Navy at War 1939–45,* Collins, London, 1960.

Sims, William S., *The Victory at Sea,* John Murray, London, 1921.

CHAPTER XIII   *The Aircraft Carrier*

Hovgaard, William, *The Modern History of Warships,* E. & F. N. Spon, London, 1920.

Kemp, P. K., *Fleet Air Arm,* Herbert Jenkins, London, 1954.

Morison, Samuel E. *The Two Ocean War,* Little, Brown and Company, Boston, 1963.

Roskill, S. W., *The Navy at War, 1939–45,* Collins, London, 1960.

Index

[For names of ships see separate listing on page 362.]

Ships

[The dates, unless otherwise stated, refer to the launching of the ships.]